AMERICAN REGIONS MATH LEAGUE
&
Power & Local Contests

2004 – 2008

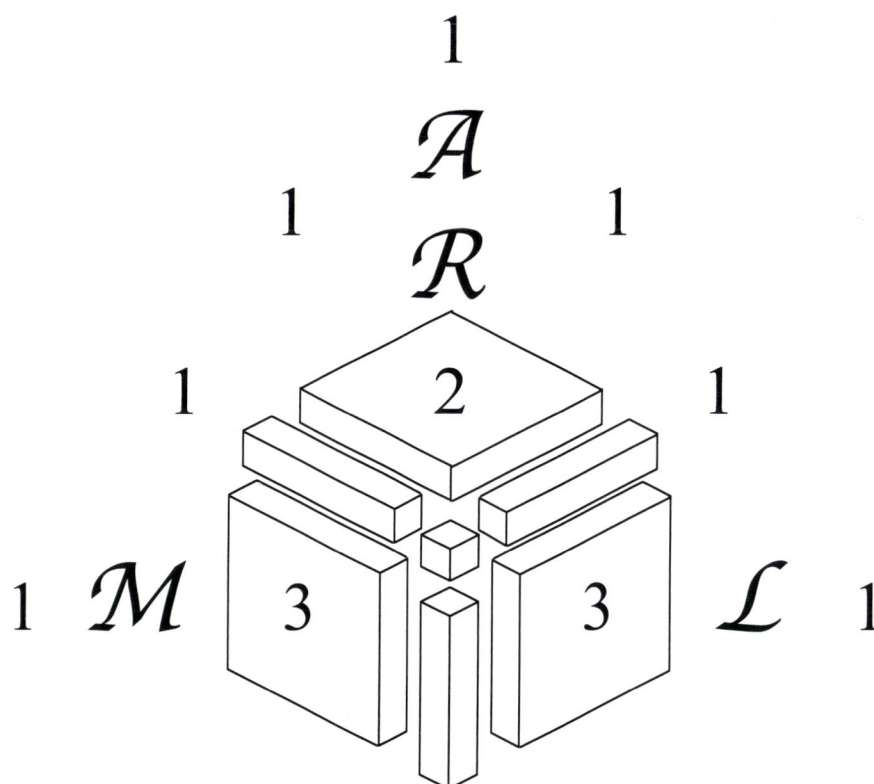

by Don Barry, Tom Kilkelly, & Paul Dreyer

Contents

From 1995 to 2000 my wife Roxy saw bits and pieces of ARML. She noted that many a night I was at my desk trying to develop problems worthy of a competition that involved the best mathematics students in the country. She watched as I searched for creative problem posers to serve on a problem writing committee. She had some sense of the struggle that it took to transform some tiny insight, some small exploratory question, into a problem both delightful and challenging. Fundamentally, however, ARML for her was one person sitting in a pool of light in dusky room, thinking and typing, and thinking some more. Then in June of 2001 she was finally able to go to ARML. Penn State was quiet when we first arrived, but as students poured out of buses the campus became vibrantly alive. She could see that I was growing nervous, fearful that a missed ambiguity in a problem would wreak havoc with scoring, wondering if we'd found all the answers, worried that the contest be too easy or too hard. But that June she looked beyond her husband and saw, to her delight and amazement, a jam-packed auditorium of 900 brightly t-shirted students working with quiet intensity to wrest answers out of our problems. She had never imagined that a mathematics competition could be that dramatic, that compelling. She had never imagined that so many teachers and students could put such an immense amount of work into preparation for this contest. She loved the pure idealism that guided and informed this community of scholars. She marveled at the creativity, competence, and accomplishments of these mathematics students, while being equally baffled by the fact that the media and general public took such little note of our efforts to develop and nurture the mathematical ability of our students.

It has been my privilege and pleasure to be the head author for ARML these past 14 years from 1995 to 2008. I write for a number of contests, but there is no contest like ARML and every head author that I've known has been emotionally invested in ARML beyond all reason. We fuss over it, worry about it, strive to make it better, and then we redouble our efforts. It is time to turn my job over to a younger person. Working for ARML has been the most enduring high point of my career as a teacher of mathematics. During that time ARML has grown and evolved. The ARML Power Contest was introduced in 1994, the number of teams has risen dramatically, a fourth site was added in Georgia in 2008, ARML Local was introduced in 2008, and IRML, the International Regions Math League, has been getting underway the past few years, IRML will enable international teams to take the ARML problems by email on the same day as the teams in the United States.

ARML was founded in 1976 as the Atlantic Region Mathematics League. It was an outgrowth of NYSML, the New York State Mathematics League, founded in 1973, and designed to serve as a competition for the best of the teams in the math leagues in New York. Both were the joint vision of Alfred Kalfus and Steve Adrian. Alfred served as the first president of ARML and Steve, along with Joe Quartararo (from 1976 to 1982), did the organizational work, site preparations, and publicity. Marty Badoian as vice president and Eric Walstein also played crucial roles in ARML's early days. The impetus for ARML came when Marty Badoian brought a Massachusetts team to NYSML in 1974 and 1975 and they did so well, losing by a point in 1974 and winning by a point in 1975, that an expanded competition seemed desirable. ARML was conceived as an interstate competition covering the eastern seaboard, formed through the joint action of the New York State Mathematics League, the New England Association of Mathematics Leagues, and leagues from New Jersey, Pennsylvania, Maryland, and Virginia. But ARML is a great contest and it soon attracted math students and math teachers from all over the country.

By 1984 ARML was renamed the American Regions Mathematics League. Currently, it takes place simultaneously at four sites, Penn State University in State College, Pennsylvania, the University of Iowa in Iowa City, Iowa, the University of Georgia in Athens, Georgia, and the University of Nevada at Las Vegas. It brings together some 1700 of the finest young mathematicians in the United States and Canada. In the past teams from Russia have competed and in the last few years teams from Taiwan, the Philippines, Columbia, and Hong Kong have been taking part. Taiwanese educators even created a similar competition for schools in Taiwan called TRML. Turkey, Bulgaria, and Vietnam competed in IRML in 2008

ARML is a competition between regions. A region may be as large as a state–there are teams from Texas, Minnesota, and Georgia, it may be half a state–eastern and western Massachusetts field teams, it may be a county such as Suffolk county in New York, it may be a city such as Chicago or New York, or a region may even be a high school. Each team consists of 15 students and a region may send more than one team.

The contest consists of 6 parts. First is the <u>Team Round</u>. A team's 15 students are in one classroom, they receive 10 problems, they have 20 minutes to solve them as a group, and up through 2008 they could use calculators. Typically, problems are divided up so that every problem is being worked on by at least one student, answers are posted, and hurried consultations take place if there is disagreement. Next comes the <u>Power Question</u>. Teams are given 60 minutes to solve a series of in-depth questions on one topic and/or prove a number of theorems on that topic. The teams' papers are graded by a hardworking group of teachers tucked away in a corner of the auditorium. Following the Power Question, the teams come together in a large auditorium for the <u>Individual Round</u>. Here, up through 2008, they solved 8 questions, given in pairs with 10 minutes for each pair, right answer only. Neither calculators nor collaboration are allowed. Initial problems are easier, but an easier problem is generally paired with a more difficult one. We try to write problems so that 80–90% of the students can solve the first one and less than 5% can solve the last one. The next round is the <u>Relay Round</u>. The teams of 15 are divided up into 5 groups of 3. Each 1st person in a group gets the same problem, each 2nd person gets the same problem, and each 3rd person gets the same problem. The first person's problem has all the information necessary to solve it, but the second person's problem requires the first person's answer, and the third person needs the second person's answer. None of the three knows the other's questions. A well-written relay problem enables the second and third team members to do considerable work while waiting. They may even be able to discover a candidate pool of likely answers to their problem.

Those four rounds are the only rounds that count for the Team and Individual competition. Scoring is as follows: each correct answer on the Team Round earns 4 points. Sometimes a team gets all 40 points, but 36 has typically been the top score and the average for all the teams has been between 20 and 24. The Power Question is worth 40 points; often one or more teams earn a perfect score. Each individual problem is worth 1 point per contestant, meaning that the team can earn as many as $8 \cdot 15 = 120$ points on this round. Generally, 90 is a great score. On the Relay Round, only the third person's answer is scored. If the group of 3 gets the problem correct within 3 minutes they earn 4 points, if within 6 minutes they earn 2 points. Thus, each relay is worth a maximum of $5 \cdot 4 = 20$ points; a score of 14 is quite good. The winning team's score for the entire contest usually lies between 160 and 190 points.

The <u>Super Relay</u> has followed the relay races the past few years. It is just for fun and is a relay race for the whole team involving 15 questions. The team that gets the correct answer to the last question is the winner, earning a round of applause and bragging rights 'til next year. To keep the Super Relay from getting bogged down, we usually slip one or two problems into the relay that can be solved without requiring the previous person's answer. Students pass answers from both ends into position 8. That student's question requires two answers in order to be solved.

The <u>Tiebreaker Round</u> follows the relays. Until 2006 ARML gave only 3 top individual prizes, forcing a playoff took place between the top scorers. With increased sponsorship, ARML was able to increase the number of awards to 10. The Tiebreaker is a dramatic moment. At each site the contenders come to the front of the auditorium, they receive the problem at the same time that it is flashed on an overhead screen. Each student is timed and the winners are determined by who gets the correct answer most quickly. Three tiebreakers are now given. A site will give tiebreakers until it either has 10 correct answers or has exhausted the problems and students. Afterwards times are compared with the other sites.

ARML is quite an undertaking. It brings together great students, it is one of the few mathematics contests that involves exciting travel, meeting lots of other students, and renewing friendships established during summer programs. It relies on the work of a large number of dedicated adults who do all the organizing and spend hours finding or writing problems to use in practice sessions. It is a contest that promotes and demands creativity and imagination. The students who take part in ARML are very experienced problem solvers, quick and insightful. Those of us who write problems for ARML respect the abilities of our participants and, consequently, we spend hours developing problems that spring from high school mathematics, yet are out of the ordinary, problems that can't be attacked in rote fashion. We don't just take a theorem and write a problem that employs it. We ask questions, we imagine situations we'd never thought of before, we try out this idea and that possibility, we run into dead-ends, and we occasionally stumble across a really neat idea and that's the one that makes it into an ARML competition. There are many different topics on each year's ARML, but more important, there is a wide variety of ways of thinking.

This publication makes available the problem sets and solutions for the 2004 to 2008 ARML contests. Four earlier publications contain ARML problems from its beginning in 1976 to 2003 and NYSML problems from its beginning in 1973 to 1992. The first was *NYSML–ARML Contests 1973–1982*, published in 1983 by Mu Alpha Theta. The second was *NYSML–ARML Contests 1983–1988* by Gilbert Kessler and Lawrence Zimmerman, published by the National Council of Teachers of Mathematics in 1989. The third was *ARML –NYSML Contests 1989–1994* by Lawrence Zimmerman and Gilbert Kessler, published by MathPro Press in 1995. The fourth was The *American Regions Math League & ARML Power Contests* by Don Barry and Thomas Kilkelly, published by ARML in 2003.

ARML has an executive board that organizes each contest. Alfred Kalfus was president from 1976 until 1989 when Mark Saul of Bronxville High School, NY took over. Mark retired in 2001 and Tim Sanders, director of the Great Plains Mathematics League, took over. In June of 2004, J. Bryan Sullivan became president. Current board members include Marty Badoian, Steve Adrian, Linda Berman, J. Bryan Sullivan, Paul Dreyer, Barbara Chao, Mike Curry, Don Slater, and Steve Condie.

Don Barry has been the head author from 1995 to 2008 and during that time he has received a number of great problems, solutions, and a lot of spirited help from James Albrecht, Gabriel Carroll, Paul Dreyer, Ed Early, Zuming Feng, Zac Franco, Chris Jeuell, Paul Karafiol, Andy Niedermaier, Rick Parris, Leo Schneider, Bridget Tenner, and Eric Wepsic. The following teachers at Phillips Academy in Andover, Massachusetts have helped enormously in editing, reviewing, and occasionally suggesting problems: Chris Odden, David Penner, Bob Perrin, Bill Scott, and Sam Vandervelde. Our work has benefited from and, we hope, built upon the fine work done by ARML's previous problem writers including Steve Conrad, Dr. Norman Schaumberger, Dr. Erwin Just, Irwin Kaufman, Howard Shapiro, Harry Ruderman, Gilbert Kessler, and Larry Zimmerman. When Larry and Gil stepped down as the ARML authors after the 1994 contest, they made sure that their answer to the last relay problem was (10, 4), a symbolic way of signing off. The attentive reader of this book will notice that as I step down after the 2008 contest, I followed suit in the last relay problem.

I would like to dedicate this book to my wife, Roxy, whose cheerful patience, support and encouragement have been so invaluable and to James Albrecht who was emerging as a good ARML problem writer before his untimely death.

Don Barry, dbarry@andover.edu
Phillips Academy, Andover, MA 01810

Don Barry is on the left and J. Bryan Sullivan, President of ARML, is on the right.

In 1995, under the leadership of its president, Mark Saul, ARML introduced the ARML Power Contest. Modeled on the Power Question which involves, as Mark noted, "cooperative effort in exploring a problem situation through the solution of chains of related problems", ARML began to offer a competition by mail. In November and February, each participating team receives a set of problems based on a major theme. Some of the problems require a numerical answer, some require justification, while others require that a proof be written. The mathematics of the problems has been geared so that students in an honors class, a math club, or on a math team can have a unique, challenging, yet mostly successful problem solving and mathematics writing experience. There is no limit to the size of the team, but the time for solving the problem set is limited to 45 minutes. Currently, the team's solutions are mailed to the author where they are graded by the author and some of his colleagues. There are 40 points per contest; the team score is the sum of the scores of the two contests. A team may represent a region, not just a school, but the contest must be taken by all members of the team at the same time and place. The contest has grown steadily. As of the 2008-2009 academic year there were 76 teams from the United States, Canada, Colombia, and Bulgaria participating.

The Power Question and the Power Contest are both designed to simulate actual mathematical research activity. This is not easy. As Mark noted,

> "Power Contest problems are difficult to write. They must provide meaningful problem situations both for the novice and veteran mathletes. They must attract schools with strong traditions in mathematics competitions, yet offer experiences for students new to such events. Thus, they must build mathematically significant results out of mathematically trivial materials."

Tom Kilkelly, Director of ARML Power Contest

Since 1998 Tom Kilkelly has been the main author, coordinator, and grader of the ARML Power Contest. In developing the problems he has been assisted at times by Andy Niedermaier, a former ARML participant from Minnesota and Ivaylo Kortezov from Sofia, Bulgaria. The idea for a Power Contest question usually starts off quite small and simple but then grows as the problem is made assessable and inviting for all participating teams yet also challenging and discriminating for even the best teams in the competition.

Special thanks to Carla, my wife, whose patience, support and encouragement have been essential for my participation in this project. I want to say that I really enjoy the research, problem solving, and mathematical writing challenges that the competition provides.

Thomas Kilkelly,
Wayzata High School
4955 Peony Lane N.
Plymouth, MN 55446.
kilkelly@ties2.net

ARML Local was created to offer schools an opportunity to either practice for ARML or to take part in a contest similar to ARML at a local site. If a school is not already taking part in ARML, we hope that if it finds ARML Local to be a valuable experience, a school will be encouraged to support its students to participate in ARML. A team consists of up to 6 students and a school may field up to four teams of 6 students each. The local site administrator downloads the problems on the date of the contest, administers the test, corrects the problems, and emails back the team's results. The answers to all problems are numerical, there are no proofs to correct.

ARML Local consists of four parts, none of which allowed calculators in 2008.

The Team Round consists of 10 questions. The team of students works together for 40 minutes to find the answers to the problems.

The Theme Round takes 60 minutes and consists of around ten questions based on a common topic. Unlike the Power Question at ARML, the Theme Round does not involve proof. The reason for this is that it would be impossible to ensure consistency of grading across so many different sites.

The Individual Round consists of 10 questions given in pairs with 10 minutes allowed for each pair.

The Relay Rounds depart from the approach used at ARML to some degree by taking advantage of the fact that teams consist of 6 members. First of all, there are three rounds not two. Secondly, the first relay is for three teams of two, the second is for two teams of three, and the third is for one team of all six students. The times allotted for the relays are 6, 8, and 10 minutes respectively.

More information about the contest is available at http://arml.com/arml_local/

ARML Local was written in 2008 by Paul Dreyer who is also the head coordinator of ARML Local and Doug Ray who manages the Dr. Numsen Academic Meet Companion website at http://academicmeet.com.

In 2008, the contest was sponsored by a grant from the National Security Agency, which enabled us to allow teams to compete in the inaugural contest free of charge.

2004: Don Barry, Gabriel Carroll, Paul Dreyer, Ed Early, Zuming Feng, Zac Franco, Chris Jeuell, Paul Karafiol, and Eric Wepsic.

Reviewers: Rick Parris, David Penner, and Bob Perrin. Leo Schneider helped with editing.

2005: James Albrecht, Don Barry, Paul Dreyer, Ed Early, Zuming Feng, Zac Franco, Chris Jeuell, Paul Karafiol, Leo Schneider, and Eric Wepsic.

Reviewers: Rick Parris and David Penner.

2006: James Albrecht, Don Barry, Paul Dreyer, Ed Early, Zuming Feng, Zac Franco, Chris Jeuell, Paul Karafiol, David Penner, Leo Schneider, Bridget Tenner, and Eric Wepsic.

Rick Parris reviewed the problems and Tom Hull helped with the Power Question.

2007: James Albrecht, Don Barry, Paul Dreyer, Ed Early, Zuming Feng, Zac Franco, Chris Jeuell, Paul Karafiol, Andy Niedermaier, David Penner, Leo Schneider, Bridget Tenner, and Eric Wepsic.

Rick Parris, David Penner, and Bill Scott reviewed the problems.

2008: Don Barry, Paul Dreyer, Ed Early, Zuming Feng, Zac Franco, Chris Jeuell, Paul Karafiol, Andy Niedermaier, David Penner, Leo Schneider, Bridget Tenner, and Eric Wepsic.

Reviewers: Rick Parris and Bill Scott

Problem Writers for the ARML Power Contest

Nov. 2004:	Thomas Kilkelly	Feb. 2005:	Thomas Kilkelly
Nov. 2005:	Thomas Kilkelly	Feb. 2006:	Andy Niedermaier (U.C. Davis)
Nov. 2006:	Ivaylo Kortezov (Sofia Math Circle) Thomas Kilkelly	Feb. 2007:	Thomas Kilkelly
Nov. 2007:	Andy Niedermaier	Feb. 2008:	Thomas Kilkelly
Nov. 2008:	Thomas Kilkelly		

Proof Readers for all 5 years: William Skerbitz, Stephen Heilig, Carla Kilkelly

2004 Team Competition

Division A

1. Thomas Jefferson HS A 166
2. San Francisco Bay Area A 150
3. New York City A 144
4. Georgia A 142
5. Chicago A 137
6. Montgomery A 134

Division B

1. Washington A 107
2. New York City Y 99
3. Indiana Gold 94
4. San Francisco Bay Area B 93

2004 Individual Competition

1. Aaron Pixton .... Upstate New York A 8
2. Jongmin Baek .... San Francisco Bay Area A 8
3. Anders Kaseorg .... North Carolina A 8

2005 Team Competition

Division A

1. Lehigh Valley Fire 172
2. Chicago A 164
3. Phillips Exeter Red 162
4. Montgomery A 159
5. Thomas Jefferson HS A 157
6. AAST Mu 154
7. North Carolina A 153

Division B

1. Wisconsin Red 134
2. Texas Silver 133
3. Florida 131
4. Alabama 128
4. Georgia B 128

2005 Individual Competition

1. Ryan Ko .... Phillips Exeter Academy A 7

Unfortunately, we've misplaced the names of the second and third place winners.

2006 Team Competition

Division A

1. North Carolina A — 186
2. Montgomery A — 184
3. Lehigh Valley Fire — 177
3. Texas Gold — 177
5. Chicago A — 173
6. San Francisco Bay Area A — 169
7. Phillips Exeter Red — 167

Division B

1. Colorado — 148
Int. 1 Taiwan D — 147
Int. 2 Taiwan C — 134
Int. 3 Taiwan B — 133
2. Western Massachusetts A — 123
3. Chicago Blue — 121
4. Montgomery B — 119
4. Ohio A — 119

2006 Individual Competition D.E. Shaw Winners

1. Samuel Dittmer — Indiana Gold
2. Jeffrey Chen — Texas Gold
3. Zachary Abel — Texas Gold
4. Brian Lawrence — Montgomery A
5. Daniel L. Schafer — Thomas Jefferson HS A
6. Jennifer Iglesias — Chicago A
7. Charles Tam — Indiana Gold
8. Nathan Benjamin — Indiana Gold
9. Shaunak Kishore — Lehigh Valley Fire
10. Jeffrey Manning — Southern California A

2007 Team Competition

Division A

1. Phillips Exeter Red — 171
2. Lehigh Valley Fire — 169
3. New York City A — 163
4. North Carolina A — 162
5. Georgia A — 161
6. Texas Gold — 160
7. Chicago A — 159

Division B

Int 1. Taiwan A — 128
Int 2. Taiwan B — 127
1. South Carolina Doom — 116
2. Massachusetts E — 115
3. San Diego A — 113
4. North Carolina B — 112
4. Southern California B — 112

2007 Individual Competition D.E. Shaw Winners

1. Tao Ran Chen — New York City A
2. Howard Tong — Georgia A
3. Jay Whang — Southern California A
3. Ping-Han Chung — Taiwan A
4. Seva Tchernov — Alabama
5. Sunny Kam — Nassau A
6. Linda Yu Liu — Georgia A
7. Tedrick Leung — Southern California A
8. Arnav Tripathy — North Carolina A
9. Sam Elder — Colorado
10. Gye Hyun Baek — Phillips Exeter Red

2008 Team Competition

Division A

1.	New York City A	170
2.	Phillips Exeter Red	168
3.	North Carolina A	162
4.	San Francisco Bay Area A	161
5.	Southern California A	160
6.	Massachusetts A	157
7.	Georgia A	154
7.	Chicago A	154

Division B

Int 1.	Paradise Mall Hong Kong	141
1.	Vermont All-Stars	122
2.	AAST Mu B	115
3.	San Francisco Bay Area B	114
4.	Chesapeake	109
5.	Oregon	108
6.	Connecticut A	106

2008 Individual Competition D.E. Shaw Winners

1.	Qinxuan Pan	Montgomery A
2.	Vlad Firoiu	Eastern Massachusetts A
3.	Daniel Li	Thomas Jefferson HS A
4.	Jeff Manning	Southern California A
5.	Colin Sandon	Vermont
6.	Zhuo Ming Yang (Aubrey)	Southern California A
7.	Allan Yuan	Michigan
8.	Kevin Chen	Texas Gold
8.	Yat Wui Cheung	Hong Kong
9.	Thomas Davids	Colorado
10.	David Rolnick	Vermont

ARML Power Contest Prize Winners

2004-05	1. Thomas Jefferson HS	Alexandria, VA	Coach: Pat Gabriel
	2. Academy for Advancement of Science and Technology	Hackensack, NJ	Coach: Joe Holbrook
	3. Illinois Math and Science Academy	Aurora, IL	Coach: Micah Fogel
2005-06	1. Stuyvesant HS	New York, NY	Coach: Richard Geller
	2. Phillips Exeter Academy	Exeter, NH	Coach: Zuming Feng
	3. Sofia Math Circle	Sofia, Bulgaria	Coach: Evgenia Sendova
2006-07	1. Western Washington ARML	Seattle, WA	Coach: Bev Hesterberg
	2. Sofia Math Circle	Sofia, Bulgaria	Coach: Evgenia Sendova
	3. Colorado ARML	Boulder, CO	Coach: Silva Chang
2007-08	1. Georgia ARML	Conyers, GA	Coach: Chuck Garner
	2. Colorado ARML	Boulder, CO	Coach: Silva Chang
	2. Thomas Jefferson HS	Alexandria, VA	Coach: Pat Gabriel

ARML Local Prize Winners

Inaugural Competition 2008

Archimedes Division

1. Thomas Jefferson HS	138	Alexandria, VA	Pat Gabriel/Jen Allard
2. Lehigh Valley	126	Radnor, PA	Don Davis
3. Wayzata Gold	117	Wayzata, MN	Tom Kilkelly

Bernoulli Division

| 1. South Burlington HS | 58 | South Burlington, | Jean Ohlson |
| 2. Chesapeake | 47 | Columbia, MD | Catherine Asaro |

Individual Winners

1. Jonathan Mei	10	Buchholz 1	Gainesville, FL
1. Palmer Mebane	10	Chesapeake	Columbia, MD
1. Haitao Mao	10	Thomas Jefferson C	Alexandria, VA

The *Alfred Kalfus Founder's Award* is given each year for long-term service to ARML. Al Kalfus was the founder and first president of both NYSML and ARML. He was devoted to his students and dedicated to excellence. Some measure of the man can be found in a preface that he wrote to the first book of ARML problems covering the 1976 to 1982 contests: "Meanwhile, enjoy the problems given in these pages. Remember, they were posed not to stump you, but to provoke your mathematical ingenuity, to guide you to clever tricks and new methods of attack, to open new facets of topics to the uninitiated, and to offer you the unique joy that only the solving of a truly challenging problem can bring." This award was first given in 1985.

The *Samuel L. Greitzer Coach Award* is given each year for outstanding service to a regional team. For many years Dr. Samuel Greitzer, a professor at Rutgers University, coached the United States IMO team. He also served as the editor for *Arbelos*, a small journal designed for high school students that was full of challenging mathematics problems and investigations. The award was first given in 1987.

The *Harry and Ruth Ruderman Award* is awarded at ARML to the winning team of the ARML Power Contest. Harry Ruderman influenced and inspired generations of students and teachers. He was a prolific writer, problem poser, and lecturer. For over a decade, he served as a contributor and reviewer of ARML questions as well as being the head judge. It was first awarded in 1996.

The *Douglas Cameron Baker Memorial Award* is given in honor of Douglas Baker, a former member of the Chicago ARML team who died much too young. It is given to two students, one from the Chicago team and one chosen nationally, who best exemplify the qualities that Douglas brought to the competition—an enthusiasm for the contest, and enjoyment of the social interaction with students, and a love of mathematics. It was first awarded in 2007.

The *Zachary Sobol Award* is awarded for outstanding contributions by a student to his or her ARML team or to the competition itself. It was given in honor of Zachary Sobol who was an active, very enthusiastic participant on the Montgomery County, Maryland team from 1981 through 1983. He was famous for Sobol diagrams, circles that resembled vaguely closed curves. He died in 1986 and a fund in his memory was set up by parents and friends. It was first given in 1986 and was retired after the 2006 competition.

ARML

2004

Thomas Jefferson HS made it three in a row in 2004 with a very strong showing on a difficult contest. Team round scores were low this year with only three teams earning more than 28 points. With a remarkable 36 points, TJ had a 4 point lead over Georgia A and AAST Mu after the team round. With a strong 35 on the Power Question, a score matched only by Missouri A, TJ had 12 point lead over Georgia going into the Individual Round. San Francisco Bay A rallied with 77 points on the individual round, but TJ with 142 points had a 12 point lead over San Francisco, an 18 point lead over New York City A, with Georgia dropping off the pace. TJ was consistently strong on the relays as well, winning the competition by 16 points over San Francisco with a score of 166 with New York City A in third place with 144 points.

There were 25 teams in Division A this year and 63 teams in Division B.

Josh Zucker was awarded the Alfred Kalfus Founder's Award. Josh was instrumental in bringing California teams into ARML and served as a coach for the San Francisco Bay Area team for many years. He was site chairman for the years that ARML was at San Jose State University. Outside of ARML he founded the East Palo Alto College Track math circle and he's been the director of the annual Julia Robinson Mathematics Festival. He's been described as a whirlwind of activity, inspiring teachers and students throughout the Bay area while serving as a teacher in colleges, high schools, distance learning programs, and summer programs.

Carol Miller of the Chicago team was awarded the Samuel L. Greitzer Coach Award. Carol has been one of the most influential coaches of the Chicago Area ARML team for more than twenty years. She was responsible for the creation of the third and fourth teams, enabling Chicago to take twice as many students as before. Her commitment to ARML and the Chicago team has been unwavering and influential throughout her career.

The St. Louis Math Circle of St. Louis, MO was awarded the Harry and Ruth Ruderman Award for winning the ARML Power Contest.

The following were awarded the Zachary Sobol Award: Jaemin Bae of AAST in New Jersey, Peter Goldstein of Western Massachusetts, and Si-Hyun Km of Southern California.

T–1. Suppose $20.04 is expressed using any combination of pennies, nickels, dimes, and/or quarters with at most 50 of each type of coin. Compute the positive difference between the greatest and least number of coins possible.

T–2. Let S be the shape just to the right. An infinite number of copies of S are placed on an infinite floor as indicated to the far right. The edges of S are integers x and y. Compute the least value of x if 35% of the area is covered by shape S.

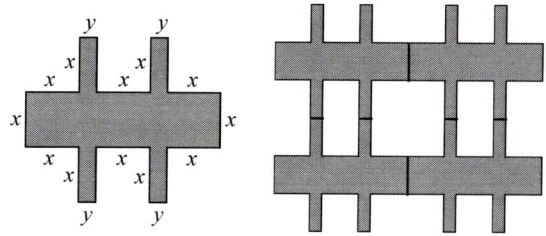

T–3. $ABCDE$ is inscribed in a circle with $AB = BC = CD = DE = 4$ and $AE = 1$. Compute $(1 - \cos \angle B)(1 - \cos \angle ACE)$.

T–4. Let $ABCDEFGHI$ be a regular 9-sided figure. A *trip* is defined to be any sequence of 4 letters such that no two consecutive letters are the same. $AGIB$ and $ACAB$ are trips while $AACB$ is not. Compute the number of distinct trips from A to B.

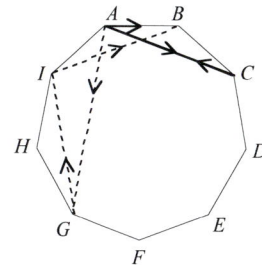

T–5. For <u>integers</u> a and T, $T \neq 0$, a parabola whose general equation is $y = ax^2 + bx + c$ passes through the points $A(0, 0)$, $B(2T, 0)$ and $C(2T + 1, 28)$. Let N be the sum of the coordinates of the vertex point. Determine the largest value of N.

T–6. Compute all values of b for which the following system has a solution (x, y) in real numbers:

$$\sqrt{xy} = b^b$$
$$\log_b\left(x^{\log_b y}\right) + \log_b\left(y^{\log_b x}\right) = 4b^4$$

T–7. If $\dfrac{a-b}{c} = \dfrac{b+c}{a} = \dfrac{a-c}{b}$, compute all possible values of $\dfrac{a}{a+b+c}$.

T–8. Points P and Q lie on $y = 2x$ and $y = \dfrac{x}{2}$ respectively such that the coordinates of P and Q are positive integers less than or equal to 99. Compute the number of ordered pairs (P, Q) such that the trisection points of $\overline{PQ}$ are lattice points.

T–9. Consider the sequence of numbers 24, 2534, 253534, 25353534, 2535353534, . . . Let N be the first number in the sequence that is divisible by 99. Compute the number of digits in the base ten representation of N.

T–10. Pyramid $EARLY$ has rectangular base $EARL$ and apex Y, $ER = \sqrt{1105}$, and $\overline{EY} \perp \overline{RY}$. If EA, AR, EY, AY, RY, and LY are distinct integers, compute the area of the smallest face of the pyramid.

3

1.   42

2.   26

3. $\dfrac{1}{64}$ = 0.015625

4.   57

5.   60

6. $0 < b \le \dfrac{\sqrt{2}}{2}$

7. $-1, \dfrac{1}{2}$

8.   800

9.   176

10. $\dfrac{5\sqrt{119}}{4}$

T–1. The least is 50 quarters, 50 dimes, 50 nickels, and 4 pennies for a total of 154 coins. The greatest does not succumb so easily to the greedy algorithm. Fifty of each coin would give us $20.50, so we need to exclude the least number of coins that give $0.46. That is 1 quarter, 2 dimes, and 1 penny. Thus, the greatest number of coins comes from 49 quarters, 48 dimes, 50 nickels, and 49 pennies for a total of 196 coins. The difference is $196 - 154 = \boxed{42}$.

T–2. Enclose S in a rectangle whose area is $3x(3x + 2y)$. To obtain the area of S, subtract the areas of the six squares of side x from the rectangle giving $3x(3x + 2y) - 6x^2 = 3x(x + 2y)$. Thus, $\dfrac{3x(x + 2y)}{3x(3x + 2y)} = .35 = \dfrac{7}{20}$. Rearranging yields $21x + 14y = 20x + 40y \rightarrow x = 26y$. Since x and y are integers, the least value of x occurs when $y = 1$ making $x = \boxed{26}$.

T–3. Since $\Delta ABC \cong \Delta EDC$ by SAS, $AC = CE$. Let $AC = x$. By the Law of Cosines, $x^2 = 4^2 + 4^2 - 2 \cdot 4 \cdot 4 \cos \angle B = 32(1 - \cos \angle B)$. Also, $1^2 = x^2 + x^2 - 2x \cdot x \cos \angle ACE = 2x^2(1 - \cos \angle ACE)$. Substituting the value of x^2 from the first equation into the second gives the following:

$1 = 2 \cdot 32(1 - \cos \angle B)(1 - \cos \angle ACE)$. Thus, $(1 - \cos \angle B)(1 - \cos \angle ACE) = \boxed{\dfrac{1}{64}}$.

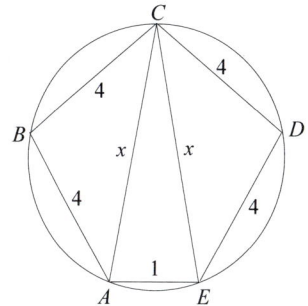

T–4. A trip may be of the form $A\,B\,y\,B$. There are 8 values for y so there are 8 such trips. Or a trip may be of the form $A\,x\,y\,B$ where x is not B. There are $7 \cdot 7 = 49$ of those. So there are $8 + 49 = \boxed{57}$ possible trips.

Alternate solution: Suppose there are n vertices. We can divide the trips into three types. If the trip is $A\,x\,A\,B$, then there are $1 \cdot (n - 1) \cdot 1 \cdot 1 = n - 1$ trips. If the trip is $A\,B\,y\,B$, then there are $1 \cdot 1 \cdot (n - 2) \cdot 1 = n - 2$ trips. Note that we use $n - 2$ to eliminate duplications with the first type. Finally, we have a trip of the type $A\,x\,y\,B$ and there are $1 \cdot (n - 2)(n - 3) \cdot 1 = (n - 2)(n - 3)$ of those. The sum is $(n - 1) + (n - 2) + (n - 2)(n - 3) = (n - 1) + (n - 2)^2$. In this case we have $8 + 7^2 = 57$.

T–5. By symmetry the parabola also passes through $(-1, 28)$. Since the zeros are 0 and $2T$, the vertex point lies on $x = T$ and the equation of the parabola can be expressed as $y = ax(x - 2T)$, making the y-value of the vertex equal to $aT(T - 2T) = -aT^2$. For $x = -1$ we have $a = \dfrac{28}{2T + 1}$, giving the integer values of (T, a) as $(3, 4)$, $(-1, -28)$, and $(-4, -4)$. The vertices for those values are $\left(3, -4 \cdot 3^2\right) = (3, -36)$, $\left(-1, -(-28)(-1)^2\right) = (-1, 28)$, and $\left(-4, -(-4)(-4)^2\right) = (-4, 64)$ respectively. The sum of the coordinates of the vertices is –33, 27, and 60 respectively. Answer: $\boxed{60}$.

5

T–6. Let $m = \log_b x$ and $n = \log_b y$. Take the $\log_b$ of both sides of the first equation to obtain

$\log_b \sqrt{xy} = \log_b \left(b^b \right) \;\to\; \frac{1}{2}\left(\log_b x + \log_b y \right) = b \;\to\; m + n = 2b$. The second equation can be

rewritten as $\left(\log_b y \right)\left(\log_b x \right) + \left(\log_b x \right)\left(\log_b y \right) = 4b^4 \;\to\; mn + mn = 4b^4 \;\to\; mn = 2b^4$.

Thus, m and n are the roots of $z^2 - (m+n)z + mn = 0 \;\to\; z^2 - 2bz + 2b^4 = 0$. For these roots to be

real, then $\left(-2b \right)^2 - 4 \cdot 1 \cdot \left(2b^4 \right) \geq 0 \;\to\; 1 \leq 2b^2 \;\to\; -\frac{1}{\sqrt{2}} \leq b \leq \frac{1}{\sqrt{2}}$. Since $b > 0$, the solution set is

$\boxed{0 < b \leq \dfrac{\sqrt{2}}{2}}$.

T–7. Let $K = \dfrac{a-b}{c} = \dfrac{b+c}{a} = \dfrac{a-c}{b}$. Then $a - b = Kc$, $b + c = Ka$, and $a - c = Kb$. Adding these three

equations yields $2a = K(a+b+c)$, so $\dfrac{a}{a+b+c} = \dfrac{K}{2}$. Since $b + c = Ka$, then

$a + b + c = a + Ka = a(K+1)$. Thus, we also have $\dfrac{a}{a+b+c} = \dfrac{a}{a(K+1)} = \dfrac{1}{K+1}$ making $\dfrac{K}{2} = \dfrac{1}{K+1}$

$\to\; K^2 + K - 2 = 0 \;\to\; K = -2$ or 1. Thus, the possible values for $\dfrac{a}{a+b+c}$ are $\boxed{-1 \text{ and } \dfrac{1}{2}}$.

These values are possible. For $a = 2$, $b = 1$, and $c = 1$, then $\dfrac{a-b}{c} = \dfrac{b+c}{a} = \dfrac{a-c}{b} = 1$ and

$\dfrac{a}{a+b+c} = \dfrac{1}{2}$. For $a = -1, b = 1$, and $c = 1$, then $\dfrac{a-b}{c} = \dfrac{b+c}{a} = \dfrac{a-c}{b} = -2$ and $\dfrac{a}{a+b+c} = -1$.

T–8. Let the coordinates of P and Q be $P(p, 2p)$ and $Q(2q, q)$.

Since P and Q are lattice points, then $0 < 2p \leq 99$ and

$0 < 2q \leq 99$ gives integers p and q such that $1 \leq p, q \leq 49$.

The trisection points are $A\left(p + \dfrac{2q-p}{3}, 2p + \dfrac{q-2p}{3} \right)$ and

$B\left(2q - \dfrac{2q-p}{3}, q - \dfrac{q-2p}{3} \right)$. Thus, for integral m and n,

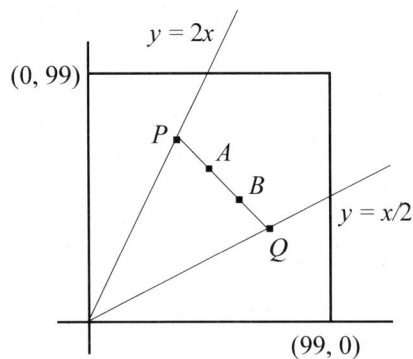

$2q - p = 3m$ and $q - 2p = 3n$. Subtracting the second

equation from the first yields $p + q = 3(m-n) \;\to\; p+q$ is divisible by 3. There are three cases:

1) $p \equiv 0 \,(\text{mod }3) \;\to\; q \equiv 0 \,(\text{mod }3)$. Thus, p takes on any one of 16 values from 3 to 48 as does q. Thus there are $16 \cdot 16$ pairs of (P, Q).

2) $p \equiv 1 \,(\text{mod }3) \;\to\; q \equiv 2 \,(\text{mod }3)$. In this case, p takes on any one of 17 values from 1 to 49 while q takes on any one of 16 values from 2 to 47. Here there are $17 \cdot 16$ pairs.

3) $p \equiv 2 \,(\text{mod }3) \;\to\; q \equiv 1 \,(\text{mod }3)$ giving $16 \cdot 17$ pairs as in case 2.

Thus, the total number of pairs of points (P, Q) equals $16 \cdot 16 + 17 \cdot 16 + 16 \cdot 17 =$

$16(16 + 17 + 17) = 16 \cdot 50 = \boxed{800}$.

6

T–9. To go from each term to the next term, apply the transform $x \to 100x + 134$. This is the same (mod 99) as $x \to x + 35$. Starting at 24, the nth term after the first is divisible by 99 iff $24 + 35n \equiv 0 \pmod{99}$ $\Leftrightarrow$ $2 + 2n \equiv 0 \pmod{11}$ and $6 + 8n \equiv 0 \pmod 9$ $\Leftrightarrow$ $n \equiv 10 \pmod{11}$ and $n \equiv 6 \pmod 9$ $\Leftrightarrow$ $n \equiv 87 \pmod{99}$. Since $n = 87$ is the first solution to this equation, the 88th term is divisible by 99 and this has $\boxed{176}$ digits.

Alternate solution: Let N_d be the number in the sequence with d digits. We have divisibility by 11 if the alternating sum of the digits is divisible by 11. Starting with 24 the alternating sum is –2 and each insertion of a 53 reduces the sum by –2, so the alternating sum of the digits in N_d is $A_d = -d$. We have divisibility by 9 if the sum of the digits is divisible by 9. Since the sum of the digits of 24 and 53 is 6 and 8 respectively, the sum of the digits in N_d is $S_d = 4d - 2$. Since N_d is divisible by $99 = 11 \cdot 9$ if and only if $A_d \equiv 0 \pmod{11}$ and $S_d \equiv 0 \pmod 9$, solve $-d \equiv 0 \pmod{11}$ and $(4d - 2) \equiv 0 \pmod 9$. This amounts to solving the system $-d = 11t$ and $4d - 2 = 9r$ for integral t, r, and d. Eliminating d we have

$$9r = -44t - 2 = -45t + t - 2 \to r = -5t + \frac{t-2}{9}.$$ Clearly, t must be negative. Starting with –1, we obtain our first solution at $t = -7$ and $r = 34$, but this gives $d = 77$ and d must be even. The next solution is at $t = -16$, giving $r = 78$, making $d = 176$.

T–10. In *ARMLog 95* a theorem sometimes known as the British Flag Theorem was proved: Given rectangle $ABCD$ and point P, then $PA^2 + PC^2 = PB^2 + PD^2$. This is true if P lies inside, outside, or above the rectangle. In this problem, by the British Flag Theorem or by repeated use of the Pythagorean Theorem, we have $YE^2 + YR^2 = YA^2 + YL^2$.

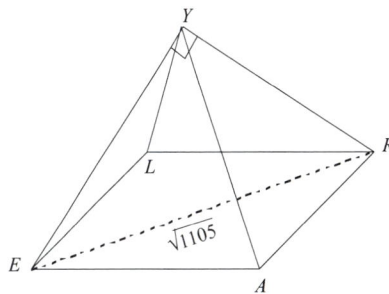

By the Pythagorean Theorem, each of these is equal to $EA^2 + AR^2 = ER^2 = 1105$. Note that 1105 can be written as the sum of two squares in 4 different ways: $4^2 + 33^2 = 9^2 + 32^2 = 12^2 + 31^2 = 23^2 + 24^2 = 1105$. Thus, to form the edges of *EARLY*, the ordered pairs (EA, AR), (EY, RY), and (AY, LY) must be drawn from the set $\{(4, 33), (9, 32), (12, 31), (23, 24)\}$. We cannot use (23, 24). If we did, the triangle inequality would be violated in one of the triangles *EAY*, *ARY*, *RLY* and *LEY*. To see this, first let 23 and 24 be the sides of base *EARL*. Then either (4, 9), (4, 12), or (9, 12) would be lengths of two segments from the base to vertex *Y*. These lengths would form two sides of a triangle whose third side is either 23, 24, or $\sqrt{1105} \approx 33.24$, violating the triangle inequality.

7

Second, let 23 and 24 be edges rising to *Y* from opposite corners of the base. Let 12 and 31 be the sides of *EARL* and let 9 and 32 be the lengths of the edges rising to *Y* from the other pair of opposite corners. We are forced to have a 9-12-23 or a 9-12-24 triangle, again violating the triangle inequality. In a similar fashion, the triangle inequality is violated for all pairs of (4, 9), (4, 12), and (9, 12) where one pair serves as the edges of the base and the other as risers to *Y*.

Since (23, 24) cannot be used, we must use (12, 31), (9, 32) and (4, 33). Segments with lengths of 4 and 9 must form two sides of a triangle. For example, if (4, 33) forms the base, a segment of length 9 will rise from one of the four corners, forming a triangle with sides 4 and 9. If (9, 32) forms the base, a segment of length 4 will rise from one of the four corners. If segments of length 4 and 9 are both ascending to *Y*, they will also form two sides of a triangle. The only segment that can be the third side without violating the triangle inequality is the 12. This means there is a face with sides 4, 9, and 12. It must have the smallest area (try all other combinations) and by Heron's formula its area is

$$\sqrt{\frac{25}{2} \cdot \left(\frac{25}{2} - 4\right) \cdot \left(\frac{25}{2} - 9\right) \cdot \left(\frac{25}{2} - 12\right)} = \boxed{\frac{5\sqrt{119}}{4}}.$$

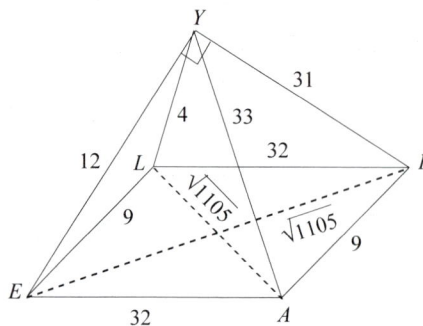

Note: We could also think of each possible pyramid as half an octahedron inscribed in a sphere of diameter $\sqrt{1105}$. Viewed in this way, it doesn't matter which pair of numbers is used to form the base. Then the trouble with (23, 24) is that each length is smaller than the differences between (4, 33) and (9, 32) and at least one of (4, 33) and (9, 32) must be used to form faces with (23, 24).

8

Let S denote a finite sequence of numbers. A *subsequence* of S consists of some terms of S in their original order. S is considered to be a subsequence of itself. The empty sequence, a sequence of zero terms which we denote by $\emptyset$, is also a subsequence of S. For any sequence S, let $N(S)$ be the number of distinct subsequences of S. For example, if $S = 3, 4, 3, 4$, then $N(S) = N(3, 4, 3, 4) = 12$ because S has the following 12 distinct subsequences:

$\emptyset$	3	4	3, 4
3, 3	4, 4	4, 3	3, 4, 3
3, 4, 4	3, 3, 4	4, 3, 4	3, 4, 3, 4

1. Find $N(S)$ for each of the following sequences S:

   a) 1, 2, 2, 1   b) 4, 4, 4, 2, 4   c) 6, 6, 6, 6, 6, 6, 6   d) 1, 2, 3, 4, 5, 6

2. a) Suppose that S is a subsequence of T. Prove that $N(S) \leq N(T)$.

   b) Let T be the sequence obtained from S by writing the terms of S in reverse order. Show that $N(S) = N(T)$.

3. Let S be a sequence with k terms. Show that $k + 1 \leq N(S) \leq 2^k$.

For sequences S and T, we will write ST for the sequence obtained by adding, i.e., appending the terms of T in their original order to the end of the terms of S. For example, if $S = 1, 2, 3$ and $T = 4, 2, 2$, then $ST = 1, 2, 3, 4, 2, 2$ and $TS = 4, 2, 2, 1, 2, 3$. Also, for n a number, we will use n to represent the one-term sequence whose term is n. If $S = 1, 2, 3$, then by nS we mean the sequence $n, 1, 2, 3$.

4. a) If n is a number that does not appear in the sequence S, prove that $N(nS) = 2N(S)$.

   b) Suppose that n does not appear in S, but may appear in the sequence T. Prove that $N(nSnT) = 2N(SnT) - N(T)$.

5. Using problem 4 or otherwise, compute $N(1, 2, 3, 2, 3, 4, 3, 2, 3, 2)$. Explain your reasoning.

6. Find an example of a sequence S with 11 terms such that $N(S) = 2004$. Prove that your answer is correct.

7. a) If S and T are any two sequences, prove that $N(ST) \leq N(S) \cdot N(T)$.

   b) If S has k terms, prove that $N(ST) \geq \dfrac{N(S) \cdot N(T)}{k + 1}$.

8.   The sequence U is a *final segment* of S if there exists a sequence T such that $S = TU$. Prove that for any non-empty sequence S, there exists a collection $U_1, U_2, \ldots, U_k$ of different final segments of S such that $N(S) - 1$ can be written as $N\left(U_1\right) + N\left(U_2\right) + \ldots + N\left(U_k\right)$.

9.   Let S be a sequence with k terms. Prove that $N(S) \neq 2^k - 3$.

10.   Let S be a sequence with k terms. Prove that at least one of the numbers

$$N(S), N(SS), N(SSS), \ldots, N(\underbrace{SS \ldots S}_{k+1}) \text{ is odd.}$$

1. a) There are 11 subsequences:

$$\varnothing \qquad 1 \qquad 2 \qquad 1,2$$
$$1,1 \qquad 2,2 \qquad 2,1 \qquad 1,2,2$$
$$1,2,1 \qquad 2,2,1 \qquad 1,2,2,1$$

b) There are 13 subsequences:

$$\varnothing \qquad 2 \qquad 4 \qquad 4,4 \qquad 4,2$$
$$2,4 \qquad 4,4,4 \qquad 4,4,2 \qquad 4,2,4$$
$$4,4,4,2 \qquad 4,4,4,4 \qquad 4,4,2,4 \qquad 4,4,4,2,4$$

c) Subsequences may have any length from zero to seven terms, and for each length, we obtain just one possible subsequence, since all the terms must be 6. Therefore, there are 8 subsequences.

d) For each term we may choose whether to include it or not in our subsequence. Since all terms are distinct, all the subsequences we obtain in this manner will be different. Thus, there are $2^6 = 64$ different subsequences.

2. a) Every subsequence of S is also a subsequence of T. Thus, $N(S) \le N(T)$.

b) If U is a subsequence of S then the sequence obtained by writing U backwards is a subsequence of T. Conversely, if V is a subsequence of T, then the sequence obtained by writing V backwards is a subsequence of S. Since we have one-to-one correspondence between the subsequences of S and the subsequences of T, these two collections are of the same size.

3. First, let's show that $N(S) \ge k + 1$. Consider the following subsequences: $\varnothing$, the subsequence consisting of the first term of S, the subsequence consisting of the first two terms of S, the subsequence consisting of the first three terms of S, and so on, up to all of S. This gives us $k + 1$ subsequences of S and since their lengths are different, they are all distinct. So, $N(S) \ge k + 1$.

Second, let's show that $N(S) \le 2^k$. To construct a subsequence of S we simply go through the terms of S and decide, for each term, whether or not to include it. This gives us 2^k subsequences. Some repetitions may occur, but, in any event, every subsequence will appear at least once. Thus, $N(S) \le 2^k$.

4. a) Any subsequence of nS either starts with the term n or it doesn't. If it does, the rest of the subsequence is a subsequence of S. Conversely, any subsequence of S becomes a subsequence of nS if we stick n on at the beginning. So, we have $N(S)$ such subsequences. If our subsequence doesn't start with n, it is simply a subsequence of S and, conversely, no subsequence starts with n. So we have $N(S)$ such subsequences. Thus, altogether we have $2N(S)$ subsequences of nS.

4. b) The reasoning is similar. If a subsequence of $nSnT$ starts with n, then the remaining portion is a subsequence of SnT, and we obtain $N(SnT)$ such subsequences. If our subsequence doesn't start with n, it is simply a subsequence of $N(SnT)$, so we again have $N(SnT)$ such subsequences, except that we must now subtract off the number of subsequences of SnT that start with n. In any such subsequence, stripping off the initial n leaves a subsequence of T since there is no n in S. Conversely, any subsequence of T can be made into a subsequence of SnT by sticking an n before it. So, there are $N(T)$ subsequences of SnT that start with n. Therefore, the number of subsequences of $nSnT$ is $2N(SnT) - N(T)$.

5. Problem 4 gives an algorithm for computing the number of subsequences recursively. We calculate the number of subsequences of the last term, then the last two terms, then the last three terms, and so forth. So, to compute $N(1, 2, 3, 2, 3, 4, 3, 2, 3, 2)$ do the following:

$N(\varnothing) = 1$	
$N(2) = 2$	This is by observation or using 4a with $S = \varnothing$
$N(3, 2) = 2N(2) = 4$	By 4a with $S = 2$
$N(2, 3, 2) = 2N(3, 2) - N(\varnothing) = 7$	By 4b with $S = 3$, $T = \varnothing$
$N(3, 2, 3, 2) = 2N(2, 3, 2) - N(2) = 12$	By 4b with $S = 2$, $T = 2$
$N(4, 3, 2, 3, 2) = 2N(3, 2, 3, 2) = 24$	By 4a
$N(3, 4, 3, 2, 3, 2) = 2N(4, 3, 2, 3, 2) - N(2, 3, 2) = 41$	By 4b
$N(2, 3, 4, 3, 2, 3, 2) = 2N(3, 4, 2, 3, 2) - N(3, 2) = 78$	By 4b
$N(3, 2, 3, 4, 3, 2, 3, 2) = 2N(2, 3, 4, 3, 2, 3, 2) - N(4, 3, 2, 3, 2) = 132$	By 4b
$N(2, 3, 2, 3, 4, 3, 2, 3, 2) = 2N(3, 2, 3, 4, 3, 2, 3, 2) - N(3, 4, 3, 2, 3, 2) = 233$	By 4b
$N(1, 2, 3, 2, 3, 4, 3, 2, 3, 2) = 2N(2, 3, 2, 3, 4, 3, 2, 3, 2) = 446$	By 4a

6. One such sequence is 6, 3, 1, 8, 7, 6, 5, 4, 3, 2, 1. To see that this meets the requirement, notice that $N(8, 7, 6, 5, 4, 3, 2, 1) = 2^8 = 256$ as indicated by problem 1d or by repeated application of (4a). Then by (4b), we have $N(1, 8, 7, \ldots, 2, 1) = 2 \cdot 256 - 1 = 511$. By (4b) again we have $N(3, 1, 8, \ldots, 2, 1) = 2 \cdot 511 - 4 = 1018$. Finally, we have $N(6, 3, 1, 8, \ldots, 2, 1) = 2 \cdot 1018 - 32 = 2004$.

7. a) Every subsequence of ST consists of a subsequence of S followed by a subsequence of T. There may be more than one way to perform this splitting, but in any case, the two parts uniquely determine the whole subsequence of ST. So the number of subsequences of ST is at most the number of ways to choose the two parts which is $N(S) \cdot N(T)$.

    b) We now ask: for a given subsequence U of ST, how many different possible decompositions into an S-part and a T-part are there? The part coming from S consists of the first i terms of U for some i, and the part coming from T consists of the remaining terms. The value of i then uniquely determines the part coming from S and the part coming from T. But since S only has k terms, then $i \leq k$. In other words, our subsequence of ST has at most $k+1$ possible decompositions into a part in S and a part in T, one decomposition for each value of i. Since there are $N(S) \cdot N(T)$ possible pairs of parts and each subsequence of ST decomposes into at most $k+1$ such pairs, we see that there are at least $\dfrac{N(S) \cdot N(T)}{k+1}$ subsequences of ST. Thus, $N(ST) \geq \dfrac{N(S) \cdot N(T)}{k+1}$.

8. Let $n_1, n_2, \ldots, n_k$ be the different terms appearing in S. For each $i = 1, \ldots, k$, let U_i be the final segment of S beginning just after the first occurrence of n_i. Note that $N(S) - 1$ is the number of non-empty subsequences of S. Each such subsequence begins with one of the terms $n_1, n_2, \ldots, n_k$, so if we can show that $N(U_i)$ is the number of subsequences of S beginning with n_i, we will be done. But in any subsequence of S beginning with n_i, removing the first term gives a subsequence of S that must occur after the first n_i, i.e. a subsequence of U_i. Conversely, any subsequence of U_i can be turned into a subsequence of S by sticking n_i in front of it. So, the subsequences of S beginning with n_i correspond to the subsequences of U_i, thereby completing the proof.

    Alternately, we can prove much more. Let m be the length of S. Let V_i be the sequence consisting of the last i terms of S for each $i = 0, 1, \ldots, m$. These final segments satisfy $N(V_{k+1}) \leq 2N(V_k)$, so the numbers $N(V_k)$ form a sub-binary sequence starting $\{1, 2, \ldots\}$. So, every number from 1 to $\sum N(V_k)$ can be written as the sum of distinct $N(V_k)$'s. To prove this, note, as is easily shown by induction, that $1 + 2 + \ldots + N(V_i) \leq N(V_{i+1})$. Then assume that $1, 2, \ldots, N(V_i)$ generates every number from 1 to $1 + 2 + \ldots + N(V_i)$ and let $1 + 2 + \ldots + N(V_i) < n \leq 1 + 2 + \ldots + N(V_{i+1})$. Then $n - N(V_{i+1})$ is one of those numbers from 1 to $1 + 2 + \ldots + N(V_i)$ and can be written as a sum of elements of $\{1, 2, \ldots, N(V_{i+1})\}$. Since $N(S) - 1 = N(V_m) - 1 < 1 + 2 + \ldots + N(V_m)$, the result applies to $N(S) - 1$.

9. Suppose otherwise. For each $i = 0, 1, \ldots, n$, let U_i be the sequence consisting of the last i terms of S. Then $N(U_0) = 1$ and by problem 4, for each $i > 0$, we have $N(U_i) = 2N(U_{i-1})$ or $2N(U_{i-1}) - N(U_j)$ for some $j < i - 1$. We first claim that $N(U_i) = 2^i$ for $i \leq n - 2$ because if otherwise, then by problem 2 we have $N(U_i) \leq 2^i - 1$. If that is so, then write $S = T_i U_i$ where T_i has $n - i$ terms, and then by problem 7a we have $N(S) \leq 2^{n-i}(2^i - 1) \leq 2^n - 4$, and that is a contradiction.

Next we claim that $N\left(U_{n-1}\right) = 2^{n-1}$ or $2^{n-1} - 1$ because otherwise we would have

$N\left(U_{n-1}\right) \leq 2^{n-1} - 2$ and $N\left(S_n\right) \leq 2^n - 4$, a contradiction. First, suppose that $N\left(U_{n-1}\right) = 2^{n-1}$. Then by our earlier application of problem 4, $N(S) = 2^n - 3$ requires that $N\left(U_j\right) = 3$ for some j. But every $N\left(U_j\right)$ so far has been a power of 2 so this is impossible. Therefore, $N\left(U_{n-1}\right) = 2^{n-1} - 1 =$ $2N\left(U_{n-2}\right) - N\left(U_0\right)$ and by problem 4 this means that the first term of U_{n-1}, which is the second term of S, equals the last term of U_{n-1}, and also that this term never appears in S in between these two positions. But then $N(S) = 2^n - 3 = 2N\left(U_{n-1}\right)$ means, by the same logic, that the first term of S equals the last term and that this term never appears between these two positions. However, this term appears in the second position of S. So, we have a contradiction unless S has at most 2 terms. But we can check that $N(S) = 2^n - 3$ is not possible for $n \leq 2$, so we have completed the proof.

Alternately, as in #3, generate 2^k subsequences of S and let L be the list of those subsequences. There may be repetition, meaning that some of the subsequences may be duplicates. If $N(S)$ is to equal $2^k - 3$, then there must be exactly 3 duplicates in L. We will show that this is impossible. First, let S' be a duplicate of maximum length. Observe that for $N(S)$ to equal $2^k - 3$, then S' can have no more than 2 terms. If S' had 3 or more terms, then there would be subsequences of S' that would also be duplicated. For example, assume that $S' = a\,b\,c$. For $a\,b\,c$ to be a duplicate, we would have to have $a\,b\,c\,c$, $a\,b\,b\,c$, or $a\,a\,b\,c$ as subsequences of S. Then either the subsequences $a\,b\,c$, $a\,b$, $b\,c$, and b, the subsequences $a\,b\,c$, $a\,b$, $b\,c$, and b, or the subsequences $a\,b\,c$, $a\,b$, $a\,c$, and a would appear twice, generating many more than 3 duplicates in L. In similar fashion if $S' = a\,a\,b$ or $a\,a\,a$, more than 3 duplicates would be generated from the subsequence that led to duplicates of S'. Thus, we need only consider three cases corresponding to the three possible lengths of S':

  i) If the length of S' is 0, then there are no duplicated subsequences and so $N(S) = 2^k$.

  ii) If the length of S' is 1, then there is one duplicated letter a. If $S = a\,a\,T$, for some sequence T, then there would be duplicated subsequences of more than 1 term and that would be a contradiction.
  If $S = a\,T\,a\,U$, we have the same problem. If $S = a\,T\,a$, then T cannot contain a and T must have no duplicates since if T has a duplicate b, then we would have duplicates $a\,b\,a$ of length 3, contradicting our assumption that the length of S' is 1. Thus, there are no other duplications so $N(a\,T\,a) = 2^k - 1$.

iii) If the length of S' is 2, then S must equal $a\,T\,a\,b$ or $a\,b\,T\,b$ where a and b are not necessarily distinct. As in (ii) arrangements such as $a\,a\,T\,b$ are impossible because they generate duplications of length 3 or more. By (2b) we know that $a\,T\,a\,b$ and $a\,b\,T\,b$ have the same number of subsequences so we need consider only $a\,T\,a\,b$. As in (ii) T can't contain a or any duplications. If T contains at least one b, then we would have two subsequences of a, two of b, and three of $a\,b$, ensuring that $N(S) \neq 2^k - 3$.

If T doesn't contain any b's, then by (4b), $N(a\,T\,a\,b) = 2N(T\,a\,b) - N(b) = 2^k - 2$.

Thus, it is impossible for $N(S)$ to equal $2^k - 3$.

10.   Intuitively, the problem of deciding whether $N(U)$ is odd for some sequence U can be accomplished using the following "hopping" procedure. Imagine that we can hop from one term of U to another, from left to right and that we can even hop to a space after the end of U. If we are on any term x of U, we find the next occurrence of the same term x in U and hop to the position immediately after this next x. If this x lies at the end of U then we hop to the space after the end of U. If there is no subsequence occurrence of x then we stop hopping. We claim that $N(U)$ is odd precisely when if we start from the first term of U, we can reach the position after U by repeated hopping. We can prove this by induction on the length of U: the base case where U is empty is trivial since we start at the end of U. Otherwise, if the first term x of U does not appear again in U, then by problem 4a, $N(U)$ is even. If x does reappear, then by 4b, $N(U)$ has the same parity as $N(V)$ where V is the final segment starting from the position after the next x, and by induction, $N(V)$ is odd if and only if subsequent hopping gets us to the position after the end of U. This proves that the hopping method works.

More formally, consider an infinite sequence $a_1, a_2, a_3, \ldots$ such that each term appearing in the sequence appears infinitely many times. Define a function f on positive integers as follows: given m, if $t > m$ is the next value such that $a_t = a_m$, then $f(m) = t + 1$. Then, if p is one of the numbers

$f(1), f(f(1)), f(f(f(1))), \ldots$, then $N\!\left(a_1, a_2, \ldots, a_{p-1}\right)$ is odd. The proof is a straightforward induction using problem 4b as described in the paragraph above. Now, let our infinite sequence be

$a_1, a_2, \ldots a_k, a_1, a_2, \ldots a_k, \ldots a_1, a_2, \ldots a_k, \ldots$. It is clear from the periodicity of the sequence that our function f satisfies $f(m + k) = f(m) + k$ for any k. Therefore, f gives us a well-defined function f_k from the set of integers modulo k to itself. Moreover, we claim that f_k is a permutation of these integers. To see this, it suffices to notice that f_k is onto. For example, given any value of c_k modulo k, we can choose $c > k + 1$ to assume that value. Then the value of the term a_{c-1} must have occurred at some earlier point in the sequence, at a_{c-1-k} for example. Let a_m be the most recent occurrence. Then $f(m) = c$, so f_k assumes the value c_k as desired.

15

Since f_k is a permutation of the set of integers modulo k, if we start with the value 1 and repeatedly apply f_k, we will eventually get back to 1. Moreover, because there are only k values in this set, we need to iterate f_k at most k times. Translating this back in terms of f, we see that one of the numbers $f(1), f(f(1)), \ldots, \underbrace{f(f(\cdots f(1)\cdots))}_{k}$ is congruent to 1 modulo k. Let this value be $kn + 1$. Thus,

$N(a_1, a_2, \ldots, a_{kn}) = N(\underbrace{SS \cdots S}_{n})$ is odd. Moreover, for any m, $f(m) \leq m + k + 1$ because our infinite

sequence is periodic, so the next occurrence of a_m is at most k terms later. Therefore, since $kn + 1$ was obtained from 1 by iterating f at most k times, we have $kn + 1 \leq k(k + 1) + 1 \;\rightarrow\; n \leq k + 1$. This completes the proof.

Incidentally, no better bound than $k + 1$ will do. By letting $S = 1, 2, \ldots, k$ and using the same procedure, we can see that $N(S), N(SS), \ldots, N(SS \cdots S)$ with at most k repetitions will all be even.

Alternately, for a sequence U of the form $nSnT$ as in problem 4b, write $U_1 = SnT$ and $U' = T$ so that the result in (4b) can be written as $N(U) = 2N(U_1) - N(U')$. So U' is the truncation of U after the second occurrence of the first term in U. For example, if $U = 21231$, then $U' = 31$. Since $N(U) \equiv N(U') \bmod 2$, $N(U)$ will be odd if some one of $U', U'', U''', \ldots = \varnothing$. Thus, for $U = SSS \ldots S$, we start at the end and go backwards, adding two occurrences of the term immediately preceding it to see how many truncations are needed to get there. Since S is repeated in U, we treat it as cyclical. For example, if $S = 21231$, let the decimal point represent our place.

21231.	(starting at the end)
2.1231	
21.231	(new cycle)
2123.1	(new cycle)
212.31	(new cycle)
.21231	

Thus, four cycles are needed and five truncations of $21231\ 21231\ 21231\ 21231$ give $\varnothing$. In general, since we stop when we first return 0 (the start/end of S), there can be no repeats and by the pigeonhole principle, we will arrive there after at most k steps. The largest step occurs at singletons of S (3 in the example) in which case the decimal point moves $1 + \dfrac{1}{k}$ cycles. The maximum required is $k\left(1 + \dfrac{1}{k}\right) = k + 1$ cycles or copies of S.

I–1. Let a, b, c, d, and e be distinct elements of $\{-10, -9, \ldots, 9, 10\}$.

Compute the least value of $a + e$ given the following equations:

$$a - b = 2$$
$$c - b = -3$$
$$c - d = 4$$
$$e - d = -5$$

I–2. In the unit circle with center O, $\overset{\frown}{AC} \cong \overset{\frown}{CE} \cong \overset{\frown}{EA}$, chords $\overline{AD}$, $\overline{CF}$, and $\overline{EB}$ are equidistant from O, and the four inscribed circles are congruent. Compute the area of any one of the four small circles.

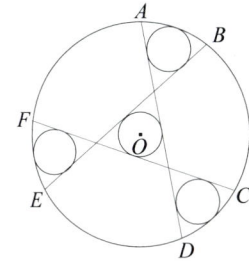

I–3. For $0 < k < 6$, the graphs of $\dfrac{(x-k)^2}{9} + y^2 = 1$

and $\dfrac{x^2}{9} + y^2 = 1$ intersect at A and C and have

x-intercepts at B and D respectively. Compute the value of k for which $ABCD$ is a square.

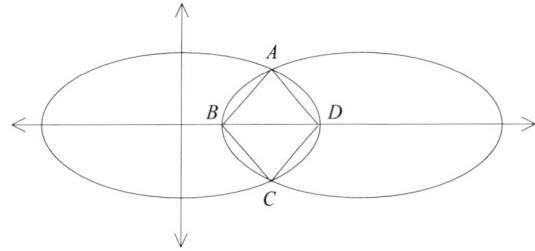

I–4. If $\sqrt[3]{2} = a + \cfrac{1}{b + \cfrac{1}{c + \cfrac{1}{d + \cdots}}}$ where $a, b, c, d, \ldots$ are positive integers, compute b.

I–5. Compute the area of the polygon whose vertices are the solutions in the complex plane to
$x^7 + x^6 + x^5 + x^4 + x^3 + x^2 + x + 1 = 0$. Express the area in simplest form as $\dfrac{a\sqrt{b} + c}{d}$.

I–6. The Fibonacci sequence is defined as $a_1 = 1, a_2 = 1$ and $a_n = a_{n-1} + a_{n-2}$ for each $n > 2$.
Compute $\displaystyle\sum_{j=1}^{2004} \left(i^{2004 - a_j} \right)$ where $i = \sqrt{-1}$.

I–7. Compute the number of integer values of n, $1 \le n \le 2004$, such that for each value of n the following inequality has exactly two integer solutions: $\left| \dfrac{nx}{2004} - 1 \right| > \dfrac{n}{2004}$.

I–8. In a game, A flips a fair coin two times. B then flips the coin until B's last two flips form a different sequence than A's. For example, if A flips HH, then B would stop flipping after each of HT, HHT or HHHT, and B's sequence would be HT. C then flips the coin until either A's sequence or B's occurs in consecutive flips. The player whose sequence occurs is the winner. Compute the probability that A wins.

1. –6

2. $\dfrac{\pi}{25}$

3. $\dfrac{24}{5}$

4. 3

5. $\dfrac{3\sqrt{2}+1}{2}$

6. $-668i$

7. 1992

8. $\dfrac{33}{64}$

I–1.   Multiply the second and fourth equations by –1 to obtain:

$$a - b = 2$$
$$b - c = 3$$
$$c - d = 4$$
$$d - e = 5$$

Add the equations to obtain $a - e = 14$, then add $2e$ to both sides, obtaining $a + e = 2e + 14$. Since the minimum value of $2e$ is –20, then the minimum of $a + e = -20 + 14 = \boxed{-6}$. This occurs for $a = 4$, $b = 2$, $c = -1$, $d = -5$, and $e = -10$.

Method #2: Adding the equations in the original system gives $a - 2b + 2c - 2d + e = -2 \rightarrow$ $a + 2(c - b - d) + e = -2$. Since $c - b = -3$ we have $a + 2(-3 - d) + e = -2 \rightarrow a + e = 2d + 4$. To minimize $a + e$, pick d as small as possible, but make sure all other conditions are satisfied. For example, if $d = -10$, then $a + e = -16$, but $e - d = -5$ makes $e = -15$ which lies outside the set. The smallest value of d that gives a valid value for e is $d = -5$. This makes $a + e = -6$ as above.

I–2.   Let the radius of any of the small circles be r and note that $\overline{PC}$ lies on chord $\overline{FC}$, $\overline{MD}$ on $\overline{AD}$, and $\overline{PM}$ on $\overline{BE}$. MNP is an equilateral triangle by the symmetries in the problem. Let $OT = r$, then $ON = 2r$, $RS = r$, and $RN = 2r$. Thus, the radius of the large circle OS equals $5r$. Since $5r = 1$,

the area of a small circle is $\pi \left(\dfrac{1}{5} \right)^2 = \boxed{\dfrac{\pi}{25}}$.

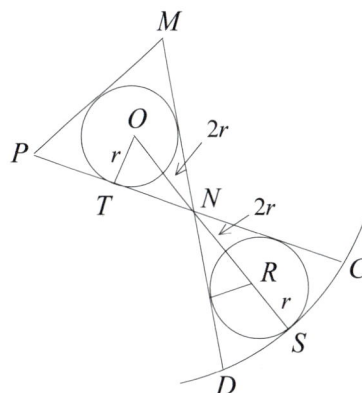

I–3.   From $\left(\dfrac{(x-k)^2}{9} + y^2 = 1 \right) - \left(\dfrac{x^2}{9} + y^2 = 1 \right)$ we obtain $(x-k)^2 - x^2 = 0 \rightarrow x = \dfrac{k}{2}$. Substituting into

the second equation yields $\dfrac{k^2}{36} + y^2 = 1 \rightarrow y = \dfrac{\sqrt{36 - k^2}}{6}$ as the y-coordinate of A. In general, $ABCD$ is

a rhombus since $\overline{AC}$ is the perpendicular bisector of $\overline{BD}$ and vice versa. It is a square if $BD = AC$. Given

$B(-3 + k, 0)$ and $D(3, 0)$ then $BD = 6 - k$; $AC = 2y = \dfrac{\sqrt{36 - k^2}}{3}$. Thus, $6 - k = \dfrac{\sqrt{36 - k^2}}{3} \rightarrow$

$10k^2 - 108k + 288 = 0 \rightarrow (5k - 24)(k - 6) = 0$. Thus, $k = 6$ or $\dfrac{24}{5}$. We reject 6 since that makes the

ellipses tangent. Answer: $\boxed{\dfrac{24}{5}}$.

Note: for the general case $\dfrac{(x - k)^2}{a^2} + \dfrac{y^2}{b^2} = 1$ and $\dfrac{x^2}{a^2} + \dfrac{y^2}{b^2} = 1$ the answer is $\dfrac{2a(a^2 - b^2)}{a^2 + b^2}$.

I–4.   Since $1 < \sqrt[3]{2} < 2$, then $a = 1$, giving $\sqrt[3]{2} - 1 = \cfrac{1}{b + \cfrac{1}{c + \cfrac{1}{d + \ldots}}}$. Thus, $\sqrt[3]{2} - 1 < \dfrac{1}{b}$ $\rightarrow$ $\dfrac{1}{\sqrt[3]{2} - 1} < b$

$\rightarrow$ $b = \left[\dfrac{1}{\sqrt[3]{2} - 1} \right] = \left[\dfrac{1}{\sqrt[3]{2} - 1} \cdot \dfrac{\sqrt[3]{2}^2 + \sqrt[3]{2} + 1}{\sqrt[3]{2}^2 + \sqrt[3]{2} + 1} \right] = \left[\dfrac{\sqrt[3]{2}^2 + \sqrt[3]{2} + 1}{2 - 1} \right] = \left[\sqrt[3]{4} + \sqrt[3]{2} + 1 \right]$. Since

$1 < \sqrt[3]{2} < \sqrt[3]{4} < 2$, then b must equal 3 or 4. Since $2 < 1.3^3 = 2.197$ and $4 < 1.6^3 = 4.096$, then

$\sqrt[3]{2} + \sqrt[3]{4} < 2.9$, so $b = \left[3.9 \right] = \boxed{3}$.

Method #2: As above obtain $\sqrt[3]{4} + \sqrt[3]{2} + 1 > b$ and the conclusion that b must equal 3 or 4. Let

$x + 1 = \sqrt[3]{4} + \sqrt[3]{2} + 1 \rightarrow x = \sqrt[3]{4} + \sqrt[3]{2} \rightarrow x^3 = 4 + 3\sqrt[3]{32} + 3\sqrt[3]{16} + 2 = 6 + 3 \cdot 2\left(\sqrt[3]{4} + \sqrt[3]{2} \right)$.

Thus, $x^3 = 6 + 6x \rightarrow x^3 - 6x - 6 = 0$. Let $f(x) = x^3 - 6x - 6$. Since $f(2) = -10$ and $f(3) = 3$,

then $2 < x < 3 \rightarrow 3 > x + 1 > 4$. Thus, $b < 4$, so $b = 3$.

I–5.   Let $P(x) = x^7 + x^6 + x^5 + x^4 + x^3 + x^2 + x + 1$. Let

$Q(x) = (x - 1)P(x) = x^8 - 1$. The solutions in the complex

plane to $Q(x) = 0$ are the vertices of regular octagon $ABCDEFGH$.

The solutions to $P(x) = 0$ are the solutions to $Q(x) = 0$ except for

$x = 1$. Thus, we seek the area of heptagon $BCDEFGH$. The

heptagon can be divided into six triangles each of which has the

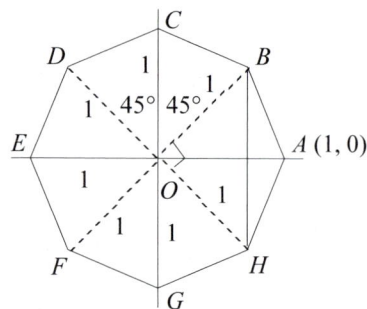

area $\dfrac{1}{2} \cdot 1 \cdot 1 \cdot \sin 45° = \dfrac{\sqrt{2}}{4}$ and right triangle BOH whose area is $\dfrac{1}{2} \cdot 1 \cdot 1 = \dfrac{1}{2}$.

The total area is $6 \cdot \dfrac{\sqrt{2}}{4} + \dfrac{1}{2} = \boxed{\dfrac{3\sqrt{2} + 1}{2}}$.

I–6. $i^{2004} = \left(i^4 \right)^{501} = 1$, so $\displaystyle\sum_{j=1}^{2004} \left(i^{2004 - a_j} \right) = \sum_{j=1}^{2004} \dfrac{1}{i^{a_j}}$. Writing out the Fibonacci sequence modulo 4 we

have $1, 1, 2, 3, 1, 0, 1, 1, 2, \ldots$ so the sequence mod 4 repeats itself every six terms. Since $\dfrac{2004}{6} = 334$, the

sum is $334\left(\dfrac{1}{i} + \dfrac{1}{i} + \dfrac{1}{i^2} + \dfrac{1}{i^3} + \dfrac{1}{i} + \dfrac{1}{i^0} \right) = 334 \cdot (-2i) = \boxed{-668i}$.

I–7. $\left| \dfrac{nx}{2004} - 1 \right| < \dfrac{n}{2004}$ $\rightarrow$ $-\dfrac{n}{2004} > \dfrac{nx}{2004} - 1 > \dfrac{n}{2004}$ $\rightarrow$ $\dfrac{2004}{n} - 1 < x < \dfrac{2004}{n} + 1$. The width of this

interval is $\left(\dfrac{2004}{n} + 1 \right) - \left(\dfrac{2004}{n} - 1 \right) = 2$. If n is a divisor of 2004, then x is bounded by two integers and

there is only 1 integer solution. For example, if $n = 2$ then $1001 < x < 1003$ and the only integer solution

is 1002. However, if n is not a divisor of 2004, then x is bounded by two non-integers and two integers can

be fit into an interval of length 2. For example, if $n = 5$, then $399.8 > x > 401.8$ and x can equal 400

and 401. Thus, we reject all positive values of n which are factors of 2004. Since $2004 = 2^2 \cdot 3 \cdot 167$,

there are $3 \cdot 2 \cdot 2 = 12$ positive factors of 2004. The number of values of n for which the inequality has two

integer solutions is, therefore, $2004 - 12 = \boxed{1992}$.

I–8. In each case we'll calculate the probability of A's outcome times the probability of B's outcome times the

probability that A wins given those outcomes of A and B. There are 4 cases:

1) Suppose A flips HH. That has a probability of 1/4. B will flip TT with probability 1/4 and TH with

probability 1/4. However, if B's first flip is H, then B continues flipping until a T comes up, so B flips HT

with probability 1/2. The probability of A flipping HH and winning is:

    i) A = HH, B = TT. By symmetry the probability is 1/2.

    ii) A = HH, B = TH. If a T is flipped first, then A loses. If an H is flipped first, then A's chance of

        winning is 1/2, so A can win 1/4 of the time.

    iii) A = HH, B = HT. The coin is flipped until an H comes up. Then A wins with a probability of 1/2

        on the next flip.

Thus, if A flips HH, A can win with probability $\dfrac{1}{4} \cdot \left(\dfrac{1}{4} \cdot \dfrac{1}{2} + \dfrac{1}{4} \cdot \dfrac{1}{4} + \dfrac{1}{2} \cdot \dfrac{1}{2} \right) = \dfrac{7}{64}$.

2) Suppose A flips TT, then the letters are reversed, so the probability that A wins stays the same and is $\dfrac{7}{64}$.

3) Suppose A flips HT with probability 1/4. Then B will flip HH with probability 1/4. The TT case is a bit trickier. B can flip TT right away with probability 1/4, but B could also flip HT and then flip a T, generating the TT outcome. This happens with probability 1/8, so B can flip TT with probability 3/8. Similarly, B can flip TH as TH or HTH with probability 3/8. The probability of A flipping HT and winning is:

    i) $A = HT, B = HH$. The coin is flipped until an H appears. Then A wins with probability 1/2 on the next toss.

    ii) $A = HT, B = TT$. If an H is flipped first, then A wins. If a T is flipped first, then A's chance of subsequently winning is 1/2, so A wins with probability $1/2 + 1/4 = 3/4$.

    iii) $A = HT, B = TH$. If an H is flipped first, then A wins. If a T is flipped first, then A loses, so A wins with probability 1/2.

Thus, if A flips HT, the probability of A winning is $\dfrac{1}{4}\left(\dfrac{1}{4}\cdot\dfrac{1}{4} + \dfrac{3}{8}\cdot\dfrac{3}{4}\cdot\dfrac{3}{8}\cdot\dfrac{1}{2} \right) = \dfrac{19}{128}$.

4) Suppose A flips TH, then the letters are reversed, so A wins with probability $\dfrac{19}{128}$.

Thus, the probability that A wins is $2\left(\dfrac{7}{64} + \dfrac{19}{128} \right) = \boxed{\dfrac{33}{64}}$.

R1–1. Compute the number of distinct positive four-digit numbers N such that the sum of the squares of the digits of N equals 20.

R1–2. Let T = TNYWR and let $K = T - 1$. Compute the probability that two distinct, randomly selected edges of a regular K-gon do not share a vertex.

R1–3. Let T = TNYWR. In simplest form $T = \dfrac{a}{b}$. Let $K = 2a + 2b$. Sally is currently K years old. $\dfrac{K}{3}$ years ago the sum of the ages of Sally's younger brother and older sister was K. If all ages in this problem are positive integers, compute the number of possible values for the current age of Sally's brother.

ARML Relay Race #2 – 2004

R2–1. For $n \neq 0$, compute the sum of the real values of x which satisfy the equation: $\log_{2^n}(2x) = \dfrac{x}{n}$.

R2–2. Let T = TNYWR. Compute the maximum value of $y = \dfrac{T}{x^2 + 2x + T}$ over all real values of x.

R2–3. Let T = TNYWR. The circles in the diagram are concentric. Chord $\overline{AB}$ of the larger circle is trisected by the smaller circle at C and D. If $AC = T$, compute the area of the ring between the circles.

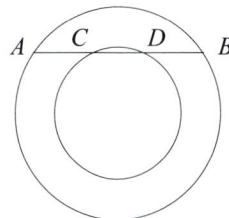

23

Relay #1:

R1–1.   12

R1–2. $\dfrac{4}{5}$

R1–3.   5

Relay #2:

R2–1.   3

R2–2. $\dfrac{3}{2}$

R2–3. $\dfrac{9\pi}{2}$

R1–1.   20 can be written as the sum of four squares in two ways, namely $4^2 + 2^2 + 0^2 + 0^2$ or $3^2 + 3^2 + 1^2 + 1^2$. In the set $\{4, 2, 0, 0\}$ there are two choices for the first digit, either 2 or 4 and the other three numbers can be permuted in $\dfrac{3!}{2!} = 3$ ways, giving $2(3) = 6$ different numbers.

For $\{3, 3, 1, 1\}$ there are $\dfrac{4!}{2! \cdot 2!} = 6$ distinct numbers.   Answer: $\boxed{12}$.

R1–2.   There are $_K C_2 = \dfrac{K(K-1)}{2}$ pairs of edges and of these exactly K pairs share a common vertex. The probability that two edges share a common vertex is $\dfrac{K}{\dfrac{K(K-1)}{2}} = \dfrac{2}{K-1}$, so the probability that the edges don't share a common vertex is $1 - \dfrac{2}{K-1} = \dfrac{K-3}{K-1}$. Since $T = 12$, then $K = 11$, making the probability equal $\dfrac{8}{10} = \boxed{\dfrac{4}{5}}$.

Alternate solution: There are K edges. Pick one. There are 2 edges that share a vertex with it, leaving $K - 3$ of the remaining $K - 1$ vertices for the second one. Hence the probability is $\dfrac{K-3}{K-1} = \dfrac{T-4}{T-6}$.

Since $T = 12$, the probability is $\dfrac{4}{5}$.

R1–3.   Let B and S denote the current ages of Sally's younger brother and older sister respectively. Then $\left(B - \dfrac{K}{3}\right) + \left(S - \dfrac{K}{3}\right) = K \rightarrow B + S = \dfrac{5K}{3}$. Since $S > K$, then $S = K + n$ where n is a positive integer.

Thus, $B + K + n = \dfrac{5K}{3} \rightarrow B = \dfrac{2K}{3} - n \rightarrow B < \dfrac{2K}{3}$ and since $B - \dfrac{K}{3} \le 1 \rightarrow B \ge \dfrac{K}{3} + 1$. Thus,

$1 + \dfrac{K}{3} \le B > \dfrac{2K}{3}$. Since $K = 18$, $7 \le B < 12$, so $B = 7, 8, 9, 10,$ or 11 and the answer is $\boxed{5}$.

R2–1.　$\log_{2^n}(2x) = \dfrac{x}{n} \;\rightarrow\; 2x = \left(2^n\right)^{x/n} \;\rightarrow\; 2x = 2^x \;\rightarrow\; x = 1 \text{ or } 2 \;\rightarrow\; \text{sum} = \boxed{3}$.

R2–2.　$T = 3$. Since $y = \dfrac{T}{x^2 + 2x + T} = \dfrac{T}{(x+1)^2 + (T-1)}$ and the maximum value

of y occurs when the denominator takes on its minimum value, the maximum occurs at

$x = -1$ and equals $\dfrac{T}{T-1} = \boxed{\dfrac{3}{2}}$.

R2–3.　Drop the altitude $\overline{OP}$ to $\overline{AB}$ and let $OP = h$. Since $CD = T$,

then $PD = \dfrac{T}{2}$ and $PB = \dfrac{3T}{2}$. Let R and r be the radii of the large

and small circle respectively. Then $h^2 + \left(\dfrac{3T}{2}\right)^2 = R^2$ and

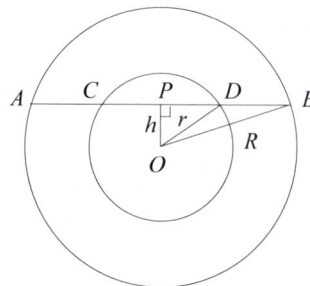

$h^2 + \left(\dfrac{T}{2}\right)^2 = r^2$. Subtract and obtain $R^2 - r^2 = 2T^2$.

The area of the ring is $2\pi T^2$ and since $T = \dfrac{3}{2}$, the desired area is $2\pi\left(\dfrac{9}{4}\right) = \boxed{\dfrac{9\pi}{2}}$.

26

1. An isosceles triangle has a perimeter of 16 and integer sides. Compute the largest possible area of the triangle.

2. Let T = TNYWR and let $K = T + 1$. In circle O, chords $\overline{AB}$ and $\overline{CD}$ are perpendicular and intersect at E. If $BE = 48$, $DE = 12$, and $AD = K$, compute CE.

3. Let T = TNYWR and let $K = T + 2$. For real x, compute the period of
$$f(x) = \tan\left(\frac{\pi x}{K} + \frac{\pi}{2K}\right) + \frac{\pi}{3K}.$$

4. Let T = TNYWR; T will not be zero. Let N range over the set of reals and consider the system $y = x + 18$ and $2x + Ty = N$. Compute the y-value of the point of intersection of the system that is closest to the origin.

5. Let T = TNYWR. In $\triangle ABC$, M is the midpoint of $\overline{BC}$ and D is on $\overline{AC}$ such that $\dfrac{CD}{AD} = T$.
If $\dfrac{\text{area } \triangle CDM}{\text{area } \triangle ABC} = \dfrac{a}{b}$ where a and b are relatively prime, compute $a + b$.

6. Let T = TNYWR and let $K = T - 2$. The sequence $18, 81, 108, 117, 126, \ldots$ consists of all positive multiples of 9 that contain 1's. Find the Kth term of the sequence.

7. Let T = TNYWR and let a and b denote the two smallest distinct prime factors of T. V_1 is the volume of a cylinder with a circumference of a and a height of b. V_2 is the volume of a cylinder with a circumference of b and a height of a. Compute $\pi\left|V_1 - V_2\right|$.

8. Let a and b be the two numbers you receive. The graphs of $\dfrac{x^2}{a^2} + \dfrac{y^2}{b^2} = 1$ and $\dfrac{x^2}{b^2} + \dfrac{y^2}{a^2} = 1$ intersect in a 1st quadrant point. Find the sum of the coordinates of the point.

27

15. Asked to compute 4^3, a student mistakenly computed $4 \cdot 3$. In what number base would the student's answer be equivalent to 4^3 in base 10?

14. Let T = TNYWR and let $K = T + 2$. If $\log_2 x + \log_4 x + \log_8 x = \log_K x^n$ for each $x > 0$, compute n.

13. Let T = TNYWR. In the diagram, $\overline{BD}$ bisects $\angle ABC$ and $\overline{CE}$ is the trisector of $\angle ACB$ that is closest to $\overline{BC}$. If $m\angle A = T$ and $m\angle DBC - m\angle ECB = \dfrac{T}{3}$, compute the degree measure of $\angle DBC$.

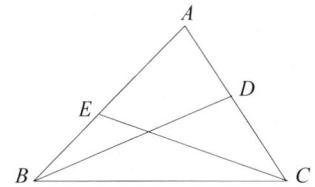

12. Let T = TNYWR. Compute the positive value of x that satisfies the equation:
$$\sqrt{Tx} \cdot \sqrt[3]{2Tx^2} \cdot \sqrt[6]{4T^4x^3} = \sqrt[4]{T^2x^4} \cdot \sqrt[5]{T^5x^5} .$$

11. Let T = TNYWR. Compute the largest integer value of x satisfying $\left| Tx - T \right| < T^2$.

10. Let T = TNYWR. The area of square $ABCD$ is $9T$. $M, N,$ and O are the midpoints of $\overline{AD}, \overline{AB},$ and $\overline{BC}$ respectively and P and Q are the trisection points of $\overline{CD}$ with P closer to C. Compute the area of $MNOPQ$.

9. Let T = TNYWR and let $K = T - 19$. K distinct boys and two distinct girls are to be seated in a row of $K + 2$ chairs. Compute the number of different arrangements if the girls can't sit next to each other. If A is your answer, pass $A + 16$ to the next student.

8. Let a and b be the two numbers you receive. The graphs of $\dfrac{x^2}{a^2} + \dfrac{y^2}{b^2} = 1$ and $\dfrac{x^2}{b^2} + \dfrac{y^2}{a^2} = 1$ intersect in a 1st quadrant point. Find the sum of the coordinates of the point.

1. 12

2. 20

3. 22

4. 9

5. 29

6. 819

7. 21

---

15. 62

14. 11

13. 36

12. 4

11. 4

10. 21

9. 12

---

8. $\dfrac{168}{5}$

1. The 2-7-7 triangle has an area of $4\sqrt{3} < 4(2) = 8$, the 4-6-6 has an area of $8\sqrt{2} > 8(1.5) = 12$, and the 6-5-5 has an area of $\boxed{12}$. That's the largest. For a fixed perimeter, the triangle closest to an equilateral triangle will have the greatest area.

2. $T = 12$ so $K = 13$. Since $EB \cdot AE = DE \cdot CE$, then

   $$48\sqrt{K^2 - 144} = 12 \cdot CE. \text{ Thus, } CE = 4\sqrt{13^2 - 144} = \boxed{20}.$$

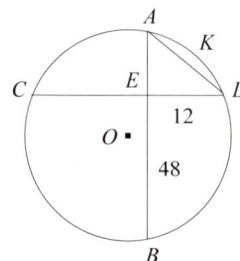

3. $T = 20$ so $K = 22$. The period is $\dfrac{\pi}{\pi/K} = K = \boxed{22}$.

4. For a particular value of T, the y-intercept of $2x + Ty = N$ can range over the y-axis, and $2x + Ty = N$ can intersect $y = x + 18$ at any point. The point of intersection closest to the origin is just the point on $y = x + 18$ that is closest to the origin. Using $(x, x + 18)$ we need the minimum of $x^2 + (x + 18)^2$. This gives $2x^2 + 36x + 324$,

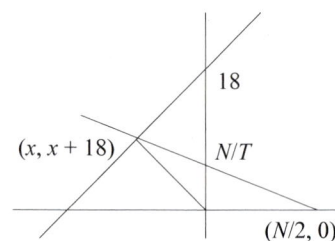

   a quadratic whose minimum occurs at $x = -\dfrac{b}{2a} = -\dfrac{36}{4} = -9$. Thus, $y = -9 + 18 = \boxed{9}$. Or just find the perpendicular distance from the origin to $y = x + 18$ by finding the intersection of the line with $y = -x$.

5. $T = 9$. Since $\dfrac{\text{area } \triangle CDM}{\text{area } \triangle ABC} = \dfrac{\frac{1}{2} \cdot y \cdot Tx \cdot \sin\theta}{\frac{1}{2} \cdot 2y \cdot (Tx + x) \cdot \sin\theta} =$

   $\dfrac{T}{2(T + 1)} = \dfrac{9}{20}$, then $a + b = \boxed{29}$.

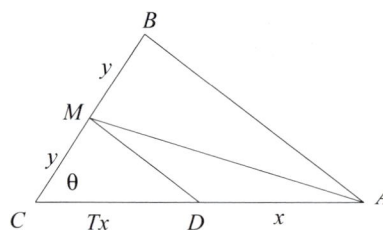

6. $T = 29$, so $K = 27$. The first two numbers are 18 and 81. If a three-digit number starts with 1 and the digits sum to 9 there are 9 numbers and if the digits sum to 18 there are two numbers, 189 and 198. If a three-digit number starts with 2, 3, 4, 5, 6, or 8 there are two numbers and if it starts with 7 there is just one number, 711. Through 711 there are $2 + 11 + 2 + 2 + 2 + 2 + 1 = 24$ terms. In the 800's we have 801, 810, and finally 819. The 27th term in the sequence is $\boxed{819}$.

7. $T = 819$. In V_1, $2\pi r_1 = a \rightarrow r_1 = \dfrac{a}{2\pi} \rightarrow V_1 = \pi\left(\dfrac{a}{2\pi}\right)^2 b$. Similarly, $V_2 = \pi\left(\dfrac{b}{2\pi}\right)^2 a$. Thus,

   $$\pi \cdot \left| \pi \cdot \dfrac{a^2 b}{4\pi^2} - \pi \cdot \dfrac{b^2 a}{4\pi^2} \right| = \dfrac{ab}{4} \cdot |a - b|. \text{ Since } 819 = 3 \cdot 3 \cdot 7 \cdot 13, \text{ pick } a = 7 \text{ and } b = 3, \text{ giving}$$

   $$\dfrac{7 \cdot 3}{4} \cdot |7 - 3| = \boxed{21}.$$

15. $12_b = b + 2 = 64 \rightarrow b = \boxed{62}$.

14. $T = 62$, so $K = 64$. Since $\log_2 x + \log_4 x + \log_8 x = \log_2 x + \log_2 x^{1/2} + \log_2 x^{1/3} = \log_2 x^{11/6} =$

     $\log_K x^n = n\log_K x$, then $\dfrac{11}{6} \cdot \dfrac{\log x}{\log 2} = \dfrac{n \log x}{\log K} \rightarrow n = \dfrac{11 \cdot \log K}{6 \cdot \log 2}$. Since $K = 64 = 2^6$, then

     $\log K = 6 \log 2$, making $n = \boxed{11}$.

13.   Since $2x + 3y + T = 180°$, then $3x + 3y = 180° - T + x$, giving

     $x + y = 60° + \dfrac{x - T}{3}$. It is given that $x - y = \dfrac{T}{3}$ so adding the

     equations yields $2x = 60° + \dfrac{x}{3}$. Thus, $x = \boxed{36°}$ and T is irrelevant.

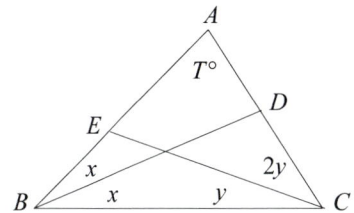

12. $T^{1/2}x^{1/2} \cdot 2^{1/3}T^{1/3}x^{2/3} \cdot 2^{1/3}T^{2/3}x^{1/2} = T^{1/2}x \cdot Tx \rightarrow 2^{2/3}T^{3/2}x^{5/3} = T^{3/2}x^2 \rightarrow 2^{2/3} = x^{1/3}$

     $\rightarrow x = \boxed{4}$. For the first time in ARML, T is irrelevant twice in a row.

11. $T = 4$. Since $-T^2 > Tx - T > T^2 \rightarrow 1 - T > x > 1 + T$, then if T is an integer, the largest integer value of x is T. Thus, $x = \boxed{4}$.

10. $9T = 36$. Let $AB = 6x$, then the area of $MNOPQ =$

     $(6x)^2 - 2 \cdot \dfrac{1}{2} \cdot (3x)^2 - 2 \cdot \dfrac{1}{2} \cdot 2x \cdot 3x = 21x^2$.

     Since $x = 1$, then $21x^2 = \boxed{21}$.

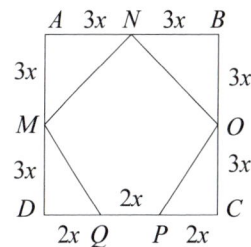

31

9. $T = 21$ so $K = 2$. Consider the position of the <u>leftmost</u> girl A and the number of positions that girl B can take. Here are the results: $\underline{K}\ \underline{K-1}\ \ldots\underline{3}\ \underline{2}\ \underline{1}\ \_\ \_$. The first seat A can sit in is the third seat from the right. Then B can only sit in the last seat. If A sits in the 4th seat from the right, then B has 2 options, if A sits in the 5th seat from the right, then B has 3 options, and so on. With A on the left, the total number of arrangements for the girls is $1 + 2 + \ldots + K = \dfrac{K(K+1)}{2}$. The girls can be permuted in 2! ways and the boys in $K!$ ways so the total number of arrangements is $\dfrac{K(K+1)}{2} \cdot 2 \cdot K! = K \cdot (K+1)!$. Since $K = 2$, the answer is $2 \cdot 3! = \boxed{12}$. Pass $12 + 16 = 28$ to the next student.

Or, note that there $K + 1$ pairs of adjacent seats and for each pair there are $K!$ ways to arrange the boys and 2! ways to arrange the girls. From $(K+2)!$ permutations, exclude $2!(K+1)K!$ permutations giving $(K+2)! - 2(K+1)! = K(K+1)!$.

8. Let $a = 21$ and $b = 28$. Multiply the first equation by a^2 and the second by b^2 and subtract, obtaining $\left(a^4 - b^4\right)y^2 = a^2 b^2\left(a^2 - b^2\right)$, giving $y^2 = \dfrac{a^2 b^2}{a^2 + b^2}$. Recognizing the symmetry in the system or multiplying the first by b^2, the second by a^2 and subtracting yields $x^2 = \dfrac{a^2 b^2}{a^2 + b^2}$. Then

$$x + y = \frac{2ab}{\sqrt{a^2 + b^2}} = \frac{2 \cdot 21 \cdot 28}{5 \cdot 7} = \boxed{\dfrac{168}{5}}.$$

1. In $\triangle ABC$, $\overline{AC} \perp \overline{BC}$, $\overline{DE} \perp \overline{BC}$,

    $DE = EC = \dfrac{1}{5}$, and the area of $\triangle ABC$

    equals $\dfrac{1}{12}$. Compute $AC + BC$.

    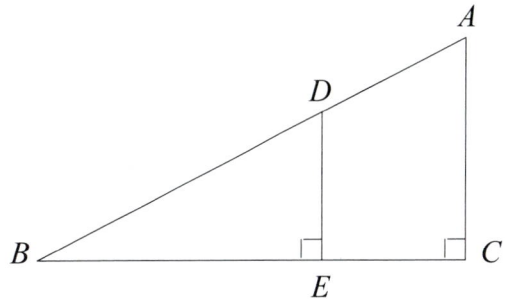

2. The graph of the function $f(x) = \sin^{-1}(2\sin x)$ consists of the union of disjoint pieces. Compute the distance between the endpoints of any one piece.

3. Let $a_1 = 0.5678 + 0.5321$, $a_2 = 0.56785678 + 0.53215321$, and in general, $a_n = 0.5678\ldots5678 + 0.5321\ldots5321$, a number that is the sum of two numbers, one with n blocks of 5678 and the other with n blocks of 5321. Compute the number of zeros in a_{2004}.

1. Let $AC = b$ and $BC = a$. Since $\triangle DEB \sim \triangle ACB$, $\dfrac{DE}{EB} = \dfrac{AC}{CB} \rightarrow \dfrac{1/5}{a - 1/5} = \dfrac{b}{a} \rightarrow$

    $\dfrac{1}{5a - 1} = \dfrac{b}{a} \rightarrow a + b = 5ab$. Since $\dfrac{1}{2}ab = \dfrac{1}{12}$ then $ab = \dfrac{1}{6} \rightarrow \boxed{a + b = \dfrac{5}{6}}$.

    Note: In this problem it can be shown that $\dfrac{1}{DE} = \dfrac{1}{AC} + \dfrac{1}{BC}$.

2. Since the domain of $\sin^{-1}$ is $[-1, 1]$, then $-1 \le 2\sin x \le 1 \rightarrow -\dfrac{1}{2} \le \sin x \le \dfrac{1}{2}$. This

    means, for example, that in $\left[-\dfrac{\pi}{2}, \dfrac{\pi}{2}\right]$, f is only defined on the closed interval $\left[-\dfrac{\pi}{6}, \dfrac{\pi}{6}\right]$.

    The endpoints of the graph of f on that interval are $\left(-\dfrac{\pi}{6}, -\dfrac{\pi}{2}\right)$ and $\left(\dfrac{\pi}{6}, \dfrac{\pi}{2}\right)$. The

    distance is $\sqrt{\left(\dfrac{\pi}{3}\right)^2 + \pi^2} = \boxed{\dfrac{\pi}{3}\sqrt{10}}$.

3. Since $0.5678 + 0.5321 = 1.0999$ and $0.56785678 + 0.53215321 = 1.10000999$, it is clear

    that for each additional block of 5678 and 5321 we obtain 3 more zeros. Thus, a_n will

    have $1 + 3(n - 1)$ zeros. For $n = 2004$, we have $1 + 2003 \cdot 3 = \boxed{6010}$.

ARML
2005

This year's contest proved to be easier than the 2004 contest. On the team round Lehigh Valley Fire, North Carolina A, Georgia A, and Iowa Power earned perfect scores of 40 and hopes were high going into the next round. Five teams earned the top score of 38 on the Power Question, leaving Lehigh Valley and North Carolina tied for the lead. The individual round proved a bit more difficult and when the dust had cleared, Phillips Exeter Red had seized the lead. The team's score of 79 on that round gave them a total of 152 and a lead of 3 over North Carolina and 4 over Chicago. Lehigh Valley Fire had stumbled badly with a 68 and looked to be out of it. But Lehigh Valley roared back on the relays, earning 26 points, outscoring Exeter by 16 points, North Carolina by 22, and Chicago by 10 to win the competition by 8 points with a score of 172. Chicago A finished second with 164 and Exeter was third with 162.

There were 27 teams in Division A and 68 teams in Division B. Several new teams joined the competition: Florida, NE Pennsylvania, Nevada, and Washington.

Don Barry was awarded the Alfred Kalfus Founder's Award. Don has been the head author since 1995. Before that he served as a coach of teams from Eastern Massachusetts where he helped run practices and wrote tryout and practice problems. He has put together a superb problem writing team, experienced and capable of challenging the best students at ARML. He also writes problems for an end of the year state contest in Massachusetts as well as an end of the year New England regional contest. He started his teaching career in Turkey and his Turkish students' interest in problem solving inspired him to start writing problems and creating math contests. He's taught and coached the math team at Phillips Academy in Andover, Massachusetts since 1980. He's equally appreciative of his Andover students for the stimulating classes that have continually supported his interest in creating non-routine problems.

Rick Armstrong of the Missouri team was awarded the Samuel L. Greitzer Coach Award. Rick has been the driving force behind establishing and promoting a Missouri ARML team. He provides a nurturing yet challenging environment for team practices, he writes and edits problems for all sorts of contests, he always has an abundance of material ready for contests, he's in close contact with his ARML students, and he established the St. Louis Math Circle.

Thomas Jefferson HS of Alexandria, VA was awarded the Harry and Ruth Ruderman Award for winning the ARML Power Contest.

The following were awarded the Zachary Sobol Award: Drew Klein of Iowa and Carey Malkiewich of Western Massachusetts.

T–1. *ABCD* is a convex quadrilateral with $AC = BC = 10$ and $AB + 1 = AD = CD = 13$.
Compute the area of *ABCD*.

T–2. Compute the smallest positive integer K such that K and $K + 1$ each have more than four positive factors.

T–3. Let A, R, M, and L be positive real numbers such that $\log(A \cdot L) + \log(A \cdot M) = 2$,
$\log(M \cdot L) + \log(M \cdot R) = 3$, and $\log(R \cdot A) + \log(R \cdot L) = 4$. Compute the value of the
product $A \cdot R \cdot M \cdot L$.

T–4. Let a and b be integers with $b > a > 1$. If $8\sqrt{.\overline{a}_b} = \dfrac{1}{.\overline{a}_b}$, compute the least value of b.

T–5. Let $N = .\overline{abcdef}$. If N has three 2's in a row in every string *abcdef*, but no more than three 2's in a row in the
entire decimal expression for N, compute the number of distinct N.

T–6. For x and y in radian measure with $0 \le x, y \le 2\pi$, compute the largest possible value of the sum $x + y$
if $2\sin x \cos y + \sin x + \cos y = -\dfrac{1}{2}$.

T–7. In the diagram, circle O has a radius of 10, circle P is internally tangent
to O and has a radius of 4. $\overline{QT}$ is tangent to circle P at T and, if drawn,
line $\overleftrightarrow{PT}$ intersects circle O at points A and B. Compute the
product $TA \cdot TB$.

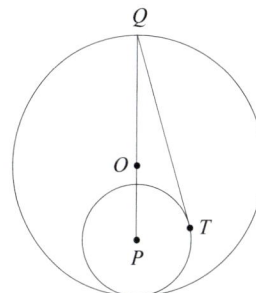

T–8. For t a real number, let $x(t) = at^3 - bt$ and $y(t) = at^3 + bt^2$ be a system of parametric equations for a
curve. If $a, b \in \{0, 1, 2, 3, \ldots, 100\}$, compute the number of ordered pairs (a, b) such that the curve has
exactly two distinct y-intercepts.

T–9. Given $A(0, 0)$ and $B(x, y)$ with $0 < x < 1$ and $y > 0$, let the slope of $\overline{AB}$ equal r. Point C lies on the line
$x = 1$ such that the slope of $\overline{BC}$ equals s with $0 < s < r$. The area of $\triangle ABC$ can be written as $k_x(r - s)$
where the value of k_x depends on x. Compute the largest possible value for k_x.

T–10. The numbers 1, 2, 3, . . . , 17, 18, 19 can be written down in a sequence that forms a 29-digit palindrome.
Compute the number of distinct 29-digit palindromes that can be formed in this way. Write the answer
without using factorial notation.

37

1. 108

2. 44

3. 1000

4. 9

5. 3240

6. $\dfrac{23\pi}{6}$

7. 60

8. 100

9. $\dfrac{1}{8} = .125$

10. 362880

T–1.   Noting Pythagorean Triples, we see that the area of $\triangle ACB$ is $6 \cdot 8 = 48$ and the area of $\triangle ADC$ is $5 \cdot 12 = 60$, making the area of $ABCD$ equal $\boxed{108}$.

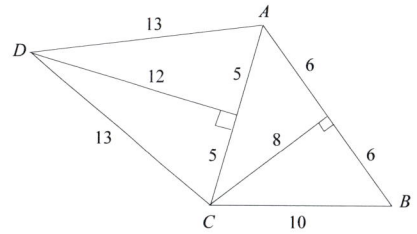

T–2.   The simplest numbers that have more than four factors are of the form p^4, p^2q, or pqr where p, q, and r are distinct primes. Trying p^4, we find that 2^4 fails since neither 15 nor 17 has four factors, but 3^4 is a candidate since 80 also has more than four factors. Trying p^2q, $2^2 \cdot 3$ fails since neither 11 nor 13 work, $2^2 \cdot 5$ fails since neither 19 nor 21 has more than four factors, and $2^2 \cdot 7$ fails since 27 and 29 fail. However, $2^2 \cdot 11$ works since 45 has six factors. We also try $3^2 \cdot 2$ but 17 and 19 are prime. Finally, $2 \cdot 3 \cdot 5$ fails since 29 and 31 are prime and $2 \cdot 3 \cdot 7$ fails since 41 and 43 are prime. Answer: $\boxed{44}$.

T–3.   From $\log(AL) + \log(AM) + \log(ML) + \log(MR) + \log(RA) + \log(RL) = 2 + 3 + 4$, we obtain $\log\left(A^3R^3M^3L^3\right) = 9 \;\rightarrow\; \log\left(ARML\right)^3 = 9 \;\rightarrow\; \log(ARML) = 3 \;\rightarrow\; A \cdot R \cdot M \cdot L = 10^3 = \boxed{1000}$.

Alternate solution: from $\log\left(A^2LM\right) = 2$, $\log\left(M^2LR\right) = 3$, and $\log\left(R^2AL\right) = 4$, we obtain $A^2LM = 100$, $M^2LR = 1000$, and $R^2AL = 10{,}000$. This gives $\dfrac{M^2LR}{A^2LM} = \dfrac{1000}{100} \;\rightarrow\; \dfrac{MR}{A^2} = 10$,

$\dfrac{R^2AL}{M^2LR} = \dfrac{10{,}000}{1000} \;\rightarrow\; \dfrac{RA}{M^2} = 10$. Thus, $\dfrac{MR}{A^2} = \dfrac{RA}{M^2} \;\rightarrow\; M^3 = A^3 \;\rightarrow\; M = A$. From

$\dfrac{R^2AL}{A^2LM} = \dfrac{10{,}000}{100} \;\rightarrow\; \dfrac{R^2}{AM} = 100 \;\rightarrow\; R^2 = 100A^2$. Thus, $R = 10A$. From $A^2LM = 100$ we obtain

$L = \dfrac{100}{A^3}$. Thus, $A \cdot R \cdot M \cdot L = A \cdot 10A \cdot A \cdot \dfrac{100}{A^3} = 1000$.

T–4.   Since $.\overline{a}_b = \dfrac{a}{b} + \dfrac{a}{b^2} + \dfrac{a}{b^3} + \cdots = \dfrac{\dfrac{a}{b}}{1 - \dfrac{1}{b}} = \dfrac{a}{b-1}$, we have $8\sqrt{\dfrac{a}{b-1}} = \dfrac{b-1}{a} \;\rightarrow\; 8 = \left(\dfrac{b-1}{a}\right)^{3/2} \;\rightarrow\;$

$\dfrac{b-1}{a} = 8^{2/3} = 4 \;\rightarrow\; b = 4a + 1$. Since $a > 1$, we have $a = 2$ and $b = \boxed{9}$.

T–5.   Let x denote any digit except 2 and let y denote any digit. Then the choices for *abcdef* in which there are three consecutive 2's but no strings of 2's longer than three are the following:

   222xyx   *x222xy*   *yx222x*   *xyx222*

Each has $9 \cdot 9 \cdot 10 = 810$ possibilities, so there are $4 \cdot 810 = \boxed{3240}$ possible *N*'s.

T–6. $2\sin x\cos y + \sin x + \cos y = -\dfrac{1}{2}$ $\rightarrow$ $4\sin x\cos y + 2\sin x + 2\cos y + 1 = 0$

$\rightarrow (2\sin x + 1)(2\cos y + 1) = 0$ $\rightarrow$ $\sin x = -\dfrac{1}{2}$ and $\cos y$ can be anything from –1 to 1 or $\cos y = -\dfrac{1}{2}$

and $\sin x$ can be anything from –1 to 1. In the first case, $x = \dfrac{7\pi}{6}$ or $\dfrac{11\pi}{6}$ and y could be anything from 0

to 2π . The largest sum is $2\pi + \dfrac{11\pi}{6} = \dfrac{23\pi}{6}$. In the second case $y = \dfrac{2\pi}{3}$ or $\dfrac{4\pi}{3}$ and x could be anything

from 0 to 2π . The largest sum is $\dfrac{4\pi}{3} + 2\pi = \dfrac{10\pi}{3} = \dfrac{20\pi}{6}$. Hence, the largest possible sum is $\boxed{\dfrac{23\pi}{6}}$.

T–7.   Extend $\overline{QP}$ and $\overline{QT}$ so that they intersect circle O at V and S,

respectively. By the Power of a Point Theorem, $AT \cdot TB = QT \cdot TS$.

Since $QV = 20 \rightarrow QP = 16$ and $PT = 4$, then $QT^2 = 16^2 - 4^2$.

Thus, $QT = 4\sqrt{15}$. Since $\Delta QVS \sim \Delta QPT$, then $\dfrac{QS}{QT} = \dfrac{QV}{QP}$ $\rightarrow$

$\dfrac{QS}{4\sqrt{15}} = \dfrac{20}{16}$ $\rightarrow$ $QS = 5\sqrt{15}$ $\rightarrow$ $TS = \sqrt{15}$. Thus,

$QT \cdot TS = 4\sqrt{15} \cdot \sqrt{15} = 60$ $\rightarrow AT \cdot TB = \boxed{60}$.

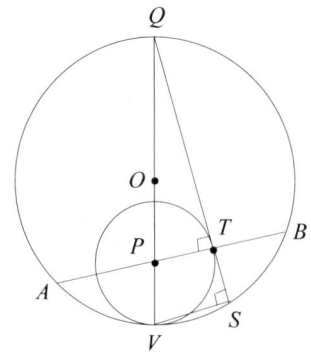

T–8.   If $b = 0$, the parametric system is $x = at^3$, $y = at^3$ whose rectangular form is $y = x$ and that can't have

two distinct y-intercepts. If $a = 0$, then we have $x = -bt$, $y = bt^2$ which turns into $y = \dfrac{x^2}{b}$ and that

can't have two distinct y-intercepts. So, $a, b \neq 0$. The zeros for x occur at $t = 0, \pm\sqrt{\dfrac{b}{a}}$. Since $y(0) = 0$,

for there to be two distinct y-intercepts, there are three cases to consider: i) $y\left(\sqrt{\dfrac{b}{a}}\right) = y\left(-\sqrt{\dfrac{b}{a}}\right)$,

ii) $y\left(\sqrt{\dfrac{b}{a}}\right) = 0$, or iii) $y\left(-\sqrt{\dfrac{b}{a}}\right) = 0$. The first is impossible since $a, b \neq 0$. The second is impossible

since $y\left(\sqrt{\dfrac{b}{a}}\right) = a \cdot \dfrac{b}{a}\sqrt{\dfrac{b}{a}} + b \cdot \dfrac{b}{a} \neq 0$ because $b \neq 0$. In the third case we have

$y\left(-\sqrt{\dfrac{b}{a}}\right) = a \cdot \dfrac{-b}{a}\sqrt{\dfrac{b}{a}} + b \cdot \dfrac{b}{a} = b\left(\dfrac{b}{a} - \sqrt{\dfrac{b}{a}}\right)$ and this equals 0 as long as $a = b$. Thus, the ordered pairs

(a, a) yield the two distinct solutions $(0, 0)$ and $(0, 2a)$ as long as a and b do not equal 0.

Thus $(a, b) = (1, 1), (2, 2), \ldots, (100, 100)$, giving $\boxed{100}$ answers.

T–9.   Let the coordinates of C be $(1, c)$. Since $\dfrac{c - rx}{1 - x} = s$ then

$c = s + (r - s)x$. Using determinants, the area of

$$\Delta ABC = \frac{1}{2}\begin{vmatrix} 1 & s + (r - s)x \\ x & rx \end{vmatrix} = \frac{1}{2}\left(x - x^2\right)(r - s).$$ The maximum

of $\dfrac{1}{2}(x - x^2)$ occurs at $x = \dfrac{1}{2}$ and equals $\dfrac{1}{8}$. Thus, $k = \boxed{\dfrac{1}{8}}$.

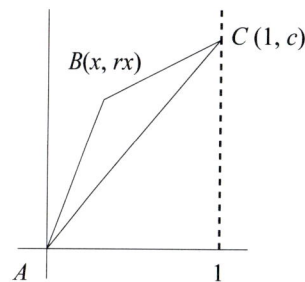

T–10.   Since 10 contains the only zero, 10 must be in the 14th and 15th positions. Call positions $1 - 13$ the front

part of the palindrome and positions $16 - 29$ the back part. If the number 11 lies in the front part in

positions n and $n + 1$, then the number 1 must lie in the back part in position $29 - n$ and a number from

12 to 19 must fill positions $29 - (n - 1) = 30 - n$ and $29 - (n - 2) = 31 - n$. If the number 11 appears

in the back part in positions n and $n + 1$, then the number 1 must appear in position $29 - n$ and a number

drawn from 12 to 19 must appear in positions $29 - (n - 1) = 30 - n$ and $29 - (n - 2) = 31 - n$. Several

conclusions can be drawn from this. First, the number 1 must be symmetric to one of the digits of the

number 11. Second, if the number 11 lies in the front part, the largest value for $n + 1$ is 13, so the largest

value for n is 12 and the smallest value for $29 - n$ is 17, implying that the number 1 cannot lie in the 16th

position. Thus, a two-digit number must lie in positions 16 and 17. If the number 11 lies in the back part

in positions n and $n + 1$, then the smallest value for n is 16 and the largest position for the number 1 would

be the 13th. Thus, the two-digit number $1A$ must follow the two-digit number 10 and the one-digit number

A must precede 10. Continuing in this fashion we see that our palindrome must have this form:

$$(I)(1H)(G)(1F)(E)(1D)(C)(1B)(A)(10)(1A)(B)(1C)(D)(1E)(F)(1G)(H)(1I)$$

with the letters $A, B, . . , I$ being any permutation of $1, 2, . . , 9$. Thus, there are $9! = \boxed{362880}$

permutations.

In Cantor County the address h of each building is an infinitely long sequence $a_1 a_2 a_3 \ldots$ where each $a_i = 0$ or 1. For example, we'll write $h = 0110100111011 \ldots$ to indicate the address of a building. If the address has a repeating block of digits as in $h = 011110011001100 \ldots$, we'll indicate that using bar notation drawn from repeating decimals, i.e., $h = 011\overline{1100}$. We will assume that all possible addresses are in use, i.e., each string refers to an actual building.

The Cantor Postal Service measures the distance between two buildings whose addresses are h_1 and h_2 in terms of the addresses. Let $h_1 = a_1 a_2 a_3 \ldots$, $h_2 = b_1 b_2 b_3 \ldots$, and let $D = \{i : a_i \neq b_i\}$. If $D \neq \varnothing$, then the *distance* between h_1 and h_2, written as $d(h_1, h_2)$, equals 2^{-n} where n is the smallest element of D. If $D = \varnothing$, then $d(h_1, h_2) = 0$. The address of the Cantor post office is $0000 \ldots = \overline{0}$.

---

1. Let $h_1 = \overline{110}$ and $h_2 = 10011110111100\ldots$.

   a) Compute $d(h_1, h_2)$.

   b) Determine the addresses of three buildings h such that $d(h_1, h) = \dfrac{1}{8}$.

   c) Determine the addresses of three buildings h, $h \neq h_1$, such that $d(h_1, h) < \dfrac{1}{8}$.

   d) Prove that $d(h_m, h_n) = 0$ if and only if $h_m = h_n$.

2. a) Georg leaves the Cantor post office, goes to Cantor High School, address $\overline{001}$, and then to the hospital, address $\overline{0011}$. Compute the difference between the length of that trip and the length of the trip from the post office directly to the hospital.

   b) Prove that d satisfies the triangle inequality. That is, if h_1, h_2, and h_3 are any three distinct addresses, then $d(h_1, h_2) + d(h_2, h_3) \geq d(h_1, h_3)$.

   c) Prove that d never satisfies the Pythagorean Theorem. That is, prove there are no distinct addresses h_1, h_2, and h_3 such that $\big(d(h_1, h_2)\big)^2 + \big(d(h_2, h_3)\big)^2 = \big(d(h_1, h_3)\big)^2$.

3. A postal route starts at the post office and delivers to an infinite sequence of buildings $h_1, h_2, h_3, \ldots$.

   A postal route is called *desirable* if $d(h_1, h_2) > d(h_2, h_3) > d(h_3, h_4) > \ldots$.

   a) Determine a postal route whose total length is 1.

   b) Prove that any desirable route has a finite total length.

The post office ordered a sorting machine A that turned out to be defective. It *deletes* the first (leftmost) three digits of a building's address and the mail is then sent to the new address. For example, the Smiths' address is $1100\overline{1100}$, but their mail is now sent to a building whose address is $011001\overline{100}$.

4. a) The Smiths now receive several buildings' mail. Give the address of one of those buildings.

    b) How many buildings' mail do the Smiths now receive? Justify your answer.

5. a) The Smiths complain to their alderman, only to discover that *his* house still receives its own mail. Demonstrate how that is possible.

    b) Determine, with proof, the number of buildings that receive their own mail under these circumstances.

6. The postal service discovers that all machines from this manufacturer delete a *consecutive string* of digits of finite length from the beginning of an address. Determine those buildings that would *never* receive their own mail, no matter how many digits are deleted.

Disgusted, the postal service composts A and orders a sorting machine B from a different manufacturer. But this machine *inserts* the digits 1001 at the beginning of every address and the mail is delivered to the new address.

7. a) Using B, is it possible that a building could get mail originally addressed to more than one other building? Justify your answer.

    b) Again, it turns out that *every* machine from the second manufacturer has a unique string of digits of finite length that it inserts at the start of an address. Prove that no matter which of this manufacturer's machines is used, there is always a building that still receives its own mail.

A neighborhood N of size $r > 0$ around h_1 consists of a set of addresses h whose distance from h_1 is less than r. It is defined by $N(h_1, r) = \{h : d(h, h_1) < r\}$.

8. a) If $h = \overline{1100}$, list three elements h_i of $N\left(h, \dfrac{1}{16}\right)$ and describe all such h_i in general.

    b) Is it possible to describe the set of all addresses at a distance of *more* than 1/16 from the Cantor post office as a neighborhood of size $r < 1/2$ around any particular address in Cantor County? If so, give the address and the value of r. If not, demonstrate why not.

9. Prove that if h_1 and h_2 are distinct addresses in Cantor County, then there exist neighborhoods $N(h_1, r_1)$ and $N(h_2, r_2)$ such that $N(h_1, r_1) \cap N(h_2, r_2) = \varnothing$.

10. The post office decides to use the digit 2 as well. Each existing building is assigned a new address whose digits are chosen from $\{0, 1, 2\}$ instead of $\{0, 1\}$. As in the old address system, a digit need not be used. However, when the post office starts assigning addresses to *new* buildings, the bureaucrats realize, to their shock, that the way in which the post office assigned new addresses to old buildings used up all the new addresses. Show that this is possible by constructing a 1-to-1 correspondence between the old addresses and the new addresses.

1. a) Since h_1 and h_2 differ for the first time in the second place, then $D = \{2, \ldots\}$ making $d(h_1, h_2) = 2^{-2} = \dfrac{1}{4}$.

   b) Such h must first differ from h_1 in the third place, i.e. $D = \{3, \ldots\}$. Thus, $h = 111\ldots$. Here are three specific answers: $111\overline{01}$, $111\overline{0}$, and $\overline{1}$.

   c) For $d(h_1, h) = \dfrac{1}{16}$, the address of h must first differ from h_1 in the fourth place, so any number of the form $1100\ldots$ works. For $d(h_1, h) = \dfrac{1}{32}$, the address of h must first differ from h_1 in the fifth place, so any number of the form $11010\ldots$ works, etc.

   d) If $h_m = h_n$, then $a_i = b_i$ for all i, so $D = \varnothing$, making $d(h_m, h_n) = 0$. If $d(h_m, h_n) = 0$ and $h_m \neq h_n$, then h_m and h_n differ in at least one digit so D is not empty and (by the Well Ordering Principle) it has a least element k making $d = 2^{-k} \neq 0$. Thus, $h_m = h_n$ iff $d(h_m, h_n) = 0$.

2. a) Let the post office be p, the high school be c and the hospital be h. Then,
   $$d(p,c) + d(c,h) = 2^{-3} + 2^{-4} = \frac{3}{16} \text{ while } d(p,h) = 2^{-3}. \text{ The difference in the lengths of the trips is } \frac{1}{16}.$$

   b) Suppose d does not satisfy the triangle inequality. Then $d(h_1, h_3) > d(h_1, h_2) + d(h_2, h_3)$. This means that $d(h_1, h_3) > d(h_1, h_2)$ and $d(h_1, h_3) > d(h_2, h_3)$. This is turn means that h_1 first differs from h_3 in a digits place i that is smaller than any i in which h_1 first differs from h_2 or h_2 first differs from h_3. But this is impossible since if h_1 and h_2 as well as h_2 and h_3 both have the same first n digits, then so do h_1 and h_3.

   <u>Alternate proof:</u> Let $h_1 = a_1 a_2 \ldots$, $h_2 = b_1 b_2 \ldots$, $h_3 = c_1 c_2 \ldots$. Suppose h_1 and h_3 first differ in the nth place, then $a_n \neq c_n$ meaning that at least one of them differs from b_n. Thus, either $d(h_1, h_2)$ or $d(h_2, h_3)$ is at least $d(h_1, h_3)$.

   c) Let $d(h_1, h_2) = 2^{-a}$, $d(h_2, h_3) = 2^{-b}$, and $d(h_1, h_3) = 2^{-c}$. We can suppose without loss of generality that $a \geq b$. From $\dfrac{1}{2^{2a}} + \dfrac{1}{2^{2b}}$ we obtain $\dfrac{2^{2b} + 2^{2a}}{2^{2b} \cdot 2^{2a}} = \dfrac{1 + 2^{2a-2b}}{2^{2a}}$. If $a > b$, then the numerator is an odd number great than 1 and can't equal $\dfrac{1}{2^{2c}}$. If $a = b$, then $\dfrac{1+1}{2^{2a}} = \dfrac{1}{2^{2a-1}}$ and that can't equal $\dfrac{1}{2^{2c}}$ either, so d does not satisfy the Pythagorean Theorem.

<u>Alternate proof #1</u>: We've shown in (2b) that one of $d\left(h_1, h_2\right)$ or $d\left(h_2, h_3\right)$ is at least as large as $d\left(h_1, h_3\right)$. But this means that $d\left(h_1, h_2\right)^2 + d\left(h_2, h_3\right)^2 > d\left(h_1, h_3\right)^2$ so the Pythagorean Theorem cannot hold. An interpretation of this is that all "triangles" in this space are acute.

<u>Alternate proof #2</u>: More generally, we'll show that no two squares of integral powers of 2 have a sum that is the square of an integer power of 2. Suppose that $2^{2x} + 2^{2y} = 2^{2z}$ for integers x, y, and z. Without loss of generality, assume that $x \geq y$. Then $2^{2y} < 2^{2x} + 2^{2y} \geq 2^{2y} + 2^{2y} = 2^{2y+1}$. Thus, $2y < 2z \geq 2y + 1$ which is impossible for integers y and z.

3.   a) If for each $h_n = a_1 a_2 \ldots a_n \ldots$, we have $a_n = 1$ and all other $a_i = 0$, then $d\left(h_n, h_{n+1}\right) = \dfrac{1}{2^n}$ and the sum of the distances is $\dfrac{1}{2} + \dfrac{1}{4} + \ldots = 1$. Or, if h_n has n 1's followed by 0's, then the distance between successive addresses is again $\dfrac{1}{2^n}$, leading to a sum of 1.

b) Every distance is a negative power of 2 so the first is at most $\dfrac{1}{2}$, the second is at most $\dfrac{1}{4}$, and so on. The sum is bounded between 0 and 1 and is therefore finite. <u>Alternately</u>, let p be the Post Office address. Since all addresses are powers of 2, it is the case that $d\left(h_2, h_3\right) \leq \dfrac{d\left(h_1, h_2\right)}{2}$. By induction, $d\left(h_n, h_{n+1}\right) \leq \dfrac{1}{2^n} \cdot d\left(p, h_1\right)$. This means that the sum of the distances is at most $d\left(p, h_1\right)\left(\dfrac{1}{2} + \dfrac{1}{4} + \ldots\right) = 2 \cdot d\left(p, h_1\right) \leq 2 \cdot \dfrac{1}{2}$. So all desirable routes have finite length.

4.   a) The Smiths get their mail from any address of the form $abc\overline{1100}$. One such address would be $100\overline{1100}$.

b) There are two choices for each of a, b, and c so the Smiths receive mail from 8 other addresses.

5.   a) The alderman could live at any address with a period of 3 such as $101\overline{101}$.

b) Any address with a period of 3 such as $abcabcabc \ldots$ would receive its own mail. There are two choices for each of a, b, and c so there are 8 addresses that would receive their own mail. Note: this includes the post office.

6. Any building whose address is not periodic, i.e., does not consist <u>solely</u> of the same block of repeating digits, would never get its own mail. An example of such a non-periodic address is $1101010\ldots = 1\overline{10}$, an address whose base 2 decimal form is $.110101010\ldots = 5/6$. Another example of a non-periodic address is $1101001000100001000001\ldots$, a number where the lengths of the strings of 0's is increasing. Those buildings that don't get their own mail can be characterized as those where the base 2 decimal form of the address is NOT a binary expansion of a simplified fraction with an odd denominator. On the other hand, a building that would get its own mail has an address that is a binary expansion of a simplified fraction with an odd denominator. Such an address is $\overline{100}$. The base 2 decimal form of the address, $.100100100\ldots$, equals $4/7$. The address can be thought of as a binary expansion of a fraction with an odd denominator. The building gets its own mail if the machine deletes a number of digits that is a multiple of 3.

7. a) No. If $1001h_1 = 1001h_2$, then h_1 must still equal h_2.

   b) Assume the machine adds a binary string M at the beginning of each address. Then the house with the periodic address $MMMM\ldots$ will still receive its own mail.

8. a) The addresses must agree in at least the first four places so any string of the form $1100h_1$ where h_1 is an address will lie in $N\left(h, \dfrac{1}{16}\right)$. Examples: $110000000\ldots$, $1100100000\ldots$, $11001100000\ldots$.

   b) No. Addresses that are at a distance of $\dfrac{1}{2}$ from the post office start with 1, those that are at a distance of $\dfrac{1}{4}$ start with 01, and those that area at a distance of $\dfrac{1}{8}$ start with 001. Imagine that all those addresses were in the neighborhood $N\left(x, \dfrac{1}{2}\right)$. That would mean that they all started with same first digit as x, but that's impossible since some addresses start with 0 and others with 1.

9. Suppose h_1 and h_2 disagree for the first time in the nth place, then $d\left(h_1, h_2\right) = \dfrac{1}{2^n}$. Let $r_1 = r_2 = \dfrac{1}{2^{n+1}}$. If x were in both $N\left(h_1, r_1\right)$ and $N\left(h_2, r_2\right)$, then $d\left(h_1, x\right) + d\left(h_2, x\right) < \dfrac{1}{2^{n+1}} + \dfrac{1}{2^{n+1}} = \dfrac{1}{2^n} = d\left(h_1, h_2\right)$, but this violates the triangle inequality from (2b). Thus, x can't lie in both neighborhoods so there are neighborhoods such that $N\left(h_1, r_1\right) \cap N\left(h_2, r_2\right) = \varnothing$.

10. We'll show that we could have mapped the original set of houses to the new addresses in such a way that every one has a unique address but that there are no addresses left over. There are two types of addresses to consider. The first type consists of those addresses of the form $M0000\ldots$ where M is a string of digits. The second type consists of all the rest of the addresses.

We'll consider the second type first. Let each such address be mapped to the element in $(0, 1)$ that has a binary expansion that is the same as the address. For example, the address $1010101010\ldots$, maps to $2/3$ since the base 2 decimal $.1010101010\ldots = \dfrac{1}{2} + \dfrac{1}{8} + \dfrac{1}{32} + \ldots = \dfrac{1/2}{1 - 1/4} = \dfrac{2}{3}$. Now convert $\dfrac{2}{3}$ to its base 3 decimal representation, being careful to use the representation that does not end in 0's. For example, instead of $.2_3$ we would use the following equivalent base 3 decimal: $.122222222\ldots$. Finally, convert the base 3 decimal to the address $122222222\ldots$. Other examples: the address whose base 2 decimal equals $5/9$ would not be converted to $.12_3$ but to $.1122222\ldots_3$ and thence to the address $11222222\ldots$. The address $01111111\ldots$ maps to $.01111111\ldots_2 = .5_{10} = .1111111\ldots_3$, giving the address $1111111\ldots$. The address $011011011\ldots \rightarrow .011011011\ldots_2 = 3/7 = .102120102120\ldots_3 \rightarrow 102120102120\ldots$. This mapping will be a bijection from all binary addresses that do not end in a string of 0's to all base 3 addresses that do not end in a string of 0's. The mapping is surjective because the first step is surjective onto $(0, 1]$ (every number has a binary expansion that does not end in 0's) as is the second (all base 3 expansions that do not end in 0's come from a building). Moreover, the mapping is also injective into this set since no two strings of 0's and 1's correspond to binary expansions of the same number unless one of the strings starts with all 0's and this same number cannot have more than one base 3 expansion (when those that end in all 0's are excepted).

Now consider the other type of addresses, those that look like $M00000\ldots$. Call them the *leftover* addresses. For each leftover address take the part up to and including the last non-zero digit. For the Post Office this is the empty string. Map that string to its reverse, i.e., $M = 10011$ would map to 11001. Then map the reversed string to its binary representation and convert to base 10, i.e. $11001_2 = 1 \cdot 2^4 + 1 \cdot 2^3 + 1 = 25_{10}$. Map the result to its base 3 representation, i.e., $25_{10} = 2 \cdot 3^2 + 2 \cdot 3 + 1 = 221_3$. Now reverse 221 to obtain 122 and end with an infinite string of 0's, thereby obtaining the address $12200000\ldots$. This mapping is a 1 to 1 correspondence over the remaining addresses. On each side (before and after) each address maps to an integer and each integer is represented uniquely by a finite string that starts with a non-zero number. This means that the mapping from either leftover address to the set of non-negative integers is bijective which means that the composition of one map and the inverse of the other is also bijective.

I–1. Compute the least positive prime p greater than 2 such that $p^3 + 7p^2$ is a perfect square.

I–2. A point P is located inside the unit square $ABCD$ with $A(0, 0)$, $B(0, 1)$, $C(1, 1)$, and $D(1, 0)$. Let Q be the midpoint of $\overline{AP}$, R be the midpoint of $\overline{BQ}$, S be the midpoint of $\overline{CR}$, and T be the midpoint of $\overline{DS}$. If point T is the same as P, compute the slope of $\overline{AP}$.

I–3. Consider an analog clock with an hour and a minute hand but no numerals. At time T A.M., a mirror image of the clock shows a time X A.M. that is 5 hours and 28 minutes later than T. Compute T in terms of hours and minutes.

I–4. $ABCD$ is a trapezoid, P is the intersection of the diagonals, $AB = 8$, and $CD = 32$. If $EPGF$ is a square, compute the height of $ABCD$.

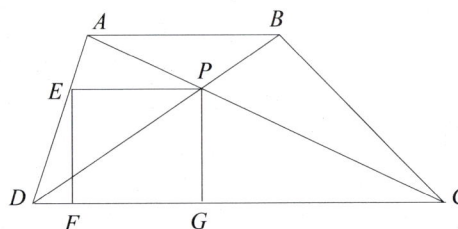

I–5. The set $S = \{a, b, c, d, e\}$ consists of distinct integers. Every sum of two distinct integers is calculated. If the number of distinct negative sums is twice the number of distinct positive sums, compute the minimum possible number of negative integers in S.

I–6. Ellipse E is defined by the equation $\dfrac{x^2}{25} + \dfrac{y^2}{16} = 1$. Compute the radius of the largest circle that is internally tangent to E at $(5, 0)$, and only intersects E at $(5, 0)$.

I–7. The point $A(\sin\theta, \cos\theta)$ is 3 units away from the point $B(2\cos 75°, 2\sin 75°)$. If $0° \le \theta < 360°$, compute θ.

I–8. Compute all real numbers a such that the equation $x^3 - ax^2 - 2ax + a^2 - 1 = 0$ has <u>exactly</u> one real solution in x.

1. 29

2. $\dfrac{1}{2}$

3. 3:16

4. 8

5. 2

6. $\dfrac{16}{5}$

7. 195° or 195

8. $a < \dfrac{3}{4}$ or $\left(-\infty, \dfrac{3}{4}\right)$

I–1.   Since $p^3 + 7p = p^2(p + 7)$, we must find the least prime p such that $p + 7$ is a perfect square. Setting $p + 7 = n^2 \rightarrow n^2 - 7 = p$, try integer values of n until a prime is reached. That prime is $\boxed{29}$.

I–2.   Using complex numbers, $A = 0, B = i, C = 1 + i, D = 1, Q = \dfrac{A + P}{2} = \dfrac{P}{2}, R = \dfrac{B + Q}{2} = \dfrac{i}{2} + \dfrac{P}{4},$

$S = \dfrac{C + R}{2} = \dfrac{2 + 3i}{4} + \dfrac{P}{8}, T = \dfrac{D + S}{2} = \dfrac{1}{2} + \dfrac{2 + 3i}{8} + \dfrac{P}{16} = P$. Solving for P we obtain $P = \dfrac{4}{5} + \dfrac{2}{5}i$.

Thus, the slope of $\overline{AP} = \dfrac{2/5}{4/5} = \boxed{\dfrac{1}{2}}$.

Alternate solution: let $P = (a, b)$. Then $Q = \left(\dfrac{a}{2}, \dfrac{b}{2}\right), R = \left(\dfrac{a}{4}, \dfrac{b + 2}{4}\right), S = \left(\dfrac{a + 4}{8}, \dfrac{b + 6}{8}\right)$, and

$T = \left(\dfrac{a + 12}{16}, \dfrac{b + 6}{16}\right)$. Thus, $a = \dfrac{a + 12}{16} \rightarrow a = \dfrac{4}{5}$ and $b = \dfrac{b + 6}{16} \rightarrow b = \dfrac{2}{5}$, and the slope is $\dfrac{1}{2}$.

I–3.   Since 3:00 A.M. and 9:00 A.M. are 6 hours apart and 4:00 A.M. and 8:00 A.M. are 4 hours apart, the desired time is about a quarter of the time from 3:00 A.M. to 4:00 A.M. More precisely, since 5 hours and 28 minutes equals 328 minutes, the hands at T A.M. are 164 minutes behind 6:00 A.M., and so we subtract 2 hours and 44 minutes from 6:00 A.M. and obtain $\boxed{3:16}$.

Alternate solution: recall that 1 hour equals 30°. We have $X - T = 5 + \dfrac{28}{60}$ hours $= \left(5\dfrac{28}{60}\right) \cdot 30° = 164°$.

So $T = \dfrac{360° - 164°}{2} = 98°$. Converting back to hours, $98° = \dfrac{98}{30}$ hrs $= 3\dfrac{16}{60}$ hrs.

I–4.   Let the side of $EPGF$ be x, let $\overline{DT}$ be the altitude of ΔDAB from D to $\overline{AB}$ extended and let $\overline{DS}$ be the altitude of ΔDEP from D to $\overline{PE}$ extended. Since $\Delta DAB \sim \Delta DEP$, then $\dfrac{DT}{DS} = \dfrac{AB}{EP} \rightarrow \dfrac{DT}{x} = \dfrac{8}{x}$, so $DT = \boxed{8}$. It is interesting that the altitude equals the shorter base and the longer base is irrelevant.

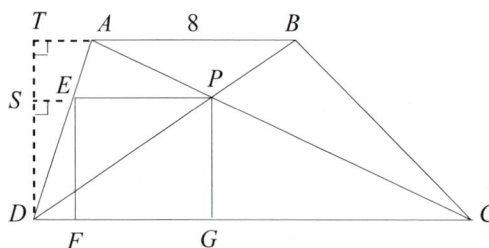

Alternate solution #1: since PAB and PCD are similar with a scale factor of 1 to 4, let $UP = h$, making $PG = 4h$. The height is $5h$. Since $EP = PG$ and P bisects $\overline{EV}$, then $EV = 8h$. Thus,

$8h = 8 + \dfrac{1}{5}(32 - 8) \rightarrow h = 1 + \dfrac{3}{5} \rightarrow 5h = 8$.

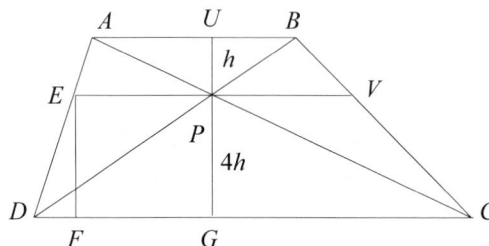

50

Alternate solution #2: Using the diagram above, let $AB = a$, $DC = b$, and the side of the square be x. Since EV is the harmonic mean between AB and CD, $x = \dfrac{ab}{a+b}$. If $UP = h$, then $\dfrac{UP}{PG} = \dfrac{h}{x} = \dfrac{a}{b} \rightarrow$

$h = \dfrac{a}{b}x = \dfrac{a}{b} \cdot \dfrac{ab}{a+b} = \dfrac{a^2}{a+b}$. The height of the trapezoid is $h + x = \dfrac{a^2}{a+b} + \dfrac{ab}{a+b} = \dfrac{a(a+b)}{a+b} = a$.

Alternate solution #3: Let $\overline{AH}$ be the altitude. By similarity, $\dfrac{EP}{AB} = \dfrac{ED}{AD} = \dfrac{HI}{AH} = \dfrac{PG}{AH}$. But $EP = PG$ so $AB = AH$.

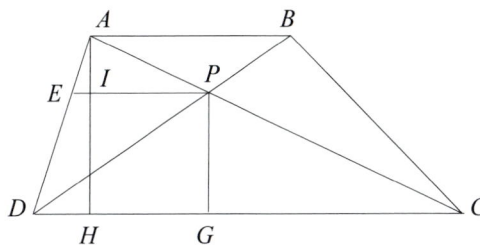

I–5.   Since there are $_5C_2 = 10$ possible sums, it is impossible for the number of distinct negative sums to be twice the number of distinct positive sums unless one sum is zero or two negative sums are the same, making 6 negative sums and three positive sums. The distinct sums of the set $\{-7, -6, -1, 4, 5\}$ are $-13, -8, -7, -3, -2, -1, 3, 4$, and 9, so three negative numbers would yield the desired result. However, the sums of $\{1, 2, 3, -3, -7\}$ are $-10, -6, -5, -4, -2, -1, 0, 3, 4$, and 5, again yielding the desired result. If a set has 4 positive numbers and one negative, then it has at most 4 negative sums. If a set has one negative number and one 0, then it has at most 3 negative sums, again not enough to double the numbers of positive sums. Thus, the least number of negative integers in S is $\boxed{2}$.

I–6.   Let the center of the circle be $(h,0)$ and the radius be r. Solving the system $(x - h)^2 + y^2 = r^2$ and $\dfrac{16}{25}x^2 + y^2 = 16$ by eliminating y gives $\dfrac{9}{25}x^2 - 2hx + h^2 - r^2 + 16 = 0$. If the curves intersect in one point, then $9x^2 - 50hx + 25(h^2 - r^2 + 16) = 0$ has one solution, so its discriminant equals 0. Thus, $(-50h)^2 - 4 \cdot 9 \cdot 25(h^2 - r^2 + 16) = 0 \ \rightarrow \ 9r^2 + 16h^2 = 144$. Since $(5, 0)$ lies on the circle, $(5 - h)^2 + 0^2 = r^2 \ \rightarrow \ r = 5 - h \rightarrow h = 5 - r$. Substituting into $9r^2 + 16h^2 = 144$, we obtain $9r^2 + 16(5 - r)^2 = 144 \ \rightarrow \ 25r^2 - 160r + 256 = 0 \ \rightarrow \ (5r - 16)^2 = 0$. Thus, $r = \boxed{\dfrac{16}{5}}$.

Note: in the general case where the ellipse is $\dfrac{x^2}{a^2} + \dfrac{y^2}{b^2} = 1$ and the circle is $(x - h)^2 + y^2 = r^2$, we have

$h = \dfrac{a^2 - b^2}{a}$ and $r = \dfrac{b^2}{a}$. The circle fits inside the ellipse because the curvature of the ellipse varies from point to point, reaching its maximum at $(5, 0)$. Look at #6 on the 1986 ARML Team Round for a much different solution to a somewhat similar problem.

I–7. $AB = \sqrt{\left(2\cos 75° - \sin\theta\right)^2 + \left(2\sin 75° - \cos\theta\right)^2} =$

$\sqrt{4\left(\cos^2 75° + \sin^2 75°\right) + \left(\sin^2\theta + \cos^2\theta\right) - 4\left(\sin\theta\cos 75° + \cos\theta\sin 75°\right)} =$

$\sqrt{4 + 1 - 4\sin\left(\theta + 75°\right)}$. For this result to equal 3, $\sin\left(\theta + 75°\right)$ must equal -1, so $\theta = \boxed{195°}$.

Alternate solution: If A were the point $(\cos\theta, \sin\theta)$, then since B lies on a circle with radius 2 and A lies on a circle of radius 1 as shown, AB would equal 3 if A lay opposite B at the point $\left(\cos(180° + 75°),\ \sin(180° + 75°)\right) = (\cos 255°, \sin 255°)$. But $A = (\sin\theta, \cos\theta)$ so we want a third quadrant angle θ such that $\sin\theta = \cos 255°$ and $\cos\theta = \sin 255°$. Clearly $\theta = 195°$.

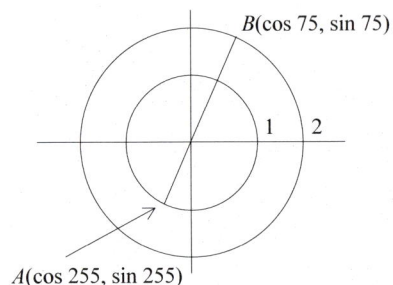

$B(\cos 75, \sin 75)$

$A(\cos 255, \sin 255)$

I–8.   One can gamble on this problem and hope that one of $x = a - 1$ or $a + 1$ works. By synthetic division we indeed find that $x = a + 1$ is a solution, and that the other factor is $x^2 + x + (1 - a)$. Since we have our one solution, the equation $x^2 + x + (1 - a) = 0$ cannot have any real roots, so $1^2 - 4(1 - a) > 0 \rightarrow$

$4a > 3 \rightarrow \boxed{a > \dfrac{3}{4}}$.

Alternate solution: Rewriting the equation as a quadratic in a we obtain $a^2 - (x^2 + 2x)a + (x^3 - 1) = 0$, giving $a^2 - (x^2 + 2x)a + (x - 1)(x^2 + x + 1) = 0$. In this form we might recognize that the coefficient of the linear term is the sum of $x - 1$ and $x^2 + x + 1$, and consequently, we can factor the quadratic in a as $\left(a - (x - 1)\right)\left(a - (x^2 + x + 1)\right) = 0$. Thus, we obtain the single real number solution from

$a - (x - 1) = 0 \rightarrow x = a + 1$ and then we find the values of a for which $x^2 + x + (1 - a) = 0$ has no real solutions as before.

R1–1.   If the product $55 \cdot 60 \cdot 65$ is written as the product of five distinct positive integers, compute the least possible value for the largest of the five integers.

R1–2.   Let T = TNYWR. Let x and y be real numbers satisfying $(x + yi)(2 + i) = T + 2Ti$. Compute the value of x.

R1–3.   Let T = TNYWR. In square $ABCD$, $AD = T$ and $DE = T - 4$. M is the midpoint of $\overline{AD}$ and F is chosen so that $\overline{AE} \perp \overline{MF}$. Compute the length of $\overline{FA}$.

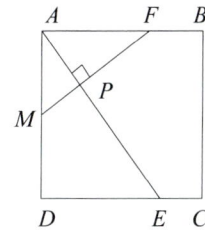

R2–1.   If $\dfrac{AB}{BC} = \dfrac{4}{3}$, compute the y-coordinate of point B.

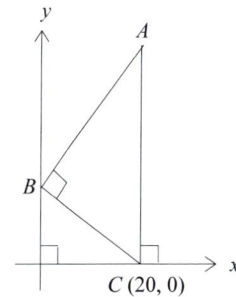

R2–2.   Let T = TNYWR. In a classroom there are T rows of desks with 4 desks to a row. Al and Betty pick different desks in the same row and Carl picks a desk in a different row. Compute the number of distinct seating arrangements for the three distinct students.

R2–3.   Let T = TNYWR. For $1 \leq x \leq T$, compute the least upper bound of the solution set to the equation $\left\lceil \log_{10} x \right\rceil = \log_{10} \lceil x \rceil$ where $\lceil x \rceil$ is the greatest integer function.

Relay #1:

R1–1.   20

R1–2.   16

R1–3. $\dfrac{32}{3}$

Relay #2:

R2–1.   15

R2–2.   10,080

R2–3.   10,001

R1–1. $55 \cdot 60 \cdot 65 = 2^2 \cdot 3 \cdot 5^3 \cdot 11 \cdot 13$. Try 13 as the largest factor. That gives $13 \cdot 12 \cdot 11 \cdot (5 \cdot 3)$ which fails or $13 \cdot 11 \cdot 10 \cdot \left(5^2 \cdot 3 \cdot 2\right)$ which fails since it is impossible to write 150 as the product of two numbers less than 10. So, 13 can't be the largest factor. Try 15 as the largest, giving $15 \cdot 13 \cdot 11 \cdot \left(5^2 \cdot 2^2\right)$. This fails since it is impossible to write 100 as the product of 10 and a number less than 10. Try 20 as the largest, giving $20 \cdot 15 \cdot 13 \cdot 11 \cdot 5$. Ans: $\boxed{20}$.

R1–2. $T = 20$. From $2x + xi + 2yi - y = T + 2Ti$, we obtain $2x - y = T$ and $x + 2y = 2T$, giving $5x = 4T$, so $x = \dfrac{4}{5}T = \dfrac{4}{5} \cdot 20 = \boxed{16}$.

R1–3. $T = 16$. Since $\Delta FAM \sim \Delta ADE$, $\dfrac{FA}{AD} = \dfrac{AM}{DE} \rightarrow \dfrac{FA}{T} = \dfrac{T/2}{T-4}$

$\rightarrow FA = \dfrac{T^2}{2(T-4)} = \dfrac{16^2}{2 \cdot 12} = \boxed{\dfrac{32}{3}}$.

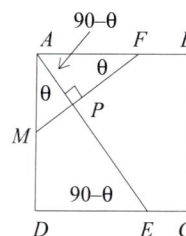

R2–1. Since ΔABC is a 3-4-5 triangle and $\Delta ABC \sim \Delta COB$, then

$\dfrac{CO}{OB} = \dfrac{4}{3}$. If $CO = 4n = 20$, then $n = 5$, making $OB = \boxed{15}$.

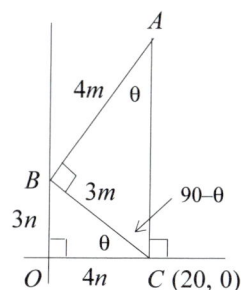

R2–2. $T = 15$. Al and Betty can pick any one of T rows and arrange themselves in any one of $4 \cdot 3 = 12$ ways. Carl can pick any one of $T - 1$ rows and pick any one of 4 seats. Therefore, the total number of different seating arrangements is $12T \cdot 4(T - 1) = 48T(T - 1) = 48 \cdot 15 \cdot 14 = \boxed{10{,}080}$.

R2–3. Since $\left\lfloor \log_{10} x \right\rfloor = 0, 1, 2, 3, \ldots$ depending on the value of x, then, in order for $\log_{10}\left\lfloor x \right\rfloor$ to be an integer, $\left\lfloor x \right\rfloor$ must be a power of 10, meaning that x cannot exceed the nearest power of 10 by 1 or more. Thus, for $1 \le x < 2$, $\left\lfloor x \right\rfloor = 1$ and $\log_{10}\left\lfloor x \right\rfloor = 0$. For $10 \le x < 11$, $\left\lfloor x \right\rfloor = 10$ and $\log_{10}\left\lfloor x \right\rfloor = 1$. For $100 \le x < 101$, $\left\lfloor x \right\rfloor = 100$ and $\log_{10}\left\lfloor x \right\rfloor = 2$, etc. Since $T = 10{,}080$, then T exceeds 10,000, and the largest solutions to the equation are values of x such that $10{,}000 \ge x > 10{,}001$. Hence, the least upper bound of the solution set is $\boxed{10{,}001}$.

1. Let b and h denote the base and height of a triangle whose area is 200. Compute the smallest value of $b + h$.

2. Let T = TNYWR. Compute the value of x that satisfies $\log_2(T - 8) = 2 + \log_4(T + x)$.

3. Let T = TNYWR and set $K = 2[T]$ where $[x]$ denotes the greatest integer function. If $f(n) = i^n + \dfrac{1}{i^n}$ where $i = \sqrt{-1}$, compute the number of integers n, $1 \le n \le 2005$, such that $f(K) + f(n) = 0$.

4. Let T = TNYWR. Compute $\dfrac{|T|}{668 - T} + \dfrac{T}{|668 - T|}$.

5. Let T = TNYWR. Compute the smallest positive value of θ in degrees such that $\tan\theta = \csc(3T) - \cot(3T)$.

6. Let T = TNYWR. P-$ABCD$ is a pyramid with a square base $ABCD$ of side 8 and $PA = PB = PC = PD = \dfrac{2}{3}T$. Let h be the height of P-$ABCD$. Compute $\dfrac{h}{\sqrt{2}}$.

7. Let T = TNYWR. The line $x + y = 2005T$ intersects the lines $y = x + 6T$ and $y = x + T$ at points A and B, respectively. Compute the length of $\overline{AB}$.

8. Let M and N be the numbers that you received. Let A be the area of the region bounded by the x-axis, the y-axis, the line $x = 2$, and the graph of $y = (M + N) - [x^2]$ where $[x]$ is the greatest integer function. Compute $[A]$.

56

15. Compute the value of $x + y$ if $\dfrac{x^2}{2005} - \dfrac{y^2}{2005} = 1$ and $\dfrac{x}{2005} - \dfrac{y}{2005} = \dfrac{1}{3}$.

14. Let T = TNYWR. In the figure, $ABCD$ is a square, C and D lie on circle O, chord $\overline{EF}$ has length 10, and $AB = 2T$. $\overrightarrow{DB}$ meets circle O at G. Compute $\dfrac{1}{BG}$.

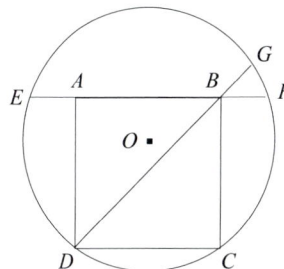

13. Let T = TNYWR. Compute the value of $\left(\cos\left(\sin^{-1} T\right)\right)^2 + T^2$.

12. Let T = TNYWR and set $K = T + 10$. For every carload of K pizzas that you order, you get an additional pizza free. If you obtained 36 pizzas, compute the number of carloads that you ordered.

11. Compute the 2005th term of the arithmetic sequence $-5956, -5956 + T, -5956 + 2T, \ldots$

10. Let T = TNYWR. Compute the sum of the squares of the first T terms of the sequence:
$$\sin\left(\frac{\pi}{14}\right),\ \sin\left(\frac{2\pi}{14}\right),\ \sin\left(\frac{3\pi}{14}\right),\ \sin\left(\frac{4\pi}{14}\right),\ \ldots$$

9. Let T = TNYWR. Compute the least positive value of x satisfying $x^2 - y^2 = 2\sqrt{3}y + T$.

8. Let M and N be the numbers that you received. Let A be the area of the region bounded by the x-axis, the y-axis, the line $x = 2$, and the graph of $y = (M + N) - [x^2]$ where $[x]$ is the greatest integer function. Compute $[A]$.

1. 40

2. 24

3. 501

4. 6

5. 9

6. $\sqrt{2}$

7. 5

- -

15. 3

14. $\dfrac{3\sqrt{2}}{8}$

13. 1

12. 3

11. 56

10. 28

9. 5

_____

8. 18

1. $\frac{1}{2}bh = 200 \rightarrow bh = 400$. By the AM-GM inequality, $\frac{b+h}{2} \geq \sqrt{bh} \rightarrow b + h \geq 2\sqrt{400} = \boxed{40}$.

2. Since $\log_{a^2} b = \frac{1}{2}\log_a b$, then $\log_2(T-8) = 2 + \log_4(T+x) = 2 + \frac{1}{2}\log_2(T+x) \rightarrow$

    $2\log_2(T-8) = 4 + \log_2(T+x) \rightarrow \log_2(T-8)^2 - \log_2(T+x) = 4 \rightarrow \log_2\left(\frac{(T-8)^2}{T+x}\right) = 4 \rightarrow$

    $(T-8)^2 = 2^4 \cdot (T+x) \rightarrow x = \frac{(T-8)^2}{16} - T$. Since $T = 40$, $x = \frac{32^2}{16} - 40 = \boxed{24}$.

3. Note that if $n = 0(\mathrm{mod}\,4)$, $f(n) = 2$; if $n = 1(\mathrm{mod}\,4)$, $f(n) = 0$; if $n = 2(\mathrm{mod}\,4)$, $f(n) = -2$, and if
    $n = 3(\mathrm{mod}\,4)$, $f(n) = 0$. Since $K = 2[T]$, K is even. If $K = 0(\mathrm{mod}\,4)$, then n must equal $2(\mathrm{mod}\,4)$,
    i.e., $n = 2, 6, \ldots, 2002$. There are 501 such numbers. If $K = 2(\mathrm{mod}\,4)$, then n must equal $0(\mathrm{mod}\,4)$,
    i.e., $n = 4, 8, \ldots, 2004$. There are also 501 such numbers. So, regardless of T, there are $\boxed{501}$ values of n.

4. If $T > 668$, then $\frac{|T|}{668-T} + \frac{T}{|668-T|} = \frac{T}{668-T} + \frac{T}{-(668-T)} = 0$. If $0 \leq T < 668$,

    $\frac{|T|}{668-T} + \frac{T}{|668-T|} = \frac{T}{668-T} + \frac{T}{668-T} = \frac{2T}{668-T}$. If $T > 0$, the sum is again 0.

    Since $T = 501$, the sum is $\frac{2 \cdot 501}{668 - 501} = \boxed{6}$.

5. $\tan\theta = \csc(3T) - \cot(3T) = \frac{1 - \cos(3T)}{\sin(3T)}$. Since $\tan\frac{x}{2} = \frac{1-\cos x}{\sin x}$, $2\theta = 3T \rightarrow \theta = \frac{3}{2} \cdot 6 = \boxed{9}$.

6. Let $\overline{PE}$ be the altitude to the base *ABCD*. *E* is the center of the square

    ABCD. $EF = FC = 4 \rightarrow EC = 4\sqrt{2}$. Then $h^2 + (4\sqrt{2})^2 = \frac{4}{9}T^2 \rightarrow$

    $h = \frac{2}{3}\sqrt{T^2 - 72}$. Since $T = 9$, then $h = 2$, making $\frac{h}{\sqrt{2}} = \boxed{\sqrt{2}}$.

    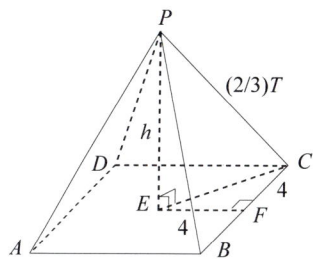

7. One could find the points $A\left(\frac{1999T}{2}, \frac{2011T}{2}\right)$ and $B(1002T, 1003T)$ and use

    the distance formula to obtain $AB = \left(\frac{5T}{2}\right)\sqrt{2}$. But $2005T$ is irrelevant since

    the two parallel lines are perpendicular to $x + y = K$ and form a 45-45-90 right

    triangle *CDE* with a hypotenuse of $5T$. Hence, $CD = AB = \frac{5T}{\sqrt{2}}$. $T = \sqrt{2}$

    makes $AB = \boxed{5}$.

    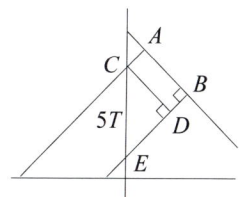

15. $\dfrac{1}{2005}(x-y)(x+y) = 1$ and $\dfrac{1}{2005}(x-y) = \dfrac{1}{3}$ $\rightarrow$ $\dfrac{1}{3}(x+y) = 1$. Thus, $x+y = \boxed{3}$.

14.   Let $AE = BF = x$. Then $(2T+x)x = (2T\sqrt{2})(BG)$ $\rightarrow$

    $\dfrac{1}{BG} = \dfrac{2T\sqrt{2}}{(2T+x)x}$. Since $2x + 2T = 10$, $x = 5 - T$, making

    $\dfrac{1}{BG} = \dfrac{2T\sqrt{2}}{(2T+5-T)(5-T)} = \dfrac{2T\sqrt{2}}{25-T^2}$. $T = 3$ $\rightarrow$ $\dfrac{1}{BG} = \boxed{\dfrac{3\sqrt{2}}{8}}$.

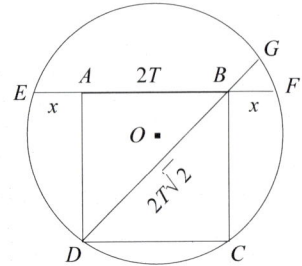

13.   From $\sin^{-1}T = \theta$, we obtain $\sin\theta = T \rightarrow \cos\theta = \sqrt{1-T^2}$. It is positive because $-\dfrac{\pi}{2} \le \theta \le \dfrac{\pi}{2}$. So,

    $\left(\cos(\sin^{-1}T)\right)^2 + T^2 = (\cos\theta)^2 + T^2 = 1 - T^2 + T^2 = \boxed{1}$. As long as $-1 \le T \le 1$, T is irrelevant.

12.   Let n be the number of carloads of K pizzas. Then $nK + n = 36 \rightarrow n(K+1) = 36 \rightarrow$

    $(n,K) = (1,35), (2,17), (3,11), (4,8), (6,5), (9,3), (12,2),$ or $(18,1)$. Since $T = 1$, $K = 11$, so $n = \boxed{3}$.

11. $a_{2005} = -5956 + 2004T = -5956 + 6012 = \boxed{56}$.

10.   Repeated use of $\sin x = \cos\left(\dfrac{\pi}{2} - x\right)$, $\sin x = \sin(\pi - x)$, and $\sin^2 x + \cos^2 x = 1$ yields

    $\sin^2\left(\dfrac{\pi}{14}\right) + \sin^2\left(\dfrac{2\pi}{14}\right) + \ldots + \sin^2\left(\dfrac{14\pi}{14}\right) = 7$. Thus, $\sin^2\left(\dfrac{\pi}{14}\right) + \sin^2\left(\dfrac{2\pi}{14}\right) + \ldots + \sin^2\left(\dfrac{14k\pi}{14}\right) = 7k$

    for k a positive integer. Since $T = 56$, $k = 4$, and the sum equals $\boxed{28}$.

9. $x^2 = (y^2 + 2y\sqrt{3} + 3) + (T - 3) = \left(y + \sqrt{3}\right)^2 + (T - 3)$. The least positive value of x occurs when

    $y = -\sqrt{3}$, making $x = \sqrt{T-3} = \sqrt{28-3} = \boxed{5}$.

---

8.   Let $M + N = T$. On the interval $[0, 1)$, $0 \le x^2 > 1 \rightarrow \left[x^2\right] = 0 \rightarrow$ the function is $y = T$, making the

    area under that portion of the graph equal to $T \cdot 1$. On $\left[1, \sqrt{2}\right]$, $1 \ge x^2 < 2 \rightarrow \left[x^2\right] = 1$, the graph is

    $y = T - 1$, giving an area of $(T-1)\left(\sqrt{2}-1\right)$. On $\left[\sqrt{2}, \sqrt{3}\right]$, $2 \le x^2 < 3 \rightarrow \left[x^2\right] = 2$, giving an area of

    $(T-2)\left(\sqrt{3}-\sqrt{2}\right)$. Finally, on $\left[\sqrt{3}, 2\right]$, $3 \le x^2 < 4 \rightarrow \left[x^2\right] = 3$, giving an area of $(T-3)\left(2-\sqrt{3}\right)$.

    Adding these together gives a total area of $2T - 5 + \sqrt{2} + \sqrt{3}$. Since $M = N = 5$, the area A equals

    $20 - 5 + \sqrt{2} + \sqrt{3}$ and $[A] = \boxed{18}$.

1. Circles P and Q, both of radius r, are inscribed in right triangle ABC as shown. If $AB = 6$, $BC = 8$, and D and E trisect $\overline{PQ}$, compute r.

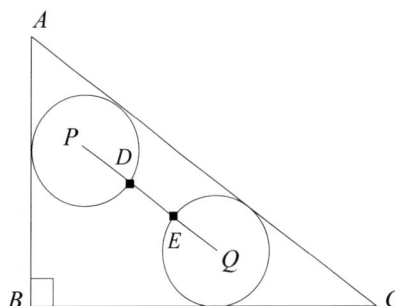

2. Compute the largest value of the product $b \cdot m$ if b and m are positive integers and $\log_b m = \dfrac{m}{128}$.

3. Let $a_1 = 101$, $a_2 = 1001$, $a_3 = 10001$, and in general, let a_n be the decimal number whose first and last digits are 1 while the n digits between are all zeros. Compute the value of k such that $\left(a_k\right)^3$ has exactly 2005 digits.

1. $PT = \dfrac{3}{5} \cdot 3r = \dfrac{9}{5}r$ and $QT = \dfrac{12}{5}r$. Since

   $PT = SV$, then $AS = 6 - r - \dfrac{9}{5}r = 6 - \dfrac{14}{5}r$.

   Similarly, $CU = 8 - r - \dfrac{12}{5}r = 8 - \dfrac{17}{5}r$.

   Since $AS = AM$ and $CU = CN$, $AC = 10 = 6 - \dfrac{14}{5}r + 3r + 8 - \dfrac{17}{5}r \;\rightarrow$

   $\dfrac{16}{5}r = 4 \;\rightarrow\; r = \boxed{\dfrac{5}{4}}$.

2. $\log_b m = \dfrac{m}{128} \;\rightarrow\; m = b^{m/128} \;\rightarrow\; b = m^{128/m}$. Since m is an integer, b can't be an integer

   unless m is a power of 2. Make a quick table of values of m, b and the product bm:

m	1	2	4	8	16	32	64	128
b	1	2^{64}	4^{32}	8^{16}	16^8	32^4	64^2	128^1
bm	1	2^{65}	2^{66}	2^{51}	2^{36}	2^{25}	2^{18}	2^{14}

   Some larger values of m such as 512 give integer values for b, but the product continues to

   drop. The maximum value of the product is $\boxed{2^{66}}$.

3. Since $a_k = 10^{k+1} + 1$, then $a_k{}^3$ has $3(k+1)+1$ digits, so $3k + 4 = 2005 \;\rightarrow\; k = \boxed{667}$.

ARML
2006

On this year's ARML there were 32 teams in Division A and 81 teams in Division B. A number of teams vied for the top position, but in the end North Carolina was the winner. The team round proved more difficult that last year's. There were just six 32's compared with four 40's on the 2005 contest. North Carolina A was tied with Lehigh Valley Fire, Texas Gold, Eastern Massachusetts A, Washington Gold, and AAST Mu after the first round. The Power Question was about the mathematics of Origami and many teams could be found folding the paper that was supplied in the PQ packet. North Carolina earned the top score of 39 and seized the lead with 71 points. San Francisco Bay Area A was second with 67 points, Montgomery A and Texas Gold were tied for third at 66. The individual round proved easier this year with a number of scores in the 80's. Georgia and North Carolina earned the top scores of 87 and North Carolina stretched its lead to 7 over Texas Gold with Lehigh Valley Fire trailing by 9. The relay races proved to be as dramatic as the previous year's. Lehigh Valley Fire made another strong move by earning a remarkable 20 on the first relay. But North Carolina held firm with an 18 and entered the final relay with a 7 point lead. The second relay was more difficult. North Carolina got 10 points and won the competition with an outstanding 186 points. Lehigh Valley got 8 but didn't hold onto second place as Montgomery A surged with 18 on the first relay and a terrific 20 on the second to threaten North Carolina's day-long lead, but in the end Montgomery A fell just a bit short with 184 points. Texas Gold and Lehigh Valley Fire tied for third with 177 points. Colorado won the B Division.

Several new teams joined the competition this year. They are Chesapeake, Colorado, Kentucky, Londonderry, NH, Maryland Home School, San Diego, New Mexico, and Utah.

Peter Shiue was awarded the Alfred Kalfus Founder's Award in recognition of the remarkable number of things he has done for ARML. Peter Shiue was instrumental helping set up the western site at UNLV. He then did all the legwork to form and train a team from Taiwan to compete at our Western site. Several years ago, he was instrumental in starting an ARML competition in Taiwan that now has over 6000 students participating at one site. He also translates the questions into Chinese.

Robert Messer of the Michigan team and Bruce White of the Ontario team were awarded the Samuel L. Greitzer Coach Award. Bob Messer is recognized for his devotion to the Michigan All-Stars and ARML from the time the team was organized in 1989 until his retirement in 2003. He organized practices, trips, grant proposals, mentoring, and a yearly newsletter, all done with a focus on math and fun. Bruce White has been a marvelously enthusiastic and successful teacher. He has taken Massey SS in Ontario, a school of modest size, to the point where it can compete successfully with teams at ARML. In so doing he has taken countless students to achievements that they could not have dreamed of otherwise.

Stuyvesant High School in New York City was awarded the Harry and Ruth Ruderman Award for winning the ARML Power Contest.

Rahul Banerjee of Western Massachusetts was awarded the Zachary Sobol Award.

T–1. A cylinder of height 10 cm and radius 6 cm is turning at 1 revolution per minute. A paintbrush 4 cm wide starts at the top as shown and slowly moves vertically down the cylinder at 1 cm/minute. Compute the time in minutes it takes for the paintbrush to paint three-fifths of the lateral surface area of the cylinder.

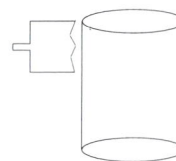

T–2. Let $[\,x\,]$ = the greatest integer less than or equal to x. Compute all values of x so that the product $\left[\,x - \dfrac{1}{2}\,\right]\left[\,x + \dfrac{1}{2}\,\right]$ is prime.

T–3. In $\triangle CBA$, $\overline{CD}$ and $\overline{AE}$ are medians, $\overline{FC} \parallel \overline{AB}$, $\overline{FEH}$, $\overline{CGD}$, and $\overline{AGE}$. The area of $FCGE = 7$ and the area of $EGDH$ is 11. Compute the area of $\triangle CBA$.

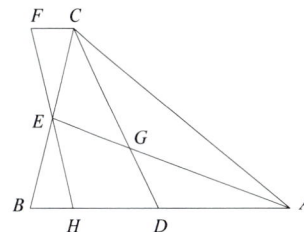

T–4. For x in radians, if $\tan x = \dfrac{a}{b}$, $\tan 2x = \dfrac{b}{a+b}$, and the least positive value for x equals $\tan^{-1} k$, compute k.

T–5. Let N be an integer such that $1 \le N \le 2006^2$. Compute the number of values of N such that there exists a factor of N, call it a, such that $\left|\sqrt{N} - a\right| \le 1$.

T–6. There are N positive integers b such that $10 \le \log_{10}\left(\log_{10} b\right) \le 100$. Let S be the sum of the digits of N. Compute the sum of the digits of S.

T–7. Shown are rows 1, 2, and 3 of Pascal's triangle. Let $\{a_i\}$, $\{b_i\}$, and $\{c_i\}$ be the sequence, from left to right, of elements in the 2005th, 2006th, and

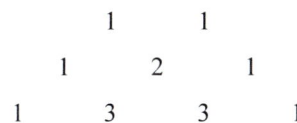

$$
\begin{array}{ccccccc}
 & & 1 & & 1 & & \\
 & 1 & & 2 & & 1 & \\
1 & & 3 & & 3 & & 1
\end{array}
$$

2007th rows, respectively, with the leftmost element occurring at $i = 0$. Compute: $\displaystyle\sum_{i=0}^{2006} \frac{b_i}{c_i} - \sum_{i=0}^{2005} \frac{a_i}{b_i}$.

T–8. An empty down elevator opens its doors on the 6th floor. It will stop at every floor unless it gets stuck. At each of the floors 6 though 2, if there is no one in the elevator, the people waiting flip a coin. If it is heads, one person gets on; if it is tails, no one gets on. At each of the floors 5 through 2, if there are 1 or 2 people in the elevator, the people waiting flip a coin. If it is heads, one person gets on and no one gets off; if it is tails, one person on the elevator gets off and no one gets on. If there are three people in the elevator at any given time, it gets stuck. Compute the probability that the elevator gets stuck before reaching the first floor.

T–9. Compute the number of ordered triples (a, b, c) of integers with $b, c \le 0$ such that $5! \cdot a^b - 4! \cdot a^c = 3456$.

T–10. Let n be a six-digit positive integer that is not a palindrome but which becomes a six-digit palindrome if two of its digits are interchanged. Compute the number of n. Note: a six-digit integer does not start with 0.

1. 3

2. $-\dfrac{3}{2} \le x < -\dfrac{1}{2}$ or $\dfrac{3}{2} \le x < \dfrac{5}{2}$ or the equivalent $\left[-\dfrac{3}{2}, -\dfrac{1}{2}\right) \cup \left[\dfrac{3}{2}, \dfrac{5}{2}\right)$

3. 36

4. $\dfrac{1}{3}$

5. 6016

6. 811

7. $\dfrac{1}{2}$ or the equivalent .5

8. $\dfrac{9}{32}$ or the equivalent .28125

9. 7

10. 4860

T–1. The shaded area is the region painted on the first revolution; the region between the two darker lines was painted on the second revolution. The area of the shaded region is 48π cm^2 but each successive revolution covers only $1 \cdot 12\pi$ cm^2 of new surface. For t = time in minutes after the first revolution,

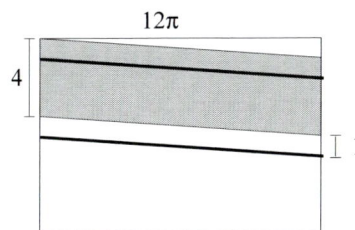

$$48\pi + 12\pi t = \frac{3}{5} \cdot 10 \cdot 12\pi \rightarrow 12t = 24. \text{ Thus, } t = 2,$$

meaning that the total time to paint 3/5 of the surface is $\boxed{3}$ minutes.

T–2. If $\left[x - \dfrac{1}{2} \right] = a$ then $a \le x - \dfrac{1}{2} < a + 1$ and $a + 1 \le x + \dfrac{1}{2} < a + 2 \rightarrow \left[x + \dfrac{1}{2} \right] = a + 1$, meaning that the two factors must be consecutive integers. Thus the product will be prime only if the factors equal 1 and 2 or -2 and -1. If $\left[x - \dfrac{1}{2} \right] = 1$, $1 \le x - \dfrac{1}{2} < 2 \rightarrow \dfrac{3}{2} \le x < \dfrac{5}{2}$. If $\left[x - \dfrac{1}{2} \right] = -2$, $-2 \le x - \dfrac{1}{2} < -1$ gives $-\dfrac{3}{2} \le x < -\dfrac{1}{2}$. Answer: $\boxed{-\dfrac{3}{2} \le x < -\dfrac{1}{2} \text{ or } \dfrac{3}{2} \le x < \dfrac{5}{2}}$ or the equivalent $\left[-\dfrac{3}{2}, \, -\dfrac{1}{2} \right) \cup \left[\dfrac{3}{2}, \dfrac{5}{2} \right)$.

T–3. Since $\overline{FC} \parallel \overline{AB}$, $\angle FCE \cong \angle EBH$, $\angle FEC \cong \angle HEB$ by the vertical angle theorem, and since E is the midpoint of $\overline{CB}$, $\overline{EC} \cong \overline{EB}$. Thus, $\triangle ECF \cong \triangle EBH \rightarrow$ the area of $\triangle ECF$ equals the area of $\triangle EBH$. The area of $FCGE$ plus the area of $EGDH$ equals 18 and that equals the area of $\triangle CBD$. Since the area of $\triangle CBD$ is half the area of $\triangle CBA$ because $\overline{CD}$ is a median, the area of $\triangle CBA$ is $\boxed{36}$.

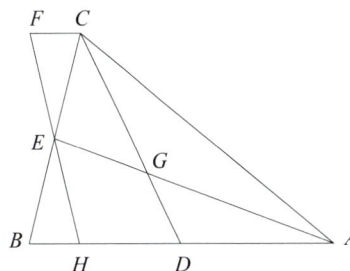

T–4. Since $\tan 2x = \dfrac{2 \tan x}{1 - \tan^2 x}$, then $\dfrac{b}{a + b} = \dfrac{2 \cdot \dfrac{a}{b}}{1 - \left(\dfrac{a}{b} \right)^2} \rightarrow \dfrac{b}{a + b} = \dfrac{2ab}{b^2 - a^2}$. Since $b \ne 0$ and $a + b \ne 0$, we cancel both to obtain $1 = \dfrac{2a}{b - a} \rightarrow 3a = b$. Thus $\tan x = \dfrac{a}{3a} = \dfrac{1}{3} \rightarrow \tan^{-1} \dfrac{1}{3} = x$. Thus, $k = \boxed{\dfrac{1}{3}}$.

T–5. If $N = a^2$, then clearly $\left| \sqrt{a^2} - a \right| \le 1$. If $N = a(a + 1)$, then since $\sqrt{a^2 + a} < \sqrt{a^2 + 2a + 1} = a + 1$, we have $a < \sqrt{N} < a + 1$ and so N will lie within 1 of a factor. If $N = a(a + 2)$, then $\sqrt{a^2 + 2a} < \sqrt{a^2 + 2a + 1} = a + 1$, so $a < \sqrt{N} < a + 1 < a + 2$ and $\sqrt{N}$ lies within 1 of a factor. Setting $N = a(a + k)$ and solving $\sqrt{a^2 + ka} < a + 1$ we have $k > 2 + \dfrac{1}{a}$, so for $k \le 3$, $\sqrt{N}$ can't lie within 1 of a factor. So, numbers of the form a^2, $a(a + 1) = a^2 + a$, and $a(a + 2) = a^2 + 2a$ satisfy the condition. These cases are disjoint since $a(a + 1)$ and $a(a + 2)$ lie between a^2 and $(a + 1)^2$, so they can't be perfect

67

squares. Thus, there are three numbers N for each perfect square between 1 and 2005^2 inclusive and one for 2006^2, making a total of $3 \cdot 2005 + 1 = \boxed{6016}$.

T–6. From $10 \le \log_{10}\left(\log_{10} b\right) \le 100$, we obtain $10^{10} \le \log_{10} b \le 10^{100} \rightarrow 10^{10^{10}} \le b \le 10^{10^{100}}$. The

number N of the values of b satisfying the inequality equals $10^{10^{100}} - 10^{10^{10}} + 1 = 999\ldots9000\ldots1$. In

$10^{10^{100}} - 10^{10^{10}}$ there are 10^{10} zeros preceded by $10^{100} - 10^{10}$ nines. Thus the sum S of the digits of N

is $\left(10^{100} - 10^{10}\right) \cdot 9 + 1 = 10^{10}\left(9 \cdot 10^{90} - 9\right) + 1$. Neglecting the 1 for a minute, we have 10^{10} times a

ninety-one digit number consisting of a leading 8, a trailing 1, and eighty-nine 9's. The sum of its digits is

$9 \cdot 90 = 810$. Adding the 1 back gives $\boxed{811}$.

T–7. Try some examples. Using rows 3, 4, and 5 we have $\left(\dfrac{1}{1} + \dfrac{4}{5} + \dfrac{6}{10} + \dfrac{4}{10} + \dfrac{1}{5}\right) - \left(\dfrac{1}{1} + \dfrac{3}{4} + \dfrac{3}{6} + \dfrac{1}{4}\right) =$

$3 - \dfrac{5}{2} = \dfrac{1}{2}$. Rows 4, 5, and 6 give: $\left(\dfrac{1}{1} + \dfrac{5}{6} + \dfrac{10}{15} + \dfrac{10}{20} + \dfrac{5}{15} + \dfrac{1}{6}\right) - \left(\dfrac{1}{1} + \dfrac{4}{5} + \dfrac{6}{10} + \dfrac{4}{10} + \dfrac{1}{5}\right) =$

$\dfrac{7}{2} - 3 = \dfrac{1}{2}$. Hmm. It looks like the answer is 1/2. Not only that, but it appears to be the case that the sum of

the ratios of each pair of rows is increasing by 1/2 and that the sum should easily be expressible in terms of

the number of the row. To establish this, note that after $\dfrac{1}{1}$, other ratios can be paired to produce sums of 1:

using rows 4 and 5 we have $\dfrac{1}{1} + \left(\dfrac{4}{5} + \dfrac{1}{5}\right) + \left(\dfrac{3}{5} + \dfrac{2}{5}\right) = \dfrac{_4C_0}{_5C_0} + \left(\dfrac{_4C_1}{_5C_1} + \dfrac{_4C_4}{_5C_4}\right) + \left(\dfrac{_4C_2}{_5C_2} + \dfrac{_4C_3}{_5C_3}\right)$. Using

rows 5 and 6: $\dfrac{1}{1} + \left(\dfrac{5}{6} + \dfrac{1}{6}\right) + \left(\dfrac{4}{6} + \dfrac{2}{6}\right) + \dfrac{3}{6} = \dfrac{_5C_0}{_6C_0} + \left(\dfrac{_5C_1}{_6C_1} + \dfrac{_5C_5}{_6C_5}\right) + \left(\dfrac{_5C_2}{_6C_2} + \dfrac{_5C_4}{_6C_4}\right) + \dfrac{_5C_3}{_6C_3}$. In

general terms we have $\dfrac{_nC_0}{_{n+1}C_0} = 1$ and then pairings such as the following: $\dfrac{_nC_r}{_{n+1}C_r} + \dfrac{_nC_{n+1-r}}{_{n+1}C_{n+1-r}}$. Since

$_nC_r = {}_nC_{n-r}$, the pairing simplifies to $\dfrac{_nC_r}{_{n+1}C_r} + \dfrac{_nC_{n+1-r}}{_{n+1}C_r} = \dfrac{_nC_r + {}_nC_{n+1-r}}{_{n+1}C_r} = \dfrac{_nC_r + {}_nC_{n-(r-1)}}{_{n+1}C_r}$

$= \dfrac{_nC_r + {}_nC_{r-1}}{_{n+1}C_r} = \dfrac{_{n+1}C_r}{_{n+1}C_r} = 1$. If the numerators are formed by $_nC_r$ where n is even, there will be an

odd number of fractions and so after the initial $\dfrac{1}{1}$, they will pair up, giving a whole number sum. If the

numerators are formed by $_nC_r$ where n is odd, there will be an even number of fractions, the first one being

$\dfrac{1}{1}$ and the rest will pair up forming a sum of 1 except for the middle fraction which will be of the form

$\dfrac{_nC_r}{_{n+1}C_r}$ where $r = \dfrac{n+1}{2}$. This fraction equals $\dfrac{n+1-r}{n+1} = \dfrac{\frac{n+1}{2}}{n+1} = \dfrac{1}{2}$. Thus if the numerator is formed by

$_nC_r$ where n is even, the sum is $1 + \dfrac{1}{2} + \dfrac{n-2}{2} \cdot 1 = \dfrac{n}{2} + \dfrac{1}{2}$. If the numerator is formed by $_{n+1}C_r$ where

$n+1$ is odd, the sum is $1 + \dfrac{(n+1)-1}{2} \cdot 1 = 1 + \dfrac{n}{2}$. The difference is $\dfrac{1}{2}$. A similar result holds if the

numerator is formed by $_nC_r$ where n is odd. Thus the difference is always $\boxed{\dfrac{1}{2}}$.

T–8. Since the elevator is initially empty, the probability that it leaves the 6th floor with 0 persons is 1/2 and the probability that it leaves with 1 person is 1/2. We could construct a massive tree graph or we could look at the probability that the elevator leaves any particular floor with a particular number of people on board, focusing on the case where it left the preceding floor with 2 people on board. In each case we can figure this out from the probabilities when it arrives at the floor. For example, the probability that it arrives on the 5th floor with 0 persons is 1/2, and the probability that it arrives with 1 person is 1/2. The probability that it leaves the 5th floor with 0 persons is $\dfrac{1}{2} \cdot \dfrac{1}{2} + \dfrac{1}{2} \cdot \dfrac{1}{2} = \dfrac{1}{2}$, the probability that it leaves the 5th floor with 1 person is $\dfrac{1}{2} \cdot \dfrac{1}{2} + \dfrac{1}{2} \cdot 0 = \dfrac{1}{4}$, and the probability that it leaves the 5th floor with 2 people is $\dfrac{1}{2} \cdot \dfrac{1}{2} + \dfrac{1}{2} \cdot 0 = \dfrac{1}{4}$. The table below summarizes the probabilities that the elevator leaves a floor with a certain number of people aboard. Note that the elevator doesn't contain 3 people until it tries to leave the 4th floor and the probability that there are 3 people on the elevator is (1/2) times the probability that the elevator left the 5th floor with 2 people. Thus, the probability that the elevator gets stuck before it can reach the first floor is $\dfrac{1}{8} + \dfrac{1}{16} + \dfrac{3}{32} = \boxed{\dfrac{9}{32}}$. Note that starting on floor 3 that the sum of the probabilities across the line doesn't equal 1.

	Number of People			
Floor Number	0	1	2	3
6	1/2	1/2	0	0
5	1/2	1/4	1/4	0
4	3/8	3/8	1/8	1/8
3	6/16	4/16	3/16	1/16
2	10/32	9/32	4/32	3/32

T–9. The equation can be rewritten as $144 = \begin{cases} 4a^b & \text{if } b = c \\ a^c(5a^{b-c} - 1) & \text{if } b > c \\ a^b(5 - a^{c-b}) & \text{if } b < c \end{cases}$

i) If $b = c$, we have $a^b = 36 \rightarrow (a, b, c) = (36, 1, 1), (6, 2, 2)$ and $(-6, 2, 2)$.

ii) If $b > c$, we have several cases to consider. If $c = 0$, we have $5a^b - 1 = 144 \rightarrow a^b = 29$. This is true for $a = 29$ and $b = 1$, giving the solution $(29, 1, 0)$. If $c > 0$, then we have $144 = a^c(5a^{b-c} - 1)$.

Note that a^c and $5a^{b-c} - 1$ have different parity since if a is odd, then $5a^{b-c} - 1$ is even and a^c will be odd. If a is even the parity is reversed. Thus, of the factor pairs $(1, 144)$, $(2, 72)$, $(3, 48)$, $(4, 36)$, $(6, 24)$, $(8, 18)$, $(9, 16)$, and $(12, 12)$ and their negatives, we need only consider $(1, 144)$, $(3, 48)$, $(9, 16)$ and their negatives. In addition, one of the factors must be 1 less than a multiple of 5. We discover that we only have a solution when $5a^{b-c} - 1 = 9 \rightarrow a^{b-c} = 2$ and $a^c = 16$, yielding the solution $(2, 5, 4)$.

iii) If $b < c$, we have several cases to consider. If $b = 0$, then $5 - a^c = 144$ giving $a^c = -139$, implying $a = -139$ and $c = 1$, giving $(-139, 0, 1)$. If $b < 0$, we have $144 = a^b(5 - a^{c-b})$. Note that a^b and $5 - a^{c-b}$ have different parity so we consider the same factor pairs as before. We discover that we have a solution for $a^b = 16$ and $5 - a^{c-b} = 9 \rightarrow a^{c-b} = -4$. The latter is true for $a = -4$ and $c - b = 1$, giving the solution $(-4, 2, 3)$.

Thus the solutions are $(a, b, c) = (36, 1, 1)$, $(6, 2, 2)$, $(-6, 2, 2)$, $(29, 1, 0)$, $(2, 5, 4)$, $(-139, 0, 1)$ and $(-4, 2, 3)$. The number of ordered triples (a, b, c) satisfying the equation is $\boxed{7}$.

T–10. Let's define *almost palindromic numbers* to be numbers that are one switch away from being palindromic.

Any six-digit almost palindrome consists of three pairs of equal digits with at least one pair distinct from the others. In addition, exactly one pair of digits is properly placed in the palindrome. We could say that this pair is in palindromic position. Furthermore, if a number is almost palindromic, there is never a need to switch the first digit in order to make a palindrome. This means we need not worry about the use of zeros except on the first digit. This leads to three cases:

Case 1: there are three distinct pairs of digits, the ones in palindromic position are in the first and last positions as indicated by the underlining. There are two possible structures for this type of number: $\underline{A}BBCC\underline{A}$ and $\underline{A}BCBC\underline{A}$. For each structure, there are 9 choices for A, 9 choices for B (since B can be 0 and A cannot) and 8 choices for C. This gives $9 \cdot 9 \cdot 8 \cdot 2 = 1296$ almost palindromes.

Case 2: there are three distinct pairs, the ones in palindromic position are in the 2nd and 5th positions or the 3rd and 4th positions. There are four possible structures for these numbers: $B\underline{A}BC\underline{A}C$, $B\underline{A}CB\underline{A}C$, $BB\underline{A}\underline{A}CC$, and $BC\underline{A}\underline{A}BC$. If $A = 0$, then there are 9 choices for B and 8 choices for C. If $A \neq 0$, then there are 8 choices for B since $B \neq 0$ and then 8 choices for C since C can equal 0. This gives $4 \cdot (1 \cdot 9 \cdot 8 + 9 \cdot 8 \cdot 8) = 2592$ almost palindromes.

<u>Case 3</u>: there are just two distinct digits, A appears four times and B appears twice. There are $_6C_2 = 15$ distinct pairs of positions in which to put the B's, but three of them result in palindromes, so there are actually only 12 distinct pairs of positions in which to place the B's. There are 9 ways to pick the leftmost digit, then 9 ways to pick the other digit. This gives $12 \cdot 9 \cdot 9 = 972$ almost palindromes.

Thus there are $1296 + 2592 + 972 = \boxed{4860}$ almost palindromes.

<u>Alternate solution #1</u>:

<u>Case 1</u>: the number of almost palindromic numbers using only two digits.

a) If there are no zeros, then there are $_9C_2$ ways of choosing the two digits, $_2C_1$ ways of choosing which one appears 4 times and $_6C_2 - 3$ ways of choosing the places of the pair to be switched. The reason for subtracting 3 is that 3 locations of the pair give a palindrome. Thus, $\dfrac{9 \cdot 8}{2} \cdot 2 \cdot 12 = 864$.

b) If there are two zeros, then there are 9 ways to choose the other digit and $_5C_2 - 2 = 8$ ways to arrange the zeros. Since we can't start with a zero there are only 10 possible arrangements, 2 of which are palindromes. Thus, $9(8) = 72$.

c) If there are four zeros then there are 9 ways to choose the other digit and 4 ways to place the non-zero pair because starting with a non-zero digit, there are 5 possible arrangements but 1 of them is a palindrome. Thus, $9(4) = 36$.

Thus there are 972 almost palindromic numbers using two digits.

<u>Case 2</u>: There are three different pairs of digits and one pair has to be in a palindromic position.

a) If there are no 0's, then there are $_9C_3$ ways of choosing the two digits, $_3C_1$ ways of choosing which pair is in the palindromic state, $_3C_1$ ways of choosing which pair of palindromic places is filled, and there are $_4C_2 - 2 = 4$ ways to arrange the non-palindromic digits since 2 of the 6 arrangements are palindromic. Thus, $\dfrac{9 \cdot 8 \cdot 7}{3 \cdot 2 \cdot 1} \cdot 3 \cdot 3 \cdot 4 = 3024$ numbers.

b) If there are two zeros, then there are two cases:

    i) If the 0's are in the palindromic positions, then there are $_9C_2$ ways to choose the other two pairs, 2 ways to locate the zeros, either in the 2nd and 5th positions or in the 3rd and 4th positions, and there are $_4C_2 - 2 = 4$ ways to arrange the non-palindromic digits since 2 of the 6 arrangements are palindromic. This gives $\dfrac{9 \cdot 8}{2 \cdot 1} \cdot 2 \cdot 4 = 288$ almost palindromic numbers.

    ii) If the 0's are not in the palindromic positions, then there are $_9C_2$ ways to choose the other two pairs and 8 ways to choose the positions where the 0's go: 2-3, 2-4, 2-6, 3-5, 3-6, 4-5, 4-6, 5-6. Note that one pair of the two other pairs of digits is in the palindromic position, one pair is not and one of that pair will switch with a 0 to obtain a palindrome. There are 2 ways to arrange one of the other two pairs in the palindromic positions, i.e., 200112 or 100221. This gives $\dfrac{9 \cdot 8}{2 \cdot 1} \cdot 8 \cdot 2 = 576$.

Thus there are 3888 almost palindromic numbers using three digits.

Grand total: $\boxed{4860}$.

Alternate solution #2:

The problem is a bit slippery since an almost palindrome such as 135351 can be turned into a palindrome in two different ways: we can interchange either the first 3 and 5, obtaining 153351 or the second 3 and 5, obtaining 135531. If we approach the problem by working from palindrome to almost palindrome we may easily over count. But this difficulty can suggest a way to approach the problem. Consider a number in which switching the numbers in the 2nd and 6th positions produces a palindrome: _ 5 _ _ _ 2 . First, note that the numbers in the 3rd and 4th places must be equal, giving, for example, _ 5 0 0 _ 2 . If switching the 5 and 2 produces the palindrome _ 2 0 0 _ 5 , then originally a 5 must lie in the first position and a 2 in the second. So our original number 550022 produces the palindrome 520025 by switching the numbers in the 2nd and 6th positions. But that means that the numbers in the 1st and 5th positions must match the numbers in the 2nd and 6th positions, otherwise the one interchange wouldn't produce a palindrome. So we need only count the number of almost palindromes with different entries in the 2nd and 6th positions and that will also count the number of almost palindromes with entries in the 1st and 5th positions. Let $a_1 a_2 a_3 a_4 a_5 a_6$ denote a six-digit number. In general, for any $1 \le i < j \le 6$, if interchanging a_i and a_j yields a palindrome, then interchanging a_{7-i} and a_{7-j} also yields a palindrome. It follows that we only need to consider these switches: $(a_2, a_6), (a_3, a_6), (a_4, a_6), (a_5, a_6)$ as well as $(a_3, a_5), (a_4, a_5)$. They are all paired with the following switches respectively: $(a_1, a_5), (a_1, a_4), (a_1, a_3), (a_1, a_2)$, and $(a_2, a_4), (a_2, a_3)$. In the first four switches of the form (a_i, a_6), $i = 2, 3, 4$, and 5, we have 9 choices for a_i (we can't use 0 because a_1 would have to be 0) and 9 choices for a_6 since $a_6 \ne a_i$ but a_6 can equal 0. These choices decide 4 digits of the number; the other two digits are equal and can be any of the 10 digits since they cannot be in the a_1 position. They will be in the following positions respectively: $(a_3, a_4), (a_2, a_5), (a_2, a_5), (a_3, a_4)$. This gives $4 \cdot 9 \cdot 9 \cdot 10$ almost palindromes of the form (a_i, a_6). In switches of the form $(a_i, a_j) = (a_3, a_4)$ or (a_4, a_5), we have 10 choices for a_i and 9 choices for a_j. These decide the 4 middle digits of the number. Since $a_1 = a_6 \ne 0$, we have 9 choices for $a_1 = a_6$ for a total of $2 \cdot 10 \cdot 9 \cdot 9$ choices. This makes for a grand total of $4 \cdot 9 \cdot 9 \cdot 10 + 2 \cdot 10 \cdot 9 \cdot 9 = 6 \cdot 810 = \boxed{4860}$ almost palindromes.

We all know how to fold a unit square into a square of area 1/4. What other fractions of a unit square's area can be constructed by folding? We're going to investigate this question and a few others…

For the purposes of this problem, there are <u>six</u> Basic Origami Operations. Each is a fold that creates a crease.

B1: Given points P and Q, you can make a fold creating a crease passing through points P and Q.

B2: Given points P and Q, you can fold P onto Q.

B3: Given lines ℓ_1 and ℓ_2, you can fold ℓ_1 onto ℓ_2.

B4: Given line ℓ and point A which can be on or off line ℓ, you can make a fold creating a crease through point A perpendicular to line ℓ. Note: A can't be an endpoint of a segment.

B5: Given line ℓ, point P not on line ℓ, and point Q not necessarily on line ℓ, you can make a fold that places P onto line ℓ while the crease passes through Q, unless no fold satisfying these conditions exists.

B6: Given points P and Q as well as lines ℓ_1 and ℓ_2, you can make a fold that simultaneously places P onto ℓ_1 and Q onto ℓ_2, unless no fold satisfying these conditions exists.

Note: in the operations above, points P and Q and lines ℓ_1 and ℓ_2 are not necessarily distinct.

To start, we're given a unit square's vertices as points and sides as segments. As with straightedge-and-compass constructions, we assume you can construct an <u>arbitrary</u> but <u>non-special</u> point or segment at will: for example, given a segment, you can construct a point P "somewhere" on that segment, but you cannot claim that P is the midpoint, or any other point with special properties, without justifying P's construction using B1–B6; similarly, given point P you can construct a segment L passing through it without further justification so long as you do not assume L has any particular properties, e.g., being perpendicular to a given segment.

---

1. a) What line is formed as a result of B2?

   b) If ℓ_1 and ℓ_2 intersect at point P, what line is formed as a result of B3?

   c) The statement of B5 is equivalent to intersecting a line with a circle. Describe the circle and the line, and justify the equivalence.

2. a) Show that B3 is a special case of B6.

   b) B5 suggests that for some locations of P, Q, and ℓ, there is no fold that would send P onto ℓ while passing through Q. Give an example of such a situation and explain why no such fold exists.

We're ready to start folding squares. To explain a particular construction, you must describe it in terms of B1–B6 above. Apart from the vertices and edges of a square, you must justify the construction of any other points or segments in terms of B1–B6. In general, you need not justify the claim that B5 or B6 is possible in a given situation.

3. a) Describe a way to fold a unit square $ABCD$ into four squares of area 1/4 in terms of B2–B6. We'll call this the Quarter construction.

3.   b)   In his dialogue *Meno,* Plato describes a way of folding a square into a square of 1/2 the original area by folding each corner into the center as shown below. Unfortunately, that presupposes that the center of the square is already located, which isn't the case. Describe the construction of a square 1/2 the area of the original in terms of B's. We'll call this the Meno construction.

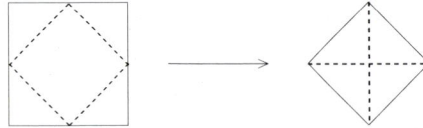

4.   Starting with a unit square and using only creases formed by Quarter and/or Meno constructions to form squares, what fractional areas p/q can be obtained where p and q are integers? Prove your result.

5.   a)   For $n = 1, 2, \ldots, 6$, how many different ways are there to obtain a square of area $1/2^n$ from a unit square using only Quarter and/or Meno constructions? Order matters.

   b)   Let $F(n)$ be the number of ways of obtaining a square of area $1/2^n$ using only Quarter and/or Meno constructions. Find and prove a formula, recursive or explicit, for $F(n)$ if order matters.

6.   One side of a square can be folded into thirds, although it's not as easy as it appears: simply saying "fold it into thirds" begs the question of how the trisection points can be constructed.

   a)   Using only B's construct points T_1 and T_2 that trisect one side of the square. Justify.

   b)   Show how to construct points that divide the side of a square into n equal pieces for any $n > 2$.

7.   Describe, with proof, what fractions p/q can be obtained as areas of squares folded from a single unit square using only creases formed by combinations of the constructions in #6, Quarter constructions and Meno constructions, possibly including more than one of each. Your proof does not have to *exclude* other fractions, but must justify the inclusion of every fraction described.

8.   a)   The diagram shows the standard straightedge-and-compass construction of a segment of length $\sqrt{r}$ (shown dotted in the diagram). Given an infinitely large sheet of paper and segments of length 1 and r, collinear with and adjacent to each other, describe an equivalent construction in terms of B's. You can't use a straightedge or compass.

   b)   Given $AE = r < 1$, describe how to construct a segment of length $\sqrt{r}$ on the unit square $ABCD$ using only B's such that no part of the segment lies outside the unit square.

9.   Describe, with proof, what fractions p/q can be obtained as areas of squares folded from a single unit square using only creases formed by combinations of the constructions in #6 & #8, Quarter constructions and Meno constructions, possibly including more than one of each. Your proof does not have to *exclude* other fractions, but must justify the inclusion of every fraction described.

10.   a)   A segment of length $\sqrt{3}/2$ can be constructed using two folds, and so a square of area 3/4 can be constructed in 5 folds including folding down the edges to make an actual square. Show how to do so.

   b)   The method developed in #9 requires 12 folds to construct a square of area 1/5 by locating all 4 vertices. Find a construction that requires fewer folds.

74

1. a) The crease is the perpendicular bisector of $\overline{PQ}$, no justification is necessary.

    b) The crease is the bisector of two of the angles formed by the two lines; no justification is necessary.

    c) Fold P onto line ℓ at P' such that the crease passes through Q. Now

    $QP = QP'$ by (1a) applied to P and P' so P' is on the circle with radius PQ

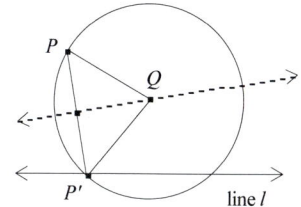

    centered at Q.

2. a) B6 does not require that ℓ_1 and ℓ_2 be distinct; in the case where $\ell_1 = \ell_2 = \ell$, the fold simply places both points onto line ℓ. Therefore, given two lines ℓ_1 and ℓ_2, mark points P and Q arbitrarily on ℓ_1; then apply B6 to place both points on ℓ_2 and that folds ℓ_1 onto ℓ_2.

    b) One situation is where P and Q are on the same side of line ℓ, but PQ is less than the distance from Q to the line ℓ. Then the circle described in (1c) fails to intersect line ℓ, as shown at the right.

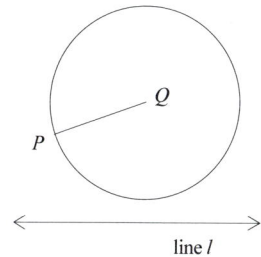

3. a) Use B2 to fold A onto point B; by (1a), the crease is the perpendicular bisector of $\overline{AB}$ and is, therefore, the perpendicular bisector of $\overline{CD}$.

    <u>Proof</u>: call the crease's intersections with $\overline{AB}$ and $\overline{CD}$ points S_1 and S_2, respectively; then AS_1S_2D is a quadrilateral with three right angles, hence a rectangle, and $S_2D = AS_1$ equals $\dfrac{AB}{2} = \dfrac{1}{2} = \dfrac{CD}{2}$.

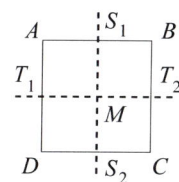

    Use B2 to fold A onto D; similar logic shows that the crease is the perpendicular bisector of $\overline{AD}$ and $\overline{BC}$, intersecting at T_1 and T_2 respectively. Finally, let M be the intersection of the creases; AS_1MT_1 is a quadrilateral with three right angles, hence a rectangle, and all sides are of length 1/2, so it is a square of area 1/4.

    b) To locate the center of the square use either the construction in (3a) or use either B2 or B1 twice; first on diagonally opposite points A & C, and then again on points B & D. The creases form the diagonals, hence intersect in the center. If B1 is used, the diagonal formed is the one joining the two points employed; if B2 is used, the other diagonal is formed. With the center of square located, use B2 four times to fold each corner to the center of the square.

Without locating the center of the square, use B2 as in (3a) to locate the midpoint of each side of the square and then use B1 on each pair of adjacent midpoints such as P and Q. Note: In folding a crease through P and Q, you fold each corner into the center.

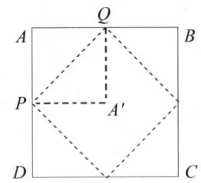

4. The Meno construction applied to a square of side length s and area s^2 produces a square of side length $\dfrac{s}{\sqrt{2}}$ and area $\dfrac{s^2}{2}$. The Quarter construction produces a square of side length $\dfrac{s}{2}$ and area $\dfrac{s^2}{4}$. In particular, doing a Meno construction twice is equivalent to doing one Quarter construction as shown by folding $ABCD$ into $EFGH$ in the diagram. So at each step, the side length can be reduced by a factor of $\dfrac{1}{\sqrt{2}}$ or $\dfrac{1}{2}$, and the area by a factor of 1/2 or 1/4. By induction, then, the possible areas formed for the smallest square are of area $1/2^n$, for n a nonnegative integer.

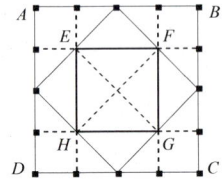

However, smaller squares can be combined into larger ones by folding back strips along two adjacent edges, as shown in the diagram at the right:

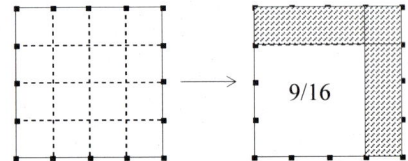

9/16

Therefore, the possible areas are of the form $\dfrac{k^2}{2^n}$, where $k \leq 2^{n/2}$.

Finally, notice that the construction at the right is *not allowed* in this problem since it uses creases other than those formed by Meno and Quarter constructions.

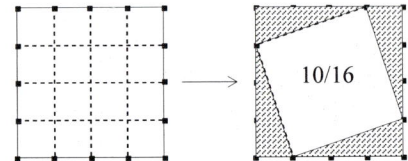

10/16

5. a) A string such as MQMMQ will mean a Meno construction, followed by a Quarter construction, followed by two Meno constructions, followed by another Quarter construction.

n	Ways to fold a unit square into a square of area $1/2^n$	$F(n)$
1	M	1
2	Q, MM	2
3	QM, MQ, MMM	3
4	QQ, QMM, MQM, MMQ, MMMM	5
5	QQM, QMQ, MQQ QMMM, MQMM, MMQM, MMMQ MMMMM	8
6	QQQ QQMM, QMQM, QMMQ, MQQM, MQMQ, MMQQ, QMMMM, MQMMM, MMQMM, MMMQM, MMMMQ, MMMMMM	13

5. b) Yes, it's the Fibonacci sequence, namely $F(n) = f_{n+1}$ where $f_{n+2} = f_{n+1} + f_n$ with $f_1 = f_2 = 1$. The basic idea can be seen in rows 3 and 4. The squares in row 3 have area 1/8. From those squares we obtain a square in row 5 of area 1/32 by a Quarter construction. So, to the end of any string of letters in row 3 we will add a Q and that new string will be entered in row 5. The squares in row 4 have an area of 1/16 and from those squares we can obtain a square of area 1/32 by using a Meno construction. So, to the end of any string of letters in row 4 we will append an M and enter the new string in row 5. Thus, row 5 will have as many members as the sum of rows 3 and 4. More formally, we have the following proof:

Proof: Let W_n be the set of all ways to form a square of area $1/2^n$ as represented by the strings described above. Thus, $F(n) = |W_n|$. Writing "xQ" for the concatenation of string x and the letter Q representing a Quarter construction, we can write $W_{n+1} = \{xQ : x \in W_{n-1}\} \cup \{yM : y \in W_n\}$. That is, a square of area $1/2^{n+1}$ can be formed by applying a Quarter construction to a square of area $1/2^{n-1}$ or it could be formed by applying a Meno construction to a square of area $1/2^n$. Note that $\{xQ : x \in W_{n-1}\} \cap \{yM : y \in W_n\} = \varnothing$ since the strings in the first set end in Q while the strings in the second set end in M. Thus we have $|W_{n+1}| = |\{xQ : x \in W_{n-1}\}| + |\{yM : y \in W_n\}| = |W_{n-1}| + |W_n|$, giving $F(n+1) = F(n-1) + F(n)$, and since $F(0) = F(1) = 1$, the assertion is proved.

6. a) There are many possible constructions, but perhaps the simplest is below:

Step 1: Using B2, fold D onto A, labeling the midpoint M.

Step 2: Without unfolding, use B2 to fold M onto $\overline{AD}$.

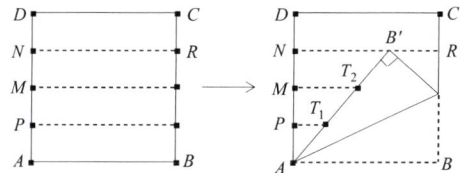

Step 3: Unfold. Recalling (3a), let N and P be the midpoints of $\overline{MD}$ and $\overline{MA}$ respectively. Label the crease passing through N as line segment $\overline{NR}$. Now use B5 to fold point B up to $\overline{NR}$ with the new crease passing through A.

Step 4: Now let T_1 and T_2 be the places where the creases through points M and P pass through $\overline{AB'}$.

Justification: (3a) shows that the creases are all perpendicular to side $\overline{AD}$, so the creases are parallel, and parallel lines that cut equal segments on one transversal (here $\overline{AD}$) cut equal segments on any transversal (here $\overline{AB'}$).

b) To split $\overline{AB}$ into k congruent segments, pick n so that $2^n > k$ and then repeatedly bisect $\overline{AD}$ a total of n times, producing $2^n - 1$ parallel creases. Then unfold the side, and using B5, fold vertex B up to the kth crease (counting from A), so that the new crease passes through A. Then the intersections of the other horizontal creases pass through $\overline{AB}$ divide $\overline{AB}$ into k equal segments, since the horizontal creases are equally spaced.

Alternately, it's not necessary to bisect $\overline{AD}$ as long as the creases formed in steps 1–3 are parallel and equally spaced. This can be achieved by picking an arbitrary point M_1 on $\overline{AD}$ near A and folding a perpendicular to $\overline{AD}$ through M_1 using B4. Now denote the image of A by M_2. Clearly, $AM_1 = M_1M_2$ by construction. Unfold and fold again through M_2 a perpendicular to $\overline{AD}$. Let the images of A and M_1 be M_4 and M_3 respectively. Now $AM_1 = M_1M_2 = M_2M_3 = M_3M_4$. Continue in this fashion until k creases are formed where $k < 2^{n-1}$. Then proceed as in steps 3 and 4 of part (6a). The only difficulty is in selecting a point M_1 such that $AM_1 \leq 1/k$, otherwise there won't be enough room to make all k folds.

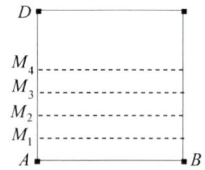

7. Now the sides can be folded into any fraction of the form $\dfrac{m}{n}$ or $\dfrac{m}{n\sqrt{2}}$, where m and n are integers, $n \geq m$.

    So the area can be folded into any fraction of the form $\dfrac{m^2}{n^2}$ or $\dfrac{m^2}{2n^2}$.

    <u>Proof:</u> use the construction in (6b) to mark points $1/n$, $2/n$, etc. of the way from A to B. Then choose the point P that is m/n of the way from A to B. Use B3 to find a corresponding point Q on $\overline{AD}$. At both P and Q use B4 to create a crease perpendicular to each side of $ABCD$. The creases meet at point R forming square $APRQ$ that has an area of $(m/n)^2 = m^2/n^2$. The Meno construction can be used on $APRQ$ to halve its area.

8. a) Given collinear points A, B, C, with $AB = 1$ and $BC = r$, first fold a crease ℓ through B with $\ell \perp \overline{BC}$ using B4. Unfold the paper and fold A onto C using B2; let O be the midpoint of $\overline{AC}$ determined by the crease. Unfold the paper and fold C onto ℓ with a crease passing through O using B5. Let C' be the image of C on crease ℓ. Now $OC = AC/2$ by B2 and $OC = OC'$ by construction, so $\overline{OC'}$ is a radius of the circle with diameter $\overline{AC}$. Since $\overline{BC'} \perp \overline{AC}$ by construction, then BC' is the geometric mean of AB and BC, i.e., $(BC')^2 = AB \cdot BC = 1 \cdot r = r \rightarrow BC' = \sqrt{r}$.

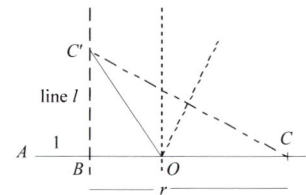

    b) Start with square $ABCD$ and point E on $\overline{AB}$ with $AE = r$. Fold point B onto E using B2 and mark the midpoint of $\overline{BE} = F$. Now $AF = r + \dfrac{1-r}{2} = \dfrac{r+1}{2}$, so AF is a radius of a circle centered at F with diameter $r + 1$. Using B4 fold a crease through E perpendicular to $\overline{AB}$; call the crease ℓ. Using B5 fold A onto ℓ with the crease passing through F. Let A' be the image of A on ℓ; note that $A'F = AF = \dfrac{r+1}{2}$.

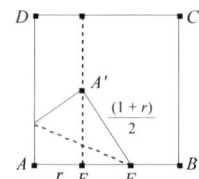

    So A' is the intersection of the circle centered at F with the perpendicular through E. Thus $(A'E)^2 = AE \cdot (r + 1 - AE) = r \cdot (r + 1 - r) = r$. Therefore, $A'E = \sqrt{r}$.

9. Using the constructions in (6) and (7), any side length of the form k/n, $k \le n$, can be constructed on the square. Using (8b), any side length of the form $\sqrt{\dfrac{k}{n}}$ can be constructed. Therefore, any area of the form k/n can be constructed. But in fact, we can do even better: by square-rooting twice, we can construct a side length of the form $\sqrt[4]{\dfrac{k}{n}}$ and thus an <u>area</u> of the form $\sqrt{\dfrac{k}{n}}$. That is, it's possible to construct a square of area $\dfrac{\sqrt{2}}{2} = \sqrt{\dfrac{1}{2}}$ using these constructions, and certainly any area of the form $(k/n)^{1/2^m}$ by repeated applications of (8b).

10. a) The altitude of a unit equilateral triangle is $\dfrac{\sqrt{3}}{2}$, and yields an area of 3/4. One

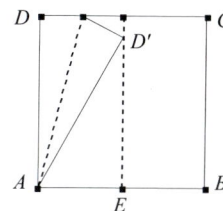

can be constructed by folding point A onto point B using B2 and labeling the midpoint E, then folding D onto the crease through E with the new crease passing through A using B5. That's 2 folds. Let the image of D be D', then $AD' = 1$,

$AE = 1/2$, and $ED' = \dfrac{\sqrt{3}}{2}$. Now fold a perpendicular to $\overline{ED'}$ through D' using

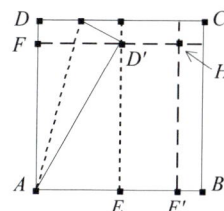

B4 and denote the intersection of that crease and $\overline{AD}$ by point F. Using B3 fold $\overline{AD}$ onto $\overline{AB}$ marking the image of F on $\overline{AB}$ as point F'. That makes 4 folds. Using B4, fold a perpendicular to $\overline{AB}$ at F'. That's 5 folds and A, F, H, and F' determine the vertices of a square whose area is 3/4.

b) One quite efficient construction is to use the method of (6b) to divide $\overline{AB}$ into five equal parts. This requires making 3 folds to subdivide $\overline{AD}$ into 8 equal parts and then folding B up to the fifth crease allowing one to subdivide $\overline{AB}$ into the five equal parts.

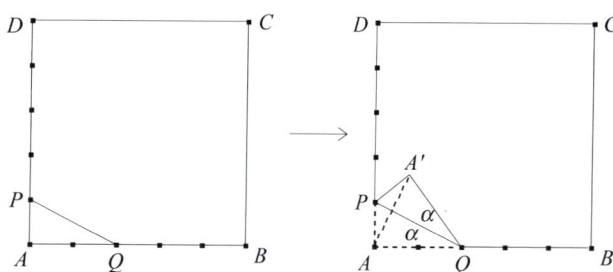

Using B3, those can also be marked off on $\overline{AD}$ using one fold, marking P such that $AP = 1/5$ and Q such that $AQ = 2/5$. That's five folds. The sixth is to fold over $\overline{PQ}$ using B1 to produce the crease $\overline{PQ}$ and point A'.

By the Pythagorean theorem, $PQ = \dfrac{\sqrt{5}}{5}$, making it the side of a square of area 1/5.

We need to construct a perpendicular to $\overline{PQ}$ through Q but that can't be constructed using B4 since Q is an endpoint of $\overline{PQ}$. However, we can still manage if we fold using B3 so that $\overline{QB}$ lands on $\overline{A'Q}$ with crease through Q,

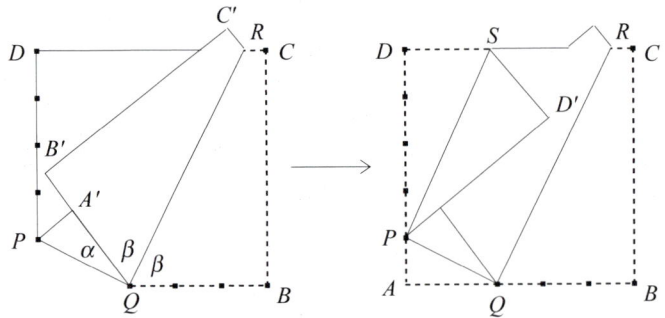

creating angle PQR. Let $m\angle AQP = m\angle PQA' = \alpha$ and $m\angle A'QR = m\angle RQB = \beta$. Since $2\alpha + 2\beta = 180°$, then $\alpha + \beta = m\angle PQR = 90°$. Using B3, fold $\overline{PD}$ onto $\overline{PA'}$ with crease $\overline{PS}$. That allows us to construct two sides of the square. That makes 8 folds.

Using B3, we fold $\overline{SP}$ onto $\overline{PQ}$, producing crease $\overline{PW}$. Using B4 we fold a crease through W that is perpendicular to $\overline{RQ}$. Points P, Q, W, and R form the vertices of a square with area 1/5. That is a total of 10 folds.

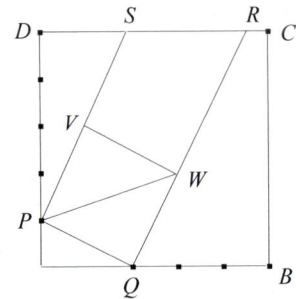

I–1. Compute the number of positive integers that have the same number of digits when expressed in base 3 and base 5.

I–2. Two 3 by 4 rectangles overlap in such a way that their sides are perpendicular. If the area and perimeter of the shaded region are 22 and 20 respectively, compute AB.

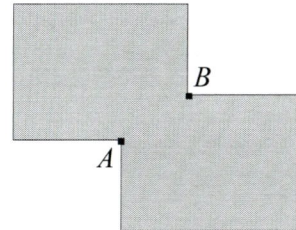

I–3. If *ABCDE* is a regular pentagon and *MNCD* is a square, compute the value of $m\angle AMN - m\angle EAM$ in degrees.

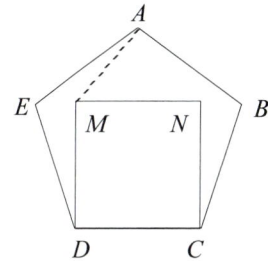

I–4. Compute the four-digit positive integer N whose square root is three times the sum of the digits of N.

I–5. Starting with $n = 1$, let $\{a_n\}$ be an infinite geometric sequence with $a_2 = 17$. Compute the smallest possible positive sum of the sequence.

I–6. Determine the sum of the *y*-coordinates of the four points of intersection of $y = x^4 - 5x^2 - x + 4$ and $y = x^2 - 3x$.

I–7. If $\log_8 a + \log_8 b = \left(\log_8 a\right)\left(\log_8 b\right)$ and $\log_a b = 3$, compute the value of a.

I–8. There are 5 computers, *A*, *B*, *C*, *D*, and *E*. For each pair of computers a coin is flipped. If it is heads, then a link is built between the two computers; if it is tails, there's no link between the two. Every message that a computer receives is sent to every computer to which it is linked. Compute the probability that every computer is able to receive messages from every other computer.

1. 8

2. $2\sqrt{3}$

3. 36

4. 2916

5. 68

6. 12

7. 16

8. $\dfrac{91}{128}$

I–1. Numbers 1 and 2 each have 1 digit in base 3 and base 5. Numbers 5, 6, 7, and 8 each have two digits in both bases. Numbers 25 and 26 each have three digits in both bases. There are no other answers since from 81 on, the base 3 representation requires more digits than the base 5. Ans: $\boxed{8}$.

I–2. The area 22 equals $24 - xy \rightarrow xy = 2$. The perimeter 20 equals $16 + 12 - 2x - 2y \rightarrow x + y = 4$. Thus,
$x^2 + 2xy + y^2 = 16 \rightarrow x^2 + 4 + y^2 = 16 \rightarrow x^2 + y^2 = 12$.
Therefore, $AB = \boxed{2\sqrt{3}}$. One could also solve the system by
setting $y = \dfrac{2}{x}$ and obtain $x + \dfrac{2}{x} = 4 \rightarrow x^2 - 4x + 2 = 0$, giving
$x = 2 - \sqrt{2}$ and $y = 2 + \sqrt{2}$.

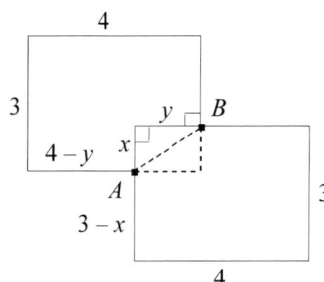

I–3. Draw line $\overleftrightarrow{PA}$ parallel to $\overline{MN}$. Set $m\angle AMN = x$ and $m\angle EAM = y$.
Since $m\angle PAM = m\angle AMN = x$, then $m\angle PAE = x - y$. Since
$m\angle RAB = x - y$, then $180 = 2(x - y) + 108 \rightarrow x - y = \boxed{36}$. Or let
$m\angle MAN = 180 - 2x$. Then $2y + (180 - 2x) = m\angle EAB = 108$, giving
$2x - 2y = 72 \rightarrow x - y = 36$.

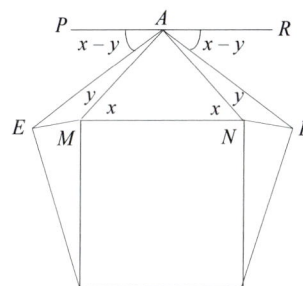

Alternate solution:

Let $m\angle EAM = x$; the other angles are as marked. Note:
$m\angle AEM = 27$. Since $m\angle EMA = 180 - (27 + x) = 153 - x$,
then $m\angle AMN = 360 - (90 + 81 + 153 - x) = 36 + x$. Thus,
$m\angle AMN - m\angle EAM = (36 + x) - x = 36$.

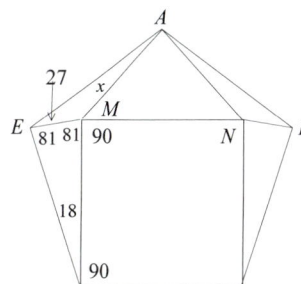

I–4. Since $\sqrt{N} = 3t$ where t is the sum of the digits of N, then $N = 9t^2 \rightarrow N$ is a multiple of 9 $\rightarrow$ the sum of the digits of N is a multiple of 9 $\rightarrow t = 9k$ for k an integer $\rightarrow \sqrt{N} = 27k \rightarrow N = k^2 \cdot 27^2$. If $k = 1$, then N is a three-digit number. If $k = 2$, then $N = 4 \cdot 27^2 = 54^2 = 2916$; the sum of its digits is 18 and $54 = 3 \cdot 18$. If $k = 3$, $N = 9 \cdot 27^2 = 81^2 = 6561$, but 6561 fails since $81 \neq 3(6 + 5 + 6 + 1)$. If $k \geq 4$, N is no longer a four-digit number. Thus, $N = \boxed{2916}$.

I–5. Let a_1 be the first term and r the common ratio. Then $a_1 = \dfrac{17}{r} \rightarrow \dfrac{a_1}{1 - r} = \dfrac{\frac{17}{r}}{1 - r} = \dfrac{17}{r - r^2}$. To minimize

the sum we need to maximize $r - r^2$ and that occurs at $r = \dfrac{1}{2}$, making the sum equal to $\dfrac{17}{1/4} = \boxed{68}$.

I–6. $x^4 - 5x^2 - x + 4 = x^2 - 3x \rightarrow x^4 - 6x^2 + 2x + 4 = 0$. Let the roots be a, b, c, and d. Since the coefficient of the x^3 term is 0, $a + b + c + d = 0$. Using the function $y = x^2 - 3x$ we obtain the following sum of the y-values of the points of intersection: $\left(a^2 - 3a\right) + \left(b^2 - 3b\right) + \left(c^2 - 3c\right) + \left(d^2 - 3d\right)$

$= \left(a^2 + b^2 + c^2 + d^2\right) - 3(a + b + c + d) = \left(a^2 + b^2 + c^2 + d^2\right) - 3(0) = a^2 + b^2 + c^2 + d^2$.

To obtain the value of $a^2 + b^2 + c^2 + d^2$ note that $(a + b + c + d)^2 = 0^2 = 0$, so squaring gives $a^2 + b^2 + c^2 + d^2 + 2(ab + ac + ad + bc + bd + cd) = 0$. Using $x^4 - 6x^2 + 2x + 4 = 0$, we know that $ab + ac + ad + bc + bd + cd = -6$ so $a^2 + b^2 + c^2 + d^2 = \boxed{12}$, the sum of the y-values.

I–7. $\log_a b = 3 \rightarrow \dfrac{\log_8 b}{\log_8 a} = 3 \rightarrow \log_8 b = 3\log_8 a$. Substituting into $\log_8 a + \log_8 b = \log_8 a \cdot \log_8 b$ gives

$4\log_8 a = 3\left(\log_8 a\right)^2$. Since $\log_8 a \neq 0$, then $4 = 3\log_8 a \rightarrow \log_8 a = \dfrac{4}{3}$ so $a = \left(2^3\right)^{4/3} = \boxed{16}$.

I–8.   Imagine that computers are vertices and links are simply segments connecting two vertices. There are 5 vertices, $_5C_2 = 10$ possible segments, and $2^{10} = 1024$ ways they can be connected. Rather than count which of the 1024 graphs connect all vertices, it is easier to count those that do not connect them all.

Case 1: none of the vertices are connected: o o o o o, so there is only $\boxed{1}$ way to do this.

Case 2: one pair is connected: o o o o–o. There are $_5C_2 = \boxed{10}$ ways to do this.

Case 3: three are connected: o o o–o–o. There are $_5C_2 = 10$ ways to pick the two unconnected vertices. If the other three vertices are connected linearly, there are 3 choices for the middle vertex. If the vertices form a triangle there's one way to do that. Thus, there $10 \cdot 4 = \boxed{40}$ not fully connected graphs here.

Case 4: two are connected and three are connected: o–o o–o–o. The same analysis as Case 3. Ans: $\boxed{40}$.

Case 5: there is an unconnected vertex and two pairs of connected vertices: o o–o o–o. There are 5 ways to pick the lone vertex. Given the remaining vertices a, b, c, and d, we could have a–b c–d, or a–c b–d, or a–d b–c, giving three choices. Ans: $5 \cdot 3 = \boxed{15}$ not fully connected graphs.

Case 6: there is a lone, unconnected vertex and four connected ones. There are 5 ways to pick the lone vertex. Concerning the other four vertices, there are $_4C_2 = 6$ possible edges so there are $2^6 = 64$ possible arrangements. To count the number of connected arrangements it is easier to count the number of ways 4 vertices aren't fully connected.

   i)   If there are no edges as in o o o o, there is 1 way.
   ii)   If there is 1 edge as in o–o o o, there are $_4C_2 = 6$ ways to select the edge.
   iii)   Two edges can be done in two ways. The first is o–o o–o and there are 3 ways to do this as in Case 4 above. The second is o–o–o o. There are 4 ways to pick the lone vertex and as in Case 3 there are 4 ways to connect three vertices, giving 16 ways. This makes for a total of $1 + 6 + 3 + 16 = 26$ not fully connected paths on 4 vertices, giving $64 - 26 = 38$ connected paths.

Since there were 5 ways to choose the lone vertex, we have $5 \cdot 38 = \boxed{190}$ ways to have one lone vertex and 4 connected vertices.

Thus there are $1 + 10 + 40 + 40 + 15 + 190 = 296$ not fully connected graphs on 5 vertices, making for $1024 - 296 = 728$ connected graphs. The probability they are all linked is $\dfrac{728}{1024} = \boxed{\dfrac{91}{128}}$.

R1–1.   Compute the number of integer solutions to $\big| |x| - 2006 \big| > 5$.

R1–2.   Let T = TNYWR. If $AB = AC$, $\overline{BD}$ bisects $\angle ABC$, $\overline{CD}$ bisects $\angle ACB$, and $m\angle A = T$, compute $m\angle BDC$.

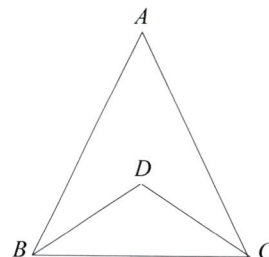

R1–3.   Let T = TNYWR. The regular hexagon intersects the y-axis in one point, a side of the hexagon lies on the x-axis, and the x-coordinate of point A is $\dfrac{T}{11}$. If the area of the hexagon is $K\sqrt{3}$, compute K.

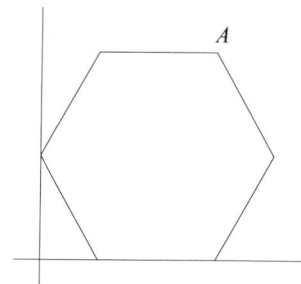

R2–1.   Let the real roots of $y = x^2 - 5x + 4$ be a and b and the real roots of $y = x^2 - 5x + k$ be c and d. If $|a - c| = |b - d| = 5$, compute the largest value of k.

R2–2.   Let T = the absolute value of TNYWR. Compute the value of $\dfrac{\left(12T^{-1} - 1\right)^{-1}}{\left(144T^{-2} - 1\right)^{-1}}$.

R2–3.   Let T = TNYWR. A triangle with sides 8, $4T$, and x with $8 < 4T < x$ is similar to a triangle with sides $4T$, x, and y with $4T < x < y$. A third triangle is similar to the first; if the length of its shortest side is y, compute the length of its longest side.

Relay #1:

R1–1. 18

R1–2. 99

R1–3. 54

Relay #2:

R2–1. –6

R2–2. 3

R2–3. $\dfrac{243}{4} = 60.75$

R1–1. $\big|\,|x| - 2006\,\big| < 5 \rightarrow -5 < |x| - 2006 < 5 \rightarrow 2001 < |x| < 2011$. Thus, $x = \pm 2002, \pm 2003, \ldots, \pm 2010$, making $2 \cdot 9 = \boxed{18}$ integer solutions.

R1–2. $T = 18$. Set $m\angle A = 4x$, then $m\angle ABC = \angle ACB = \dfrac{180 - 4x}{2} =$

$90 - 2x \rightarrow m\angle DBC = m\angle DCB = 45 - x$. Thus,

$m\angle D = 180 - (90 - 2x) = 90 + 2x$. Since $4x = 18$, then

$2x = 9$, so $m\angle D = \boxed{99}$.

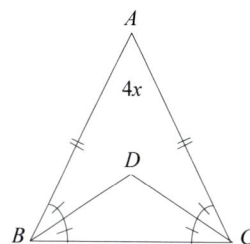

R1–3. $T = 99$. Let the side of the hexagon equal $2a$, making the area equal to $6a^2\sqrt{3}$. Since ΔDOB is a 30-60-90 triangle with $DB = 2a$, then $B = (a, 0)$ and $C = (3a, 0)$, making $\dfrac{T}{11} = 3a \rightarrow$

$a = \dfrac{T}{33} = \dfrac{99}{33} = 3$. Thus, the area is $54\sqrt{3}$, making $K = \boxed{54}$.

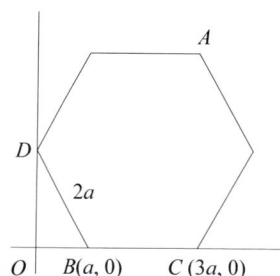

R2–1. Let $a = 1$ and $b = 4$. Then $|1 - c| = 5 \rightarrow c = -4$ or 6 and $|4 - d| = 5 \rightarrow d = 9$ or -1. Since both parabolas have $x = 5/2$ as the axis of symmetry, either c lies to the right of the axis and d lies to the left in which case $c = 6$ and $d = -1$, or vice-versa, in which case $c = -4$ and $d = 9$. The former gives $(x - 6)(x + 1) = x^2 - 5x - 6$ and the latter gives $(x + 4)(x - 9) = x^2 - 5x - 36$. The largest value of k is $\boxed{-6}$.

R2–2. $T = |-6| = 6$. $\dfrac{\left(\dfrac{12}{T} - 1\right)^{-1}}{\left(\dfrac{144}{T^2} - 1\right)^{-1}} = \dfrac{T}{12 - T} \cdot \dfrac{144 - T^2}{T^2} = \dfrac{12 + T}{T}$. Since $T = 6$, $\dfrac{12 + T}{T} = \boxed{3}$.

R2–3. $T = 3$. Since the first two triangles are similar, then corresponding sides are in the same ratio meaning that $\dfrac{8}{4T} = \dfrac{4T}{x} = \dfrac{x}{y}$, but from $\dfrac{8}{4T} = \dfrac{4T}{x}$, we realize that the sides of the first triangle form a geometric sequence. The first term is 8, making $4T = 8r$, $x = 8r^2$, and $y = 8r^3$, so the longest side of the 3rd triangle is $8r^5$. Since $T = 3$, $8r = 12 \rightarrow r = \dfrac{3}{2} \rightarrow 8\left(\dfrac{3}{2}\right)^5 = \boxed{\dfrac{243}{4}} = \boxed{60.75}$. The 8-12-18 and 12-18-27 triangles have three pairs of congruent angles and two pairs of congruent sides, but are not congruent. The problem suggests a way to construct such pairs of triangles.

87

1. Currently, Arnold is $3x$ years old and his younger sister Millie is x years old. When Millie was born, Arnold was 16 years old. Compute Arnold's age 10 years from now.

2. Let T = TNYWR. A right circular cylinder has a radius of r, a height of Tr, and a total surface area of 420π. Compute r.

3. Let T = TNYWR and set $K = 2T^2$. Compute $\log_{\sqrt[3]{K}}\left((2K - 1) + (2K - 3) + \ldots + 1\right)$.

4. Let T = TNYWR. If $x^{1/T} - x^{1/(2T)} = 12$, compute $x^{1/12}$.

5. Let T = TNYWR. A class has T boys and T girls and the heights of all the students are different. Compute the number of ways to arrange the students in a row such that all of the following conditions hold: (i) the boys are not all standing next to each other, (ii) from left to right the boys are arranged from shortest to tallest, and (iii) from left to right the girls are neither arranged from shortest to tallest, nor from tallest to shortest.

6. Let T = TNYWR. Let $K = \dfrac{2006 - T}{4}$. The <u>product</u> of the positive divisors of 36^3 equals $\left(2^{K+x}\right)\left(3^{K+y}\right)$ where x and y are integers. Compute $x + y$.

7. Let T = TNYWR. Compute the maximum value of the function
    $$f(x) = 4\sin^2 x + (T - 2)\cos x + 34.$$

8. To the right is a magic square in which the sums of the elements in the rows, columns, and diagonals are all equal. Let R be the number you receive from position 7 and T be the number you receive from position 9. Compute X.

30		
27		R
T	X	

15. Let $a_1 = 1, a_2 = 11, a_3 = 111, a_4 = 1111$, and so on. Compute the smallest value of n so that a_n is a multiple of $n + 1$.

14. Let T = TNYWR. In the figure, $\angle ABC$ is a right angle, and D is the midpoint of $\overline{BC}$. If $AB = BC = 12$, and $BE = T$, compute BF^2.

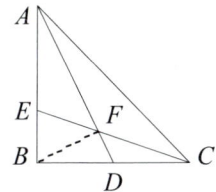

13. Let T = TNYWR and set $K = 2T^2$. Compute $\log_{\sqrt[3]{K}}\left((2K-1) + (2K-3) + \ldots + 1\right)$.

12. Let T = TNYWR. Arrange T women and T men into T rows of 2 people so that each row contains 1 woman and 1 man. Let 2^K be the highest power of 2 that is a factor of the number of ways to do this. Compute K.

11. Let T = TNYWR. Two candles of height T cm are lit. One burns down three times as fast as the other and after T minutes, it is 1/5 as tall as the other. Compute the height in centimeters of the fast burner after T minutes.

10. Let T = TNYWR. A regular polygon of $T + 1$ sides has a side length of 1, an area of K, and a perimeter of P. Compute P/K.

9. Let T = TNYWR. Triangle ABC is given with $BC = 2006$. Circle O is inscribed in $\triangle ABC$, it is tangent to $\overline{AB}$ at D, and it has a radius of $1 / T^2$. If $AD = 10$, compute the area of $\triangle ABC$.

8. To the right is a magic square in which the sums of the elements in the rows, columns, and diagonals are all equal. Let R be the number you receive from position 7 and T be the number you receive from position 9. Compute X.

30		
27		R
T	X	

1.   34

2. $\sqrt{6}$

3.   6

4.   4

5.   1430

6.   6

7.   39

----

15.   6

14.   32

13.   6

12.   14

11.   2

10. $4\sqrt{3}$

9.   42

----

8.   21

1. $3x = x + 16 \rightarrow x = 8 \rightarrow 3x + 10 = \boxed{34}$.

2. $2\pi r^2 + (2\pi r) \cdot Tr = 420\pi \rightarrow r^2 + Tr^2 = 210 \rightarrow r^2 = \dfrac{210}{1 + T}$. $T = 34 \rightarrow r = \boxed{\sqrt{6}}$.

3. $1 + 3 + \ldots + (2K - 3) + (2K - 1) = \dfrac{1 + (2K - 1)}{2} \cdot K = K^2$. Thus,

    $\log_{\sqrt[3]{K}}\left(K^2\right) = n \rightarrow K^2 = K^{n/3} \rightarrow 2 = \dfrac{n}{3}$, giving $n = \boxed{6}$. The values of T and K are unnecessary.

4. Let $y = x^{1/(2T)}$, giving $y^2 - y - 12 = 0 \rightarrow (y - 4)(y + 3) = 0 \rightarrow y = 4$ since y is an even root.

    We have $x^{1/(2T)} = 4 \rightarrow x = 4^{2T} = 2^{4T}$. So $x^{1/12} = 2^{T/3}$. Since $T = 6$, $x^{1/12} = 2^2 = \boxed{4}$.

5. There is 1 way to order the boys. There are $T!$ ways to arrange the girls if all arrangements could be used, but since the girls can't be ordered by height, we take away 2 arrangements, leaving $T! - 2$ ways to arrange the girls. There are $_{2T}C_T$ ways to choose the T places for the boys, but $T + 1$ of them can't be used since there are $T + 1$ ways for the boys to stand next to each other. Thus, the number of arrangements is

    $1 \cdot (T! - 2)\left(_{2T}C_T - (T + 1)\right)$. Since $T = 4$ we have $22\left(_8C_4 - 5\right) = 22(65) = \boxed{1430}$.

6. Since $36^3 = 2^6 \cdot 3^6$, there are $7 \cdot 7 = 49$ factors. Except for $2^3 \cdot 3^3 = 6^3$, each factor can be paired with a different factor so that the product of the pair is $2^6 \cdot 3^6$. So, the product of all the factor pairs and $2^3 \cdot 3^3$

    is $\left(2^6 \cdot 3^6\right)^{48/2} \cdot \left(2^3 \cdot 3^3\right) = 2^{147} \cdot 3^{147}$. Since $K = \dfrac{2006 - T}{4} = \dfrac{2006 - 1430}{4} = 144$, then $x = y = 3$,

    making $x + y = \boxed{6}$.

7. $f(x) = 4\sin^2 x + (T - 2)\cos x + 34 = 4(1 - \cos^2 x) + (T - 2)\cos x + 34 = -4\cos^2 x + (T - 2)\cos x + 38$.

    The maximum occurs at $\cos x = \dfrac{-(T - 2)}{2(-4)} = \dfrac{T - 2}{8}$, assuming $\dfrac{|T - 2|}{8} \le 1$, and the maximum value

    is $-4 \cdot \dfrac{(T - 2)^2}{64} + (T - 2) \cdot \dfrac{(T - 2)}{8} + 38 = \dfrac{(T - 2)^2}{16} + 38$. At $T = 6$, the max is $\boxed{39}$.

91

15. $a_5 = 11111$ and that is not divisible by 6, but $a_6 = 111111$ is divisible by 7 since $111111 = (111)(1001) = (111)(7 \cdot 11 \cdot 13)$. Also, $111111/7 = 15873$. Ans: $\boxed{6}$.

14. Place the triangle on a coordinate system with $A = (0, 12)$, $B = (0, 0)$,

$C = (12, 0)$, $D = (6, 0)$, and $E = (0, T)$. The equation of $\overline{AD}$ is

$y = -2x + 12$ and the equation of $\overline{CE}$ is $y = -\dfrac{T}{12}x + T$. They intersect at

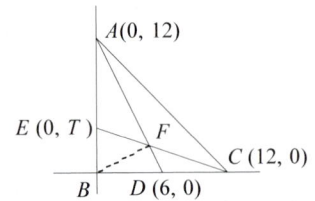

$F\left(\dfrac{12(T - 12)}{T - 24}, \dfrac{-12T}{T - 24}\right)$, making $BF^2 = \dfrac{12^2(T - 12)^2 + 12^2 T^2}{(T - 24)^2}$. Since $T = 6$, then $BF^2 = \dfrac{12^2\left(6^2 + 6^2\right)}{18^2}$ which equals $\boxed{32}$.

13. $1 + 3 + \ldots + (2K - 3) + (2K - 1) = \dfrac{1 + (2K - 1)}{2} \cdot K = K^2$. Thus,

$\log_{\sqrt[3]{K}}\left(K^2\right) = n \rightarrow K^2 = K^{n/3} \rightarrow 2 = \dfrac{n}{3}$ giving $n = \boxed{6}$. The values of T and K are unnecessary.

12. In each row there are 2 ways to arrange the man and the woman, giving 2^T ways to arrange $2T$ people in the rows. There are $T!$ ways to arrange the men and $T!$ ways to arrange the women making a total of $2^T \cdot (T!)^2$ ways to arrange everyone. Since $T = 6$, we have $2^6 \cdot (6 \cdot 5 \cdot 4 \cdot 3 \cdot 2 \cdot 1)^2 = 2^{14}(5 \cdot 3^2)^2$, so $K = \boxed{14}$.

11. Let the candles burn down at x cm/min and $3x$ cm/min respectively. Then $T - Tx = 5(T - 3xT)$ gives

$1 - x = 5(1 - 3x) \rightarrow x = \dfrac{2}{7} \rightarrow$ the height of the shorter candle equals $T - 3 \cdot \dfrac{2}{7}T = \dfrac{T}{7}$. Since $T = 14$, the height is $\boxed{2}$.

10. Let $\theta = \dfrac{360°}{T + 1}$ be the central angle, making $\dfrac{\theta}{2} = \dfrac{180°}{T + 1}$ and let h be the apothem.

Then $\tan\dfrac{\theta}{2} = \dfrac{1/2}{h} \rightarrow h = \dfrac{\cos\left(\theta/2\right)}{2\sin\left(\theta/2\right)}$. The area of the polygon

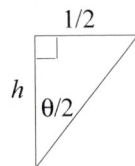

is $K = (T + 1) \cdot \dfrac{1}{2} \cdot 1 \cdot \dfrac{\cos\left(\theta/2\right)}{2\sin\left(\theta/2\right)} = \dfrac{(T + 1)\cos\left(\theta/2\right)}{4\sin\left(\theta/2\right)}$ and the perimeter $P = T + 1$. Then we have

$\dfrac{P}{K} = \dfrac{T + 1}{\dfrac{(T + 1)\cos\left(\theta/2\right)}{4\sin\left(\theta/2\right)}} = \dfrac{4\sin\left(\theta/2\right)}{\cos\left(\theta/2\right)} = \dfrac{4\sin\left(\dfrac{180°}{T + 1}\right)}{\cos\left(\dfrac{180°}{T + 1}\right)}$. Given the fact that the problem is doable without a

calculator, then the most likely T values are $T = 2, 3, 5$, and 7, giving $\dfrac{180°}{T + 1} = 60°, 45°, 30°$, and $22.5°$, making

$\dfrac{P}{K} = 4\sqrt{3}, 4, \dfrac{4\sqrt{3}}{3}$, and $4\sqrt{2} - 4$, respectively. Since $T = 2$, then $\dfrac{P}{K} = \boxed{4\sqrt{3}}$.

9. Since tangents to a circle from an exterior point are congruent, then

   $AD = AE = 10$, $BE = BF = x$, and $CF = CD = 2006 - x$. The perimeter

   is $10 + x + 2006 + 2006 - x + 10 = 4032$. Since the area of $\triangle ABC$ is

   $\dfrac{1}{2} \cdot \dfrac{1}{T^2} \cdot 4032 = \dfrac{2016}{T^2}$ and $T = 4\sqrt{3}$, then the area is $\dfrac{2016}{48} = \boxed{42}$.

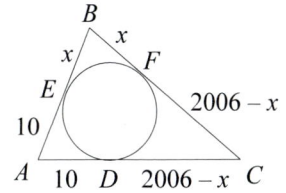

---

8. This #8 adds a new twist to the Super Relay since the problem, while not invariant, can be solved with the value of R alone, but not with the value of T alone. Let the middle square have the value of y and the lower right square have the value of z. Using column 1 and row 2, we obtain the following:

30		
27	y	R
T	X	z

   $30 + 27 + T = 27 + y + R \rightarrow 30 + T = y + R$. Using the diagonal from upper left to lower right and the elements in the 3rd row we obtain $30 + y + z = T + X + z \rightarrow y = T + X - 30$. Substituting gives $30 + T = T + X - 30 + R \rightarrow X = 60 - R$. Since $R = 39$, then $X = \boxed{21}$. Alternately, using both values, namely, $R = 39$ and $T = 42$, the sum is 99, so $y = 33$ and $z = 36$, making $X = 21$.

1. Compute the number of ways three distinct numbers can be chosen from the set

    $S = \{1, 2, 3, \ldots, 34\}$ such that the sum of the three numbers is divisible by 3.

2. Let $f(x) = mx + b$ where m and b are integers with $m > 0$. If the solution to $2^{f(x)} = 5$ is

    $x = \log_8 10$, compute the ordered pair (m, b).

3. A square has two of its vertices on the y-axis. Points $A(1, 8)$ and $B(-1, -4)$ are on sides of

    the square such that $\overline{AB}$ bisects the square. Determine the area of the square.

1. In set S there are 11 numbers divisible by 3, 12 numbers $= 1 \pmod 3$ and 11 numbers $= 2 \pmod 3$. Choosing three numbers from any one of those three sets gives a sum divisible by 3. In addition, if the three numbers chosen from S have remainders of 0, 1, and 2 respectively, the sum is divisible by 3. There are $11(12)(11)$ ways to choose three such numbers. Thus, there are $2\dbinom{11}{3} + \dbinom{12}{3} + 11^2 \cdot 12 \;=\; \boxed{2002}$ ways to choose the three numbers.

2. Let $a = \log_8 10$ be the solution. Then $2^{f(a)} = 5 \to f(a) = \log_2 5$. Since

   $a = \log_8 10 = \dfrac{1}{3}\log_2 10$, then $3a = \log_2(2 \cdot 5) \;\to\; 3a = 1 + \log_2 5 \;\to\; 3a - 1 = \log_2 5$.

   Thus, $f(x) = 3x - 1$ and $(m, b) \;=\; \boxed{(3, -1)}$.

   <u>Alternate solution</u>: Let $x = \log_8 10 = \dfrac{1}{3}\log_2 10$. Then $2^{mx+b} = 2^{(m/3)\log_2 10 + b} = 5$.

   Thus, $2^{\log_2 10^{m/3}} \cdot 2^b = 5 \;\to\; 10^{m/3} \cdot 2^b = 5 \to 2^{m/3} \cdot 2^b \cdot 5^{m/3} = 2^{m/3+b} \cdot 5^{m/3} = 5$.

   Since m and b are integers, the power of 2 must be 0 and the power of 5 must be 1. Thus,

   $\dfrac{m}{3} = 1 \;\to\; m = 3$ and $1 + b = 0 \to b = -1$. So, $f(x) = 3x - 1$ and $(m, b) \;=\; \boxed{(3, -1)}$.

3. The vertices of opposite corners must lie on the y-axis. Since the slope of $\overline{AM}$ equals the slope of $\overline{BN} = -1$, the coordinates of the vertices are $(0, 9)$ and $(0, -5)$. The

   diagonal has a length of 14, so the area is $\left(\dfrac{14}{\sqrt 2}\right)^2 = \boxed{98}$.

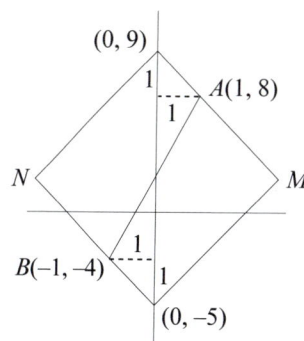

Steve Adrian, the Executive Director of ARML is on the left.

J. Bryan Sullivan, the President of ARML, is on the right.

Linda Berman is the Treasurer of ARML.

ARML
2007

This year's contest was a nail-biter that went right down to the wire. The team round was difficult again and the top score was only 32. Problem #5 was a real snake in the grass and fooled just about every team. Phillips Exeter Red, Lehigh Valley Fire, Texas Gold, Thomas Jefferson A, and Michigan Reals were all tied for first place after the first round. An excellent 39 on a Power Question involving continued fractions earned Lehigh Valley the lead with 71 points, Exeter was in second place with 68, and North Carolina A was in third with 60 points. Six teams scored in the 80's on the individual round, a fine accomplishment. Exeter moved into a tie with Lehigh Valley with an 85 and North Carolina trailed by 7 points. Two years ago Lehigh Valley surged past Exeter on the first relay, but this time relay #1 proved equally difficult for all the best teams and we entered the final relay with Exeter and Lehigh Valley still tied. New York City A moved into contention with a fine 16 on #1. It came down to the final relay. This time Exeter prevailed, but narrowly. With 6 points on #2, Exeter won ARML 2007 with a total of 171 while Lehigh Valley was second with 169. New York City did well on the second relay and vaulted into third place with a 163. Taiwan A was first in Division B and the top US team in that division was South Carolina Doom.

There were 37 teams in Division A this year and 82 in Division B. Columbia sent a team for the first time and ARML arranged for a translation into Spanish.

Eric Wepsic was awarded the Alfred Kalfus Founder's Award in recognition of his long and significant involvement with ARML. In the late 1980's Eric, an IMO team member, contributed significantly to the success of the Eastern Massachusetts team. Eric became a problem writer in 1995 and contributed some wonderful Power Questions as well as some very challenging team and individual questions. He works for D.E. Shaw and has been instrumental in securing financial support of ARML from D.E. Shaw.

Joe Holbrook of AAST in New Jersey and Steve Sigur of the Georgia team were awarded the Samuel L. Greitzer Coach Awards. Joe has been a force of nature in promoting math competitions in Bergen county to both the mathematically gifted and interested. He works round the clock to promote math. For example, he opens up a classroom stocked with vast numbers of problems books on Saturday and Sunday for students to work to improve their knowledge and ability. Anyone is welcome to pick up a book and work and as long as someone is interested, Joe will be there to help them out.

Steve Sigur has coached the Georgia ARML team for at least 15 years. He's instituted effective, fun, and intense practice sessions at which he routinely presents alternate solutions and provides positive feedback for his students. He's helped foster an optimistic and positive learning environment that further strengthens cooperation on the team. At other math contests his ARML students seek each other out to compare approaches and celebrate each other's successes. He's organized several math contests for interested students in Georgia, he's enabled students to take part in contests outside of Georgia, and he's created a website and blog for the team.

The Western Washington Math Circle was awarded the Harry and Ruth Ruderman Award for winning the ARML Power Contest.

The following were awarded the Douglas Cameron Baker Memorial Award: Paul Hlebowitsh of Iowa and Elizabeth Ann Denys of Chicago. Paul's enjoyment of mathematics has been described as irrepressible. He has organized the Fun for Friday math meetings, he's prepared the problems and solutions, he's diligent, he's taken the hardest of problem solving courses, and he does some pretty good math raps. Liz has been described as the embodiment of team spirit. She's an energetic organizer for ARML, she prepares diligently for practices despite carrying a heavy load of schoolwork and outside activities, and she's passionate about mathematics.

T–1. For integral $x > 0$, compute the number of pairs of points A and B that lie on the graph of $y = x^2$, A to the left and below B, such that the slope of $\overline{AB}$ is 2007.

T–2. Determine the number of three-digit positive integers such that if the integer is divided by the sum of its digits, the result is 19.

T–3. In rectangle *ABCD*, *M* is the midpoint of $\overline{AB}$, $EC = 10$ and $EM = 4$. Compute the area of *ABCD*.

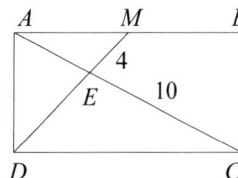

T–4. Consider the increasing list of positive integers that do not contain the digit 0, i.e., 1, 2, 3, . . . 8, 9, 11, 12, . . . Compute the 2007th integer in this list.

T–5. Compute the value of k such that the equation $\dfrac{x + 2}{kx - 1} = x$ has exactly one solution.

T–6. In a right triangle with integer sides the radius of the inscribed circle is 12. Compute the longest possible hypotenuse.

T–7. The pages of a book are numbered consecutively from 1 to n. The book is divided into 12 chapters such that the number of digits used to number the pages of each chapter is the same. Compute the least possible value for n.

T–8. Compute the sum of all integers a for which the polynomial $x^2 + ax + 10a$ can be factored over the integers.

T–9. Let [x] denote the greatest integer function. For all $x \geq 1$, let f be the function defined as follows:

$$f(x) = \begin{cases} [x] \cdot \left| x - [x] - \dfrac{1}{2[x]} \right| & \text{if } x < [x] + \dfrac{1}{[x]} \\ f\left(x - \dfrac{1}{[x]} \right) & \text{otherwise} \end{cases}$$

Let $g(x) = 2^{x - 2007}$. Compute the number of points in which the graphs of f and g intersect.

T–10. Given n points in a plane with $n > 2$, the perpendicular bisectors of all possible line segments are drawn. If the finite integer M is the largest finite possible number of intersection points of the perpendicular bisectors and 2007 divides M, compute the smallest possible value of n.

1. 1003

2. 11

3. $18\sqrt{39}$

4. 2669

5. 0

6. 313

7. 432

8. 200

9. 4,022,030

10. 299

T–1.   Given $A = \left(a, a^2\right)$ and $B = \left(b, b^2\right)$, we have $\dfrac{b^2 - a^2}{b - a} = b + a = 2007$. This gives the ordered pairs $(a, b) = (1, 2006), (2, 2005), \dots, (1002, 1005), (1003, 1004)$. Thus, there are $\boxed{1003}$ pairs of points.

T–2. $\dfrac{100a + 10b + c}{a + b + c} = 19 \rightarrow 9a = b + 2c$. Since $b + 2c \leq 27$ for digits b and c, then $a = 1, 2,$ or 3.

If $a = 3$, $(b, c) = (9, 9)$. If $a = 2$, $(b, c) \in \{(0,9), (2,8), (4,7), (6,6), (8,5)\}$ and when

$a = 1$, $(b, c) \in \{(1,4), (3,3), (5,2), (7,1), (9,0)\}$. Thus there are $\boxed{11}$ three-digit numbers that satisfy the condition.

T–3.   Since $\triangle AME \sim \triangle CED$ and $AM = \dfrac{1}{2}DC$ then $DE = 8$ and $AE = 5$.

Let $AM = x$, $AD = y$, and $DC = 2x$. Then $x^2 + y^2 = 12^2$ and

$y^2 + (2x)^2 = 15^2 \rightarrow 3x^2 = 81 \rightarrow x = 3\sqrt{3}$ and $y = 3\sqrt{13}$. The

area of $ABCD$ is $\boxed{18\sqrt{39}}$.

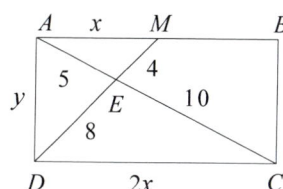

T–4.   Let $f(n)$ be the number of positive integers less than or equal to n that do not contain the digit 0. Since there are a total of 9^k k-digit numbers that do not contain the digit zero, we have $f(999) = 9^3 + 9^2 + 9 = 819$.

Since the numbers from 1000 to 1100 all contain a 0, the numbers from 1000 to 1999 add only 9^3 elements, making $f(1999) = 819 + 9^3 = 1548$. Then $f(2599) = 1548 + 5 \cdot 9^2 = 1953$ and finally

$f(2669) = 1953 + 6 \cdot 9 = 2007$. Answer: $\boxed{2669}$.

Alternate solution: If we remove the 0, we only have nine digits so there ought to be a 1-to-1 correspondence between the nine non-zero digits and base 9 numerals since there are 9^k k-digit numbers in each system. Thus, we can consider the numbers to be in base 9 and since $2007_{10} = 2670_9$, we might think that the answer is 2670, but this method overcounts by 1 since 1_{10} corresponds to 0_9. So the answer is $2670 - 1 = 2669$.

T–5. $\dfrac{x + 2}{kx - 1} = x \rightarrow x + 2 = kx^2 - x \rightarrow kx^2 - 2x - 2 = 0 \rightarrow x = \dfrac{2 \pm \sqrt{4 + 8k}}{2k}$. There is one solution if

$4 + 8k = 0$ giving $k = -1/2$. But that makes $x = -2$, giving $\dfrac{0}{-\frac{1}{2} \cdot (-2) - 1} = \dfrac{0}{0} = -2$ and that is false, so it

appears that there is no value for k that gives one solution. But if $k = 0$, then the equation is linear, not

quadratic, and we have $\dfrac{x + 2}{-1} = x$, giving the unique solution $x = -1$. Thus, $k = \boxed{0}$ gives one solution.

T–6. Since the diameter is 24, the smallest the short leg could be is 25, so consider the right triangle with

legs 25 and a, and hypotenuse b. From $25^2 + a^2 = b^2$ we have $b^2 - a^2 = 25^2 \rightarrow$

$(b - a)(b + a) = 625$. Set $b - a = 1$, $b + a = 625$ and obtain $2b = 626$ making $b = \boxed{313}$.

Any other factorization of 625 clearly yields a smaller value for b. This gives the 25-312-313 right triangle.

The radius of its inscribed circle is $\dfrac{25 + 312 - 313}{2} = 12$.

Alternate solution #1: Let the sides of the triangle be $m^2 - n^2$, $2mn$, and $m^2 + n^2$. Then

$\dfrac{m^2 - n^2 + 2mn - (m^2 + n^2)}{2} = 12 \rightarrow mn - n^2 = 12 \rightarrow n(m - n) = 12$. We can maximize $m^2 + n^2$

by choosing n is as large as possible since that will make m as large as possible. If $n = 12$ and $m - n = 1$,

then $m = 13$ and $n = 12$, giving $m^2 + n^2 = 169 + 144 = 313$.

Alternate solution #2: Letting the legs be a and b, the tangents from the acute angles have lengths of

$a - 12$ and $b - 12$. Thus, $c = a - 12 + b - 12 = (a + b) - 24$. Squaring, we obtain

$c^2 = (a + b)^2 - 48(a + b) = 576 \rightarrow a^2 + b^2 = a^2 + 2ab + b^2 - 48a - 48b + 576$. This simplifies to

$ab - 24a - 24b + 288 = 0 \rightarrow (a - 24)(b - 24) = 288$. With a fixed product, the sum would be a

minimum where $a - 24 = b - 24$ but it would take on a maximum value at an endpoint of the interval on

which a and b are defined. Here we have $b - 24 = 288 \rightarrow b = 312$ and $a - 24 = 1 \rightarrow a = 25$, giving a

maximum value for c of 313.

T–7. With twelve chapters the printer is forced to use pages with one-digit and two-digit numbers in numbering

the chapters. This creates a parity problem--some chapters will have an odd number of digits while others

will have an even number of digits. For example, if the first three chapters had three pages each, 1-3, 4-6,

and 7-9, then three digits would be used for each chapter. But it is impossible to use three digits for chapter

four since it would consist of page 10 and that would use two digits or pages 10 and 11, using four digits. If

the first chapter consisted of more than 9 pages but less than 100, then the number of digits used would be

$9 + 2x$ where x represents the number of pages with two-digit numbers. That number is odd so the second

chapter will consist of y pages with two-digit numbers and z pages with three-digit numbers and the number

of digits used will be $2y + 3z$. Thus, we have $9 + 2x = 2y + 3z$ where $x + y = 90$ and substitution gives

us $9 + 2x = 2(90 - x) + 3z \rightarrow 4x = 171 + 3z$. The first solution occurs when $z = 3$ and $x = 45$. Thus,

the first chapter consists of pages $1 - 54$ and uses $9 + 2(54 - 10 + 1) = 99$ digits. The second chapter

consists of pages $55 - 102$ and uses $2(99 - 55 + 1) + 3(3) = 99$ digits. Each additional chapter will consist

of 33 pages so the last page is $102 + 10(33) = \boxed{432}$.

T–8.   Let $P(x) = x^2 + ax + 10a$. Since P is monic, P is factorable over the integers if and only if P has integral

roots, implying that the discriminant, namely $a^2 - 40a$ must be a perfect square. So $a^2 - 40a = b^2 \rightarrow$

$a^2 - 40a + 400 = b^2 + 400 \rightarrow (a-20)^2 - b^2 = 400$. Thus, we seek ordered pair solutions to

$((a-20) + b)((a-20) - b) = 400$. Note that $(a-20) + b$ and $(a-20) - b$ have the same parity since

their sum is even. Thus, for any pair of even integers whose product is 400, by taking half their sum and

adding 20 we obtain a value of a that makes $x^2 + ax + 10a$ factorable. There are 10 pairs of even integers

whose product is 400 and since these include positive and negative factors, their sum is 0. Thus, the sum of

the 10 values of a is $10 \cdot 20 = \boxed{200}$.

<u>Alternate solution</u>: Suppose an integer p is a zero for the polynomial. Then

$$p^2 + ap + 10a = 0 \rightarrow a = -\frac{p^2}{p+10} = -p + 10 - \frac{100}{p+10} = -p - 10 + 20 - \frac{100}{p+10}. \text{ Set } r = p + 10$$

getting $a = -r - \dfrac{100}{r} + 20$. Call this function $a(r)$. We get a value of a for every positive and negative

factor of 100, but r and $\dfrac{100}{r}$ give the same value for a so we need only sum $a(r)$ over those divisors of

100 in the range $-10 \leq r \leq 10$. Also, notice that $a(r) + a(-r) = 40$ for all r. So when we add over the

ten factors r of 100 in the range $[-10, 10]$, we have five opposite pairs, so the sum is $5 \cdot 40 = 200$.

T–9.   For a fixed positive integer n we first find a formula for f over the range $\left[n, n + \dfrac{1}{n} \right)$, obtaining

$f(x) = n \left| x - n - \dfrac{1}{2n} \right| = \left| xn - n^2 - \dfrac{1}{2} \right|$. For example, when $n = 4$, we obtain $f(x) = \left| 4x - 16 - \dfrac{1}{2} \right|$ for

$4 \leq x < 4\dfrac{1}{4}$. In this example, $f(4) = f\left(4\dfrac{1}{4} \right) = \dfrac{1}{2}$ and $f\left(4\dfrac{1}{8} \right) = 0$. Similarly, in the general case,

$f(n) = f\left(n + \dfrac{1}{n} \right) = \dfrac{1}{2}$ and $f\left(n + \dfrac{1}{2n} \right) = 0$. Thus, the graph of f on $\left[n, n + \dfrac{1}{n} \right)$ is the absolute value of a

line and it forms a V with equal values at the ends as shown in the graph below:

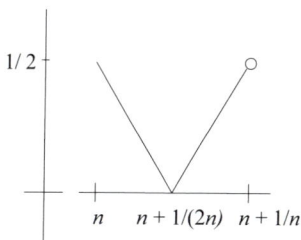

103

For the arbitrary range $n + \dfrac{k}{n} \le x < n + \dfrac{k+1}{n}$ where $0 \le k < n$, successive iterations of f give $f(x) = f\left(x - \dfrac{k}{n}\right)$. Hence, from n to $n+1$, the graph of f consists of n copies of V as shown below.

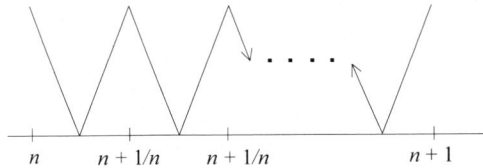

Since $g(x) = 2^{x-2007}$ is a positive increasing function and $g(2006) = \dfrac{1}{2}$, then g intersects each V of the graph of f twice in the domain $1 \le x \le 2006$. The total number of intersection points is

$$2(1 + 2 + 3 + \ldots + 2005) = 2 \cdot 2005\left(\frac{1 + 2005}{2}\right) = 2005 \cdot 2006 = \boxed{4{,}022{,}030}.$$

T–10. Given any three points, the bisectors of the sides of the triangle that they form intersect at the triangle's circumcenter. The number of intersection points is maximized when no four points lie on a circle. In this case we have at most one intersection point for each pair of lines minus the overcounting for triangles. There are $P = \left(\!\!\dbinom{\binom{n}{2}}{2}\!\!\right)$ pairs of line segments and $T = \dbinom{n}{3}$ triangles among the points. Since each point that is also a circumcenter is counted three times by P, we obtain $M = P - 2T =$

$$\frac{1}{2}\left(\frac{n(n-1)}{2}\right)\left(\frac{n(n-1)}{2} - 1\right) - \frac{2n(n-1)(n-2)}{6} = \frac{n(n-1)(n+1)(n-2)}{8} - \frac{n(n-1)(n-2)}{3} =$$

$\dfrac{n(n-1)(n-2)(3n-5)}{24}$. Note that $3n - 5$ is never divisible by 3, but that exactly one of the other three terms is and so one of n, $n-1$, or $n-2$ will cancel the factor of 3 in 24. Since $2007 = 9 \cdot 223$, if 2007 is to divide M, then M must have an additional factor of 9, meaning that M is divisible by 27; hence $n \equiv 0, 1,$ or $2 \pmod{27}$. To get divisibility by 223, $n \equiv 0, 1, 2,$ or $76 \pmod{223}$; we have $76 \pmod{223}$ since $3 \cdot 76 - 5 = 223$. Thus, we let $n = 223q + r$ for $r \in \{0, 1, 2, 76\}$ and we search for the smallest value n for which $n \equiv 0, 1,$ or $2 \pmod{27}$. By inspection, $299 = 223 \cdot 1 + 76 = 27 \cdot 11 + 2$, so $n = \boxed{299}$.

Let $a_1, a_2, a_3, \ldots$ be <u>positive</u> integers. If

$$x = a_1 + \cfrac{1}{a_2 + \cfrac{1}{a_3 + \cfrac{1}{a_4 + \ldots}}}$$

then the right hand side is called the continued fraction expansion of x. This can be determined using a process analogous to the Euclidean algorithm.

A number x is *purely periodic* with period k if there exists a $k > 0$ such that the equations to the right are true and k is the smallest such number with this property. If x is purely periodic with period k, it is represented by $\langle a_1, a_2, \ldots, a_k \rangle$.

$$a_1 = a_{k+1} = a_{2k+1} = \cdots$$
$$a_2 = a_{k+2} = a_{2k+2} = \cdots$$
$$\vdots$$
$$a_k = a_{2k} = a_{3k} = \cdots$$

Thus, $\langle 1 \rangle = 1 + \cfrac{1}{1 + \cfrac{1}{\ddots}} = \dfrac{1 + \sqrt{5}}{2}$. For the problems that follow you may use without proof the fact that

each positive number has a unique continued fraction expansion and each continued fraction expansion defines a unique positive number.

---

1. Compute the real number corresponding to each of the following infinite continued fractions:

    a) $\langle 2 \rangle$ b) $\langle 1, 3 \rangle$ c) $\langle 3, 2, 1 \rangle$

2. a) Let K be a positive integer greater than 1. Prove that the number of purely periodic numbers with period 1 that are less than K is $K - 1$.

    b) Show that there are infinitely many purely periodic numbers with period 2 that are less than 10.

3. a) Is $3 - \sqrt{6}$ purely periodic? If so, give a representation; if not, explain why not.

    b) Is $2 + \sqrt{6}$ purely periodic? If so, give a representation; if not, explain why not.

4. If $x = \langle a, b \rangle$ and $y = \langle b, a \rangle$, what is $\dfrac{x}{y}$?

5.   a) If x is purely periodic, can $\dfrac{1}{x}$ be purely periodic? If yes, give an example; if not, give a proof.

     b) If x is purely periodic, can x be rational? If yes, give an example; if not, give a proof.

6.   If x is purely periodic, show that x must satisfy $Ax^2 + Bx + C = 0$ for some integers A, B, and C.

7.   Suppose that D and E are positive integers, $x = D + \sqrt{E}$ is purely periodic, and let $\bar{x} = D - \sqrt{E}$. Show that $\bar{x} < 0$.

8.   Assume that $x = \langle a_1, a_2, ..., a_k \rangle$ and $y = \langle a_k, a_{k-1}, ..., a_1 \rangle$ are two purely periodic numbers of period k. Show that if x satisfies $Ax^2 + Bx + C = 0$, then y satisfies $Cy^2 - By + A = 0$.

9.   Suppose that D and E are positive integers, $x = D + \sqrt{E}$ is purely periodic, and let $\bar{x} = D - \sqrt{E}$. Show that $\bar{x} < -1$.

10. Suppose that n is a positive integer that is not a perfect square.

     a) Show that there is at most one integer $f(n)$ so that $f(n) + \sqrt{n}$ is purely periodic.

     b) What is the function $f(n)$?

     c) If z is a negative integer, can $z + \sqrt{n}$ be purely periodic? If yes, give an example; if not, give a proof.

     d) For what values of n is $1 + \sqrt{n}$ purely periodic? Find a purely periodic representation of $1 + \sqrt{n}$ for each of these values.

1. a) Let $x = \langle 2 \rangle$. Then $x = 2 + \cfrac{1}{2 + \cfrac{1}{2 + \cfrac{1}{2 + \ldots}}} = 2 + \cfrac{1}{x}$, so x satisfies $x^2 - 2x - 1 = 0$. The solutions to this

equation are $x + \cfrac{2 = 2\sqrt{2}}{2} + 1 = \sqrt{2}$. As x is positive, the answer is $x = 1 + \sqrt{2}$.

b) Let $x = \langle 1, 3 \rangle$. Then $x = 1 + \cfrac{1}{3 + \cfrac{1}{1 + \cfrac{1}{3 + \ldots}}} = 1 + \cfrac{1}{3 + \cfrac{1}{x}}$, so x satisfies $3x^2 - 3x - 1 = 0$. The solutions

to this equation are $x + \cfrac{3 = \sqrt{21}}{6}$. As x is positive, the answer is $x = \cfrac{3 + \sqrt{21}}{6}$.

c) Let $x = \langle 3, 2, 1 \rangle$. Then $x = 3 + \cfrac{1}{2 + \cfrac{1}{1 + \cfrac{1}{3 + \ldots}}} = 3 + \cfrac{1}{2 + \cfrac{1}{1 + \cfrac{1}{x}}}$, so x satisfies $3x^2 - 8x - 7 = 0$.

The solutions to this equation are $x + \cfrac{4 = \sqrt{37}}{3}$. As x is positive, the answer is $x = \cfrac{4 + \sqrt{37}}{3}$.

2. a) For $k \geq 1$, since $\langle k \rangle = k + \cfrac{1}{k + \cfrac{1}{k + \ldots}}$, then $k < \langle k \rangle < k + 1$. Since there are $K - 1$ pairs of consecutive

integers from $k = 1$ to K, there are $K - 1$ purely periodic numbers with period 1 less than K. Or let $x = \langle k \rangle$.

Then $x = k + \cfrac{1}{k + \cfrac{1}{\ddots}} = k + \cfrac{1}{x}$, so x satisfies $x^2 - kx - 1 = 0$. The solutions to this equation are

$x = \cfrac{k \pm \sqrt{k^2 + 4}}{2}$. As x is positive, $x = \cfrac{k + \sqrt{k^2 + 4}}{2}$. Because $k < \sqrt{k^2 + 4} < \sqrt{k^2 + 4k + 4} = k + 2$,

we can conclude that $\cfrac{k + k}{2} < x < \cfrac{k + (k + 2)}{2}$ giving $k < x < k + 1$. Thus, between every pair of integers there

is one purely periodic number with a period of 1 and there are $K - 1$ positive integers less than K.

b) There are many possible solutions to this. The most straightforward one is to consider the infinite set of purely

periodic numbers of the form $x = \langle 1, k \rangle = 1 + \cfrac{1}{k + \cfrac{1}{x}}$ for all integers $k \geq 1$. From $k + \cfrac{1}{x} > 1$ we obtain

$\cfrac{1}{k + \cfrac{1}{x}} < 1$ and this gives $1 + \cfrac{1}{k + \cfrac{1}{x}} < 2 \rightarrow \langle 1, k \rangle < 2$ for all integers $k \geq 1$.

3. a) We know that $2 = \sqrt{4} < \sqrt{6} < \sqrt{9} = 3$. Therefore $1 > 3 - \sqrt{6} > 0$. Recall that a_1 is positive and at least 1 in a purely periodic number, so any purely periodic number must be at least 1. Hence, $3 - \sqrt{6}$ is not purely periodic.

b) We know that $4 < 2 + \sqrt{6} < 5$, so if $2 + \sqrt{6}$ has a purely periodic representation, then $a_1 = 4$.

$$2 + \sqrt{6} = 4 + \left(-2 + \sqrt{6}\right) = 4 + \cfrac{1}{\cfrac{1}{-2 + \sqrt{6}}} = 4 + \cfrac{1}{\cfrac{2 + \sqrt{6}}{-4 + 6}} = 4 + \cfrac{1}{\cfrac{2 + \sqrt{6}}{2}} = 4 + \cfrac{1}{2 + \cfrac{-2 + \sqrt{6}}{2}}$$

$$= 4 + \cfrac{1}{2 + \cfrac{1}{\cfrac{2}{-2 + \sqrt{6}}}} = 4 + \cfrac{1}{2 + \cfrac{1}{2 + \sqrt{6}}}. \text{ Therefore } 2 + \sqrt{6} = \langle 4, 2 \rangle.$$

4. Notice that $x = a + \cfrac{1}{b + \cfrac{1}{a + \cfrac{1}{\ddots}}} = a + \cfrac{1}{y}$. By symmetry, $y = b + \cfrac{1}{x}$.

Therefore, $ay + 1 = xy = bx + 1 \rightarrow ay = bx \rightarrow \dfrac{x}{y} = \dfrac{a}{b}$.

5. a) If x is purely periodic, then $x > 1$. This means that $\dfrac{1}{x} < 1$, so $\dfrac{1}{x}$ cannot be purely periodic.

b) A purely periodic number cannot be rational. In fact, every positive rational number has a finite and therefore not purely periodic continued fraction representation. Let $x = \dfrac{m}{n}$, where m and n are positive integers with $m \ge n$. Write $\dfrac{m}{n} = a_1 + \dfrac{m - a_1 n}{n}$, where a_1 is the integer part of x. Note that $m - a_1 n$ is the remainder obtained by dividing m by n. If $m - a_1 n = 0$, then x is an integer. Otherwise,

$\dfrac{m}{n} = a_1 + \cfrac{1}{\cfrac{n}{m - a_1 n}}$, and we repeat the process for the rational number $\dfrac{n}{m - a_1 n}$ to generate a_2. Note

that the denominators of subsequent rational numbers are a strictly decreasing sequence of positive integers, which means that this process eventually terminates. Therefore the continued fraction expansion of a rational number will be a finite sequence of positive integers, and so it is not purely periodic.

6. Suppose $x = \langle a_1, a_2, \ldots, a_k \rangle = a_1 + \cfrac{1}{a_2 + \cfrac{1}{a_3 + \cfrac{\ddots}{a_{k-1} + \cfrac{1}{a_k + \cfrac{1}{x}}}}}$.

For $x = \langle a_1, \ldots, a_k \rangle$, define $x_i = a_i + \cfrac{1}{a_{i+1} + \cfrac{\ddots}{a_{k-1} + \cfrac{1}{a_k + \cfrac{1}{x}}}}$ for $1 \leq i \leq k$. Note that $x_1 = x$

and $x_i = a_i + \cfrac{1}{x_{i+1}}$. Note that $x_i = \dfrac{Q_i x + R_i}{S_i x + T_i}$, where:

$$Q_k = a_k$$
$$S_k = 1$$
$$R_k = 1 \qquad \text{and}$$
$$T_k = 0$$

$$Q_{i-1} = a_{i-1}Q_i + S_i$$
$$S_{i-1} = Q_i$$
$$R_{i-1} = a_{i-1}R_i + T_i$$
$$T_{i-1} = R_i$$

Therefore $x = \dfrac{Qx + R}{Sx + T}$ for non-negative integers T and positive integers Q, R, and S. Therefore

$Sx^2 + (T - Q)x - R = 0$.

7. Both x and $\bar{x}$ must be solutions to the same quadratic equation $Ax^2 + Bx + C = 0$ and their product

    equals $\dfrac{C}{A}$. Using the equation $Sx^2 + (T - Q)x - R = 0$ developed in #6, the product of the roots

    equals $-\dfrac{R}{S}$ where R and S are positive integers. Thus $\dfrac{C}{A} = -\dfrac{R}{S} < 0$. Since x must be positive,

    $\bar{x}$ must be negative.

8. The set of linear relations description in the solution to #6 can be described using a linear system of

    equations, namely:

$$\begin{pmatrix} Q_{i-1} & R_{i-1} \\ S_{i-1} & T_{i-1} \end{pmatrix} = \begin{pmatrix} a_{i-1} & 1 \\ 1 & 0 \end{pmatrix}\begin{pmatrix} Q_i & R_i \\ S_i & T_i \end{pmatrix}$$

Suppose that $x = \langle a_1, \ldots, a_k \rangle$ and $y = \langle a_k, \ldots, a_1 \rangle$. If $x = \dfrac{Qx + R}{Sx + T}$, then

$$\begin{pmatrix} Q & R \\ S & T \end{pmatrix} = \begin{pmatrix} a_1 & 1 \\ 1 & 0 \end{pmatrix}\begin{pmatrix} a_2 & 1 \\ 1 & 0 \end{pmatrix}\cdots\begin{pmatrix} a_k & 1 \\ 1 & 0 \end{pmatrix}.$$ Similarly, if $y = \dfrac{Q'y + R'}{S'y + T'}$ then

$$\begin{pmatrix} Q' & R' \\ S' & T' \end{pmatrix} = \begin{pmatrix} a_k & 1 \\ 1 & 0 \end{pmatrix}\begin{pmatrix} a_{k-1} & 1 \\ 1 & 0 \end{pmatrix}\cdots\begin{pmatrix} a_1 & 1 \\ 1 & 0 \end{pmatrix} = \begin{pmatrix} a_k & 1 \\ 1 & 0 \end{pmatrix}^T\begin{pmatrix} a_{k-1} & 1 \\ 1 & 0 \end{pmatrix}^T\cdots\begin{pmatrix} a_1 & 1 \\ 1 & 0 \end{pmatrix}^T$$

$$= \left(\begin{pmatrix} a_1 & 1 \\ 1 & 0 \end{pmatrix}\begin{pmatrix} a_2 & 1 \\ 1 & 0 \end{pmatrix}\cdots\begin{pmatrix} a_k & 1 \\ 1 & 0 \end{pmatrix}\right)^T = \begin{pmatrix} Q & R \\ S & T \end{pmatrix}^T$$

Therefore, $Q = Q'$, $R' = S$, $S' = R$, and $T' = T$. We have $Sx^2 + (T-Q)x - R = 0$ and

$Ry^2 + (T-Q)y - S = 0$, which can be written as $(-R)y^2 - (T-Q)y + S = 0$. Setting $A = S$,

$B = T - Q$, and $C = -R$ gives the desired result.

9.   Using the notation from the previous problem, we know that $Sx^2 + (T-Q)x - R = 0$ and

$Ry^2 + (T-Q)y - S = 0$. The product of the roots of the first equation is $-\dfrac{R}{S}$, and the product of the roots

of the second equation is $-\dfrac{S}{R}$. This means that if x and $\bar{x}$ with $\bar{x} < 0$ are the roots of the first equation,

then $-\dfrac{1}{x}$ and $-\dfrac{1}{\bar{x}}$ are the roots of the second equation, where $y = -\dfrac{1}{\bar{x}}$. Note that y cannot equal either

$\dfrac{1}{x}$ or $\dfrac{1}{\bar{x}}$, as the first is less than one and the second is negative. Since $y > 1$, we conclude that $-\dfrac{1}{\bar{x}} > 1$

giving $-1 > \bar{x}$ since $\bar{x} > 0$.

10.   a)   If $y = f(n) + \sqrt{n}$ is purely periodic then by (7) and (9) $-1 < \bar{y} < 0$ giving $-1 < f(n) - \sqrt{n} < 0$.

Since $\sqrt{n}$ is not an integer, there is at most one integer value that $f(n)$ can take to satisfy these inequalities.

Note: If n had been a perfect square, then there would be no such integer $f(n)$.

b) $f(n) = \left[\sqrt{n}\right]$, the largest integer less than or equal to $\sqrt{n}$.

c)   Since $\left[\sqrt{n}\right] > 0$ for any positive integer n, then by 10a and 10b, $z + \sqrt{n}$ cannot be purely periodic

since $z - \sqrt{n}$ lies outside the interval $(-1, 0)$.

d)   Since $\left[\sqrt{n}\right] = 1$ for $n = 1, 2,$ or 3, then by 10a and 10b, these are the only possible values for n. Since

1 is a perfect square, then n can only be 2 or 3. It is not hard to show that $1 + \sqrt{2} = \langle 2 \rangle$ and $1 + \sqrt{3} = \langle 2,1 \rangle$.

I–1.   In $\triangle BEC$, $m\angle EBC > m\angle ECB$. If $m\angle ABE = 4x + y$, $m\angle E = 84°$, and $m\angle ECB = x + y$, compute the number of positive integer values that y can take on.

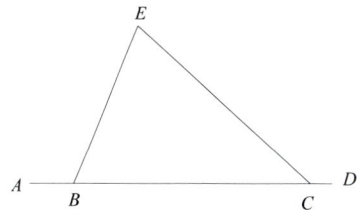

I–2.   Let $a_1 = 1$ and a_n be the number formed by putting the digits of n at the end of the digits of a_{n-1}. Thus, $a_9 = 123456789$ and $a_{10} = 12345678910$. For $k = 1$ to 2007, compute the number of a_k that are divisible by 3.

I–3.   Suppose a, b, and c are positive real numbers such that $a^2 + b^2 = c^2$ and $\log a + \log b = \log c$.

Compute $\dfrac{(a + b + c)(a - b + c)(a + b - c)(a - b - c)}{c^2}$.

I–4.   If the sum of the areas of rectangle $ABCE$ and equilateral triangles AEF and DEC exceeds the area of $\triangle BDF$ by 33, compute the area of rectangle $ABCE$.

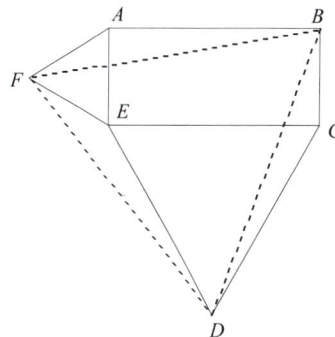

I–5.   Let $[x]$ denote the greatest integer function and let x be in radian measure. Compute all x in the interval $0 \le x \le 2\pi$ such that $f(x) = \sin[2x]$ takes on its largest value.

I–6.   Compute the smallest positive integer with exactly 26 positive composite factors, i.e., factors other than 1 or a prime number.

I–7.   Given points $M(-3, 1)$, $N(a, b)$, and $P(c, d)$ with $\overline{MN} \perp \overline{NP}$ and $a + b = c + d$, compute $b - a$.

I–8. $ABCD$ is a convex quadrilateral with $DA = DB = DC$ and $\overrightarrow{AD} \parallel \overrightarrow{BC}$. The perpendicular bisector of $\overline{CD}$ meets $\overrightarrow{AB}$ at E such that B is between A and E. If $m\angle BCE = 2m\angle CED$, compute the exact measure of $\angle BCE$ in degrees.

111

1. 19

2. 1338

3. -4

4. 132

5. $4 \le x > \dfrac{9}{2}$ which can also be written as $\left[4, 4.5\right)$

6. 720

7. 4

8. $\dfrac{360}{7}$ Note: $\dfrac{360°}{7}$, $51\tfrac{3}{7}$, $51\tfrac{3}{7}°$, and $51.\overline{428571}$ are also correct.

I–1. Since $4x + y = 84 + (x + y)$, then $x = 28$. Since $m\angle EBC < m\angle ECB$, then $180 - (84 + x + y) > x + y$, giving $96 < 2(x + y) \rightarrow 48 < 28 + y \rightarrow 20 < y$. Then $y \in \{1, 2, \ldots, 19\}$. Answer: $\boxed{19}$.

I–2. We note that a_1 is not divisible by 3 but $a_2 = 12$ and $a_3 = 123$ are. Then $a_4 = 1234$ will be 1 more than a multiple of 3, but $a_5 = 12345$ adds 2 more than a multiple of 3, thereby giving a multiple of 3, and of course, $a_6 = 123456$ adds a multiple of 3 to the digits giving a multiple of 3. In general, a_k is a multiple of 3 iff k is congruent to 0 or 2 mod 3. Thus, from $k = 1$ to 2007, two-thirds of the terms are divisible by 3, giving $\boxed{1338}$ terms.

More formally, the set of all 2007 a_n can be divided into 669 subsets of three consecutive integers of the form $\{a_{3n+1}, a_{3n+2}, a_{3n+3}\}$ for $n \geq 0$. In each of the subsets, a_{3n+1} is the only element that is not divisible by 3. This can be proved by induction. It is true when $n = 0$ since $a_1 = 1$, $a_2 = 12$, and $a_3 = 123$. Suppose it is true for $n = k$, i.e., that in $\{a_{3k+1}, a_{3k+2}, a_{3k+3}\}$, a_{3k+1} is not divisible by 3 but a_{3k+2} and a_{3k+3} are. Let the sum of the digits of a_{3k+3} be $3t$. Then the sum of the digits of a_{3k+4}, a_{3k+5}, and a_{3k+6} will be $3t + (3r + 1)$, $3t + (3r + 1) + (3s + 2) = 3(t + r + s + 1)$, and $3t + (3r + 1) + (3s + 2) + 3w = 3(t + r + s + 1 + w)$ respectively. This shows that two out of every three terms in the set are divisible by 3. Thus, $\dfrac{2}{3} \cdot 2007 = 1338$ terms are divisible by 3.

I–3. $\dfrac{\big((a + b) + c\big)\big((a + b) - c\big)\big((a - b) + c\big)\big((a - b) - c\big)}{c^2} = \dfrac{\big((a + b)^2 - c^2\big)\big((a - b)^2 - c^2\big)}{c^2} =$

$\dfrac{(2ab)(-2ab)}{c^2}$ since $a^2 + b^2 = c^2$. Since $\log a + \log b = \log c$, then $ab = c$. Thus, $\dfrac{-4(ab)^2}{c^2} = \boxed{-4}$.

I–4. Since $m\angle FED = 360° - (60° + 90° + 60°) = 150°$, triangles ABF, CDB, and EDF are all congruent. Let the area of each equal K. Then the sum of the areas of $ABCE$, AEF, and DEC equals the area of $BFEDC + 2K$. The area of BFD equals the area of $BFEDC + K$. Thus, $K = 33$. Since $\triangle FBA$ has base $\overline{AB}$ and altitude $FG = \dfrac{1}{2} AE$, the area of $\triangle FBA = 33 = \dfrac{1}{4} \cdot$ area $ABCE$.

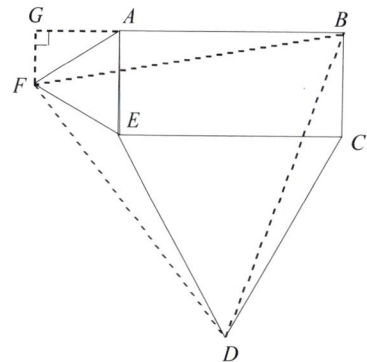

The area of $ABCE = \boxed{132}$.

Alternate solution #1: let $AB = a$, $BC = b$, and $BF = BD = FD = c$. Then using $\triangle BCD$ with $m\angle BCD = 150°$ we have $c^2 = a^2 + b^2 - 2ab\cos 150° = a^2 + b^2 + ab\sqrt{3}$ by the Law of Cosines. The area of $\triangle AFE = \dfrac{b^2\sqrt{3}}{4}$, the area of $\triangle ECD = \dfrac{a^2\sqrt{3}}{4}$, and the area of $\triangle BFD = \dfrac{c^2\sqrt{3}}{4}$ which equals

$\dfrac{(a^2 + b^2 + ab\sqrt{3})\sqrt{3}}{4}$. Thus, $ab + \dfrac{a^2\sqrt{3}}{4} + \dfrac{b^2\sqrt{3}}{4} - \left(\dfrac{(a^2 + b^2)\sqrt{3} + 3ab}{4} \right) = \dfrac{ab}{4} = 33$, making the

area of rectangle *ABEC* equal to 132.

Alternate solution #2: Once we realize that the area of $\triangle ABF$ is 33 as in the first solution, we use the sine formula for area and obtain $\dfrac{1}{2}ab\sin 150° = 33 \ \rightarrow \ \dfrac{1}{2}ab\dfrac{1}{2} = 33$ so $ab = 132$.

I–5.   Note that $\sin x$ takes on its largest values at $x = \dfrac{\pi}{2} + 2\pi k \rightarrow x = \dfrac{\pi}{2}, \dfrac{5\pi}{2}, \dfrac{9\pi}{2}, \dots$ and that $\dfrac{\pi}{2} \approx 1.57$,

$\dfrac{5\pi}{2} \approx 7.85$, and $\dfrac{9\pi}{2} \approx 14.14$. Note also that $[2x]$ takes on the integer values from 0 to 12 for $0 \le x \le 2\pi$.

To maximize $f(x) = \sin[2x]$, we need to obtain the integer greater than but closest to either 1.57 or 7.85.

The candidates are 2 and 8 but 8 is closer to an *x*-value that gives the maximum value so the solution set is

$[2x] = 8 \rightarrow \boxed{4 \le x < 4.5 \ \text{ or } \ [4, 4.5)}$.

I–6.   Suppose that $n = p_1^{a_1} \cdot p_2^{a_2} \cdot \dots \cdot p_k^{a_k}$ is our answer where $a_1 \ge a_2 \ge \dots \ge a_k$. Then *n* has

$(1 + a_1)(1 + a_2) \cdot \dots \cdot (1 + a_k)$ factors. Since there are *k* prime factors, namely $p_1, p_2, \dots, p_k$ and 1 is

included in the number of factors, then the number of composite factors can be written as

$(1 + a_1)(1 + a_2) \cdot \dots \cdot (1 + a_k) - k - 1 = 26$. This implies that number of factors would be

$(1 + a_1)(1 + a_2) \cdot \dots \cdot (1 + a_k) = k + 27$. Because *n is* the smallest number with 26 composite factors, we'll

require that the p_i be the first primes in increasing order. To determine the least value of *n* we'll pick values

of *k* and see if we can find appropriate values for the number of primes. If $k = 1$, then we seek a number

with 28 factors and one prime. The smallest would be 2^{27}. If $k = 2$, we have $(1 + a_1)(1 + a_2) = 29$ and

since 29 is prime, that's not possible. If $k = 3$, we have $(1 + a_1)(1 + a_2)(1 + a_3) = 30$ and this is solvable

for $a_1 = 4$, $a_2 = 2$, and $a_3 = 1$. The smallest value for *n* in this case is $2^4 \cdot 3^2 \cdot 5^1 = 720$. If $k = 4$, we

have $(1 + a_1)(1 + a_2)(1 + a_3)(1 + a_4) = 31$, and that's not possible since 31 is prime. If $k = 5$, we have

$(1 + a_1)(1 + a_2)(1 + a_3)(1 + a_4)(1 + a_5) = 32$ and that is solvable where all exponents a_i are equal to 1.

The least number in this case is $2 \cdot 3 \cdot 5 \cdot 7 \cdot 11 = 2310$. No greater value of *k* works since the maximum

number of terms in a decomposition of $k + 27$ into factors is $\log_2 (k + 27)$, but that has to be at least *k*.

Thus, the answer is $\boxed{720}$.

I–7. Since the slope of $\overline{MN}$ times the slope of $\overline{NP}$ equals -1, $\dfrac{b-1}{a+3} \cdot \dfrac{d-b}{c-a} = -1$. From $a+b = c+d$ we

obtain $a - c = d - b \rightarrow \dfrac{d-b}{c-a} = -1$. Thus, $\dfrac{b-1}{a+3} = 1 \rightarrow b - 1 = a + 3$. Thus, $a + b = \boxed{4}$.

I–8. It is given that $DA = DB = DC$, $\overline{AD} \parallel \overline{BC}$, $\overline{FE}$ is the perpendicular

bisector of $\overline{DC}$ and $m\angle BCE = 2m\angle CED$. Let $m\angle ADB = 2x$. Then

$m\angle DAB = m\angle DBA = 90° - x$ and $m\angle DBC = m\angle DCB = 2x$. Let O

denote the circumcircle of $\triangle BCD$ and assume that O intersects $\overline{AB}$ at two

distinct points, B and E'. Because B, C, D, and E', lie on circle O,

$m\angle CE'D = m\angle CBD = 2x$ and $m\angle DCE' = m\angle DBA = 90° - x$.

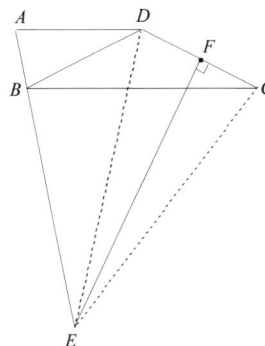

It follows that in $\triangle CDE'$, $m\angle E'DC = 180° - m\angle CE'D - m\angle DCE' = 90° - x = m\angle DCE'$. Thus,

$\triangle CDE'$ is isosceles with $CE' = DE'$. Hence, $E = E'$.

Therefore, $m\angle BCE = m\angle DCE - m\angle DCB = 90° - 3x$ and solving $m\angle BCE = 2m\angle CED$,

gives $x = 90°/7$, making $m\angle BCE = \dfrac{360°}{7}$. Answer: $\boxed{\dfrac{360}{7}}$.

R1–1. If $|a - 3| \leq 5$ and $|b + 7| \leq 1$, then $m \leq ab \leq n$ where m and n are the tightest possible bounds for the inequality. Compute $\dfrac{n}{m}$.

R1–2. Let T = TNYWR. Compute the sum of the solutions of the equation $\sin x = T$, where $0 \leq x \leq 2\pi$.

R1–3. Let T = TNYWR. The difference in surface areas of two concentric spheres is T. A circular disk is tangent to the inner sphere and its circumference is on the other sphere. Compute the <u>diameter</u> of the disk.

R2–1. In regular hexagon $ABCDEF$, $BF = 2\sqrt[4]{12}$.

Compute the area of pentagon $BCDEF$.

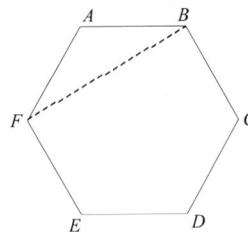

R2–2. Let T = TNYWR. In cube $ABCDEFGH$, $AB = 4T$. A plane passing through M and parallel to face $ABGF$ cuts off the right side of the cube, leaving a figure whose surface area is half the area of $ABCDEFGH$. Compute BM. Pass back an answer without units.

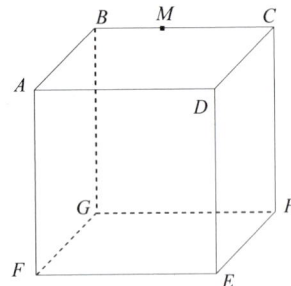

R2–3. Let T = TNYWR. Compute the number of three-term increasing arithmetic sequences that can be formed using the elements of the set $\{1, 2, 3, \ldots, T\}$.

Relay #1:

R1–1. $-\dfrac{1}{4}$

R1–2. 3π

R1–3. $\sqrt{3}$

Relay #2:

R2–1.   10

R2–2.   10

R2–3.   20

R1–1. $|a - 3| \le 5 \to -2 \le a \le 8$ and $|b + 7| \le 1 \to -8 \le b \le -6$. Thus, $m = -64$ and that occurs when

$a = 8$ and $b = -8$, and $n = 16$ and that occurs when $a = -2$ and $b = -8$. Thus, $\dfrac{n}{m} = \boxed{-\dfrac{1}{4}}$.

R1–2.   If $T = 0$, $x = 0, \pi,$ or 2π so the sum is 3π. If $0 < T < 1$, $x = t$ or $\pi - t$ for some number t,

so the sum is π. If $T = 1$, $x = \dfrac{\pi}{2}$ so the sum is $\dfrac{\pi}{2}$. If $-1 < T < 0$, $x = \pi + t$ and $2\pi - t$ so the sum

is 3π. If $T = -1$, $x = \dfrac{3\pi}{2}$ so the sum is $\dfrac{3\pi}{2}$. Since $T = -\dfrac{1}{4}$, the sum is $\boxed{3\pi}$.

R1–3. $T = 3\pi$. Let the radii of the inner and outer spheres be r_1 and r_2,

respectively. $\overline{AB}$ is the diameter of the circle. The difference in surface

areas of the spheres is $4\pi r_2{}^2 - 4\pi r_1{}^2 = T \;\to\; r_2{}^2 - r_1{}^2 = \dfrac{T}{4\pi}$. Since

$\left(\dfrac{AB}{2}\right)^2 = r_2{}^2 - r_1{}^2$, then $AB = 2\sqrt{r_2{}^2 - r_1{}^2} = 2\sqrt{\dfrac{3\pi}{4\pi}} = \boxed{\sqrt{3}}$.

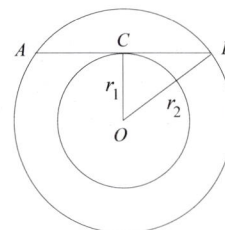

R2–1.   The area of the hexagon is twice the area of the equilateral triangle

with side length BF. The area of the hexagon is

$2 \cdot \dfrac{BF^2 \sqrt{3}}{4} = \dfrac{\left(2\sqrt[4]{12}\right)^2 \cdot \sqrt{3}}{2} = \dfrac{\left(4\sqrt{12}\right)\sqrt{3}}{2} = 12$. The pentagon

has five-sixths the area of the hexagon, so the answer is $\boxed{10}$.

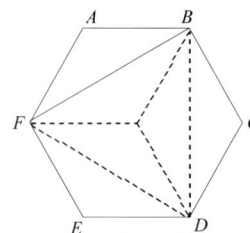

Alternately, if $AB = AF = x$, then by the Law of Cosines, $BF^2 = 2x^2 - 2x^2 \cos 120° =$

$2x^2 - 2x^2\left(-\dfrac{1}{2}\right) = 3x^2$. Thus, $4\sqrt{12} = 3x^2 \to x^2 = \dfrac{8}{\sqrt{3}}$. The area of the hexagon equals

$6\left(\dfrac{x^2\sqrt{3}}{4}\right) = 6\left(\dfrac{8}{\sqrt{3}} \cdot \dfrac{\sqrt{3}}{4}\right) = 12$. Thus, the area of the pentagon is $\dfrac{5}{6} \cdot 12 = 10$.

R2–2.   The surface area of $ABCDEFGH$ is $6(4T)^2 = 96T^2$. The area of the figure is

$2(4T)^2 + 4 \cdot 4T \cdot BM = 32T^2 + (16T)BM$. Thus, $32T^2 + (16T)BM = 48T^2$ making $BM = T$.

Pass back $\boxed{10}$.

118

R2–3. Shown below is a table of the number of arithmetic sequences based on the common difference d for values of T starting with 3:

d / T	1	2	3	4	5	TOTAL
3	1					1
4	2					2
5	3	1				4
6	4	2				6
7	5	3	1			9
8	6	4	2			12
9	7	5	3	1		16
10	8	6	4	2		20

For any value of T there are $T - 2$ choices for the middle term if $d = 1$ since 1 and T can't be used, $T - 4$ choices for the middle term if $d = 2$ since $1, 2, T - 1$, and T can't be used, etc. If T is odd, the total is just the sum of the first $\dfrac{T - 1}{2}$ odd numbers and equals $\left(\dfrac{T - 1}{2}\right)^2$. If T is even, the sum is equal to twice the sum of the first $\dfrac{T - 2}{2}$ numbers and equals $2\left(\dfrac{1 + (T - 2) / 2}{2}\right)\left(\dfrac{T - 2}{2}\right) = \dfrac{T(T - 2)}{4}$.

Since $T = 10$, the sum is $\boxed{20}$.

Alternate solution: If the common difference d is odd, a three-term arithmetic progression is either odd-even-odd or even-odd-even. If d is even the arithmetic progression is either even-even-even or odd-odd-odd. In either case, the first and third elements have the same parity. For the set $\{1, 2, \ldots, T = 2n\}$, to find a three-term arithmetic progression, one need only to find the first and third numbers of the same parity, then the middle term is fixed. For $T = 2n$, there are $_nC_2$ pairs of even numbers and $_nC_2$ pairs of odd numbers so we have $2\left(_nC_2\right) = n(n - 1) = \dfrac{T}{2}\left(\dfrac{T}{2} - 1\right) = \dfrac{T(T - 2)}{4}$.

For $T = 2n + 1$, there are n even numbers and $n + 1$ odd numbers giving

$$_nC_2 + {_{n+1}C_2} = n^2 = \left(\dfrac{T - 1}{2}\right)^2 \text{ sequences.}$$

Alternate solution: A valid sequence has first term a and common difference d, such that these values satisfy $1 \le a \le T - 2, d \ge 1$, and $a + 2d \le T$. For a fixed a, the number of possible values of d is $\left[\dfrac{T - a}{2}\right]$. The total number of increasing arithmetic sequences is $\displaystyle\sum_{a=1}^{T-2} \left[\dfrac{T - a}{2}\right]$.

With $T = 10$, the sum is $4 + 4 + 3 + 3 + 2 + 2 + 1 + 1 = 20$.

1. If $x + y + z = 0$ and $x + y + z^2 = 6$, compute the largest possible value of $x + y$.

2. Let $T = $ TNYWR. If $\sqrt{8x} - \sqrt{8y} = T$ and $\sqrt{72x} + \sqrt{72y} = 30$, compute the value of x.

3. Let $T = $ TNYWR. The side of the largest square is T; the side of each successive square is 4/7 the side of the preceding square. Compute the total perimeter of the figure.

and so on

4. Let $T = $ TNYWR. Suppose T % of a weatherman's predictions are incorrect. If the weatherman makes one prediction per day, compute the difference between the expected number of incorrect predictions in 2107 days and 2007 days.

5. Let $T = $ TNYWR and set $K = T + 5$. Compute the probability that a randomly selected element of the set $\left\{6^1, 6^2, 6^3, ..., 6^{K-1}, 6^K\right\}$ has more than 500 positive divisors.

6. Let $T = $ TNYWR. $ABCD$ is a trapezoid, $\overline{AB} \parallel \overline{CD}$, $AB = 2$, $CD = 8$. $\overline{AC}$ and $\overline{BD}$ intersect at P. If the area of $\triangle ABP = T$, compute the area of $\triangle BDC$.

7. Let $T = $ TNYWR. Triangle ABC is equilateral and has area $(T - 2)\sqrt{3}$. Point D is chosen such that $\overline{AC} \perp \overline{CD}$ and $CD = 1$. Compute AD.

8. Let M be the number you receive from position 7 and N be the number you receive from position 9. Let $P(x) = x^3 + ax + b$ where a and b are constants. If the remainder when $P(x)$ is divided by $x - 1$ is M, and the remainder when $P(x)$ is divided by $x - 2$ is N, find the remainder when $P(x)$ is divided by $x - 3$.

120

15. The lines $y = x$ and $y = mx$ meet at a 15° angle. Compute the largest possible value for m.

14. Let T = TNYWR. If $\dfrac{Ti + 7}{i - 1} = a + bi$ for real a and b, and $i = \sqrt{-1}$, compute $2(a^2 + b^2)$.

13. Let T = TNYWR. If the roots of $Tx^2 - 2Tx - 2T + 26 = 0$ equal $\log_{10} a$ and $\log_{10} b$, compute ab.

12. Let T = TNYWR. Given $\dfrac{T}{10}$ identical balls and three jars, jar 1, jar 2, and jar 3, compute the number of ways to put all the balls into the jars if each jar must contain at least as many balls as its number.

11. Let T = TNYWR. A and B are two right-circular cones. B is the center of A's base and C is the center of B's base. Circle C intersects A's surface. If $AB = T$, $BC = 5$, and the radius of circle B is 6, compute the radius of circle C.

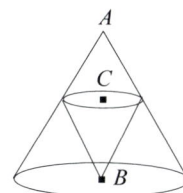

10. Let T = TNYWR. If $(1 - \sin\theta)^2 + (1 - \cos\theta)^2 = T$, compute $\sin\theta + \cos\theta$.

9. Let T = TNYWR and set $K = |4T|$. In rectangular box $ABCDEFGH$, $AD = K$, $AB = 12$, and $CF = 3$. M and N are midpoints of $\overline{AB}$ and $\overline{CD}$ respectively. Compute the volume of pyramid $MNEF$.

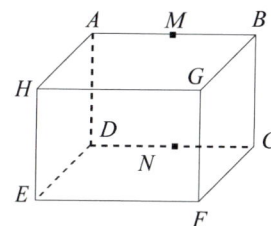

8. Let M be the number you receive from position 7 and N be the number you receive from position 9. Let $P(x) = x^3 + ax + b$ where a and b are constants. If the remainder when $P(x)$ is divided by $x - 1$ is M, and the remainder when $P(x)$ is divided by $x - 2$ is N, find the remainder when $P(x)$ is divided by $x - 3$.

121

1. 2

2. $\dfrac{9}{2}$

3. 30

4. 30

5. $\dfrac{2}{5}$

6. 8

7. 5

---

15. $\sqrt{3}$

14. 52

13. 100

12. 15

11. 4

10. $-\dfrac{1}{2}$

9. 12

8. 31

1. Subtract $x + y + z = 0$ from $x + y + z^2 = 6$ to obtain $z^2 - z = 6 \rightarrow z = 3$ or -2 giving $x + y + 3 = 0$ or $x + y - 2 = 0$. The largest possible value for $x + y$ is $\boxed{2}$.

2. $\sqrt{72x} + \sqrt{72y} = 30 \rightarrow \sqrt{8x} + \sqrt{8y} = 10$. Adding $\sqrt{8x} - \sqrt{8y} = T$ gives $2\sqrt{8x} = T + 10$. Since $T = 2$, we have $4\sqrt{2x} = 12 \rightarrow 2x = 9$. Thus, $x = \boxed{\dfrac{9}{2}}$.

3. The two sets of horizontal segments form two geometric series with first term T and a common ratio of $\dfrac{4}{7}$,

   giving a total of $2\left(T + \dfrac{4}{7}T + \left(\dfrac{4}{7}\right)^2 T + \ldots\right) = 2\left(\dfrac{T}{1 - \dfrac{4}{7}}\right) = \dfrac{14T}{3}$. The first vertical segment has length T,

   the rest of the vertical segments fill up one side so their sum is T, giving a total perimeter of

   $2T + \dfrac{14T}{3} = \dfrac{20T}{3}$. Since $T = \dfrac{9}{2}$, the perimeter is $\boxed{30}$.

4. $2107 \cdot \dfrac{T}{100} - 2007 \cdot \dfrac{T}{100} = \dfrac{100T}{100} = T$. Since $T = 30$, the answer is $\boxed{30}$.

5. Since $6^n = 2^n \cdot 3^n$ the number of positive factors of 6^n is $(n+1)(n+1)$. Thus, $(n+1)^2 < 500$ giving $n + 1 > 22 + h$ for $0 > h > 1$. Hence, $n \geq 22$ and since $K = T + 5 = 35$, then $22 \leq n \leq 35$. There are 14 values of n and the probability is $\dfrac{14}{35} = \boxed{\dfrac{2}{5}}$.

6. Since $\triangle BAP \sim \triangle DCP$ with a scale factor of 4, then the area of $\triangle DCP$ is 16 times the area of $\triangle BAP$. Since $PC : PA = 4 : 1$, and triangles BAP and BPC have the same altitude from B, the area of $\triangle BPC$ is 4 times the area of $\triangle BAP$. Since the area of $\triangle BAF$ is T, the area of $\triangle BDC$ is $20T$. Since $T = 2/5$, the area of $\triangle BDC$ is $\boxed{8}$.

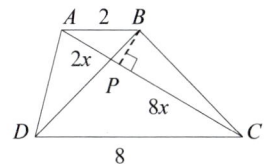

7. The area of equilateral triangle ABC with side x equals

   $\dfrac{x^2\sqrt{3}}{4} = (T - 2)\sqrt{3}$. Thus, $x^2 = 4T - 8$. Since $T = 8$,

   $x^2 = 24$. Thus, $AD^2 = 1^2 + 24 \rightarrow AD = \boxed{5}$.

- -

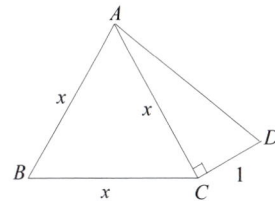

15. Since the line $y = x$ forms a 45° angle with the x-axis, the line $y = mx$ either forms a 30° or a 60° angle with the x-axis. We choose the larger angle and since $\tan 60° = \sqrt{3}$, then $m = \boxed{\sqrt{3}}$.

14. $\dfrac{Ti + 7}{i - 1} \cdot \dfrac{i + 1}{i + 1} = \dfrac{(7 - T) + (7 + T)i}{-2} \rightarrow 2(a^2 + b^2) = \dfrac{2\left((7 - T)^2 + (7 + T)^2\right)}{(-2)^2} = \dfrac{98 + 2T^2}{2} =$

   $49 + T^2 = 49 + \left(\sqrt{3}\right)^2 = \boxed{52}$.

13. From $x^2 - 2x - 2 + \dfrac{26}{T} = 0$ we have $\log a + \log b = 2 \to \log(ab) = 2 \to ab = 10^2$. Thus, $ab = 100$ regardless of T as long as T is such that the equation has real roots. In this case, $T = 52$, giving

$$x^2 - 2x - \frac{3}{2} + 0 \to x + \frac{2 = \sqrt{10}}{2} \approx 2.5811, \ -.5811. \text{ Thus, } \log_{10} a \approx 2.5811, \log_{10} b \approx -.5811, \text{ making}$$

$a \approx 10^{2.5811}$, $b \approx 10^{-.5811}$ and clearly $ab = \boxed{10^2}$.

12. Put 1 ball in jar 1, 2 balls in jar 2, and 3 balls in jar 3. Let $K = (T/10 - 6)$ be the number of remaining balls. Then the remaining balls can be distributed in any way among the three jars. One could make a table for various values of T. Or one could think this way: Imagine that the K balls are laid in a row. A distribution of balls to the 3 jars is the same as separating the balls by placing two sticks between the balls. Shown below when $K = 4$ are ways of representing three distributions of the remaining balls:

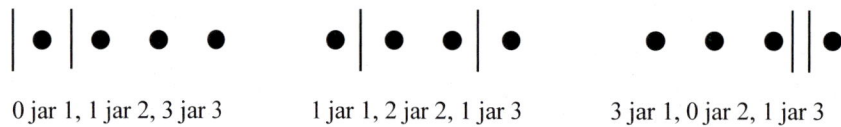

0 jar 1, 1 jar 2, 3 jar 3   1 jar 1, 2 jar 2, 1 jar 3   3 jar 1, 0 jar 2, 1 jar 3

Then the number of distributions equals the number of placements of K balls and 2 sticks in a row of $K + 2$ elements, i.e., $_{K+2}C_2 = \dfrac{(K+2)(K+1)}{2}$. Since $T = 100$, then $K = 4$, so $\dfrac{(4+2)(4+1)}{2} = \boxed{15}$.

11. Let x be the radius of circle C. By similar triangles $\dfrac{T}{6} = \dfrac{5}{6 - x} \to$

$x = \dfrac{6T - 30}{T}$. Since $T = 15$, $x = \boxed{4}$.

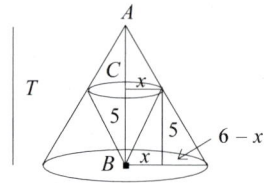

10. $(1 - \sin\theta)^2 + (1 - \cos\theta)^2 = T \to 1 - 2\sin\theta + \sin^2\theta + 1 - 2\cos\theta + \cos^2\theta = T \to 3 - 2(\sin\theta + \cos\theta) = T$

$\to \sin\theta + \cos\theta = \dfrac{3 - T}{2} = \boxed{-\dfrac{1}{2}}$ since $T = 4$.

9. Area of base $ENF = \dfrac{1}{2} \cdot CF \cdot EF = \dfrac{1}{2} \cdot 3 \cdot 12 = 18$. Height $= AD = K$.

Since $K = \left| 4 \cdot -\dfrac{1}{2} \right| = 2$, the volume is $\dfrac{1}{3} \cdot 18 \cdot 2 = \boxed{12}$.

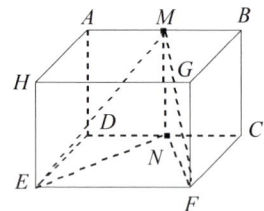

---

8. $x^3 + ax + b = (x - 1)Q(x) + M \to 1 + a + b = M \to a + b = M - 1$ when we substitute 1 for x. Likewise, $2a + b = N - 8$. Solving for a and b we obtain $a = N - M - 7$ and $b = 2M - N + 6$, giving $P(x) = x^3 + (N - M - 7)x + (2M - N + 6)$. The remainder when we divide $P(x)$ by $x - 3$ is just $P(3)$ and that equals $27 + (3N - 3M - 21) + (2M - N + 6) = 2N - M + 12$. Since $N = 12$ and $M = 5$, $P(3) = \boxed{31}$.

1. Compute the largest solution to $2x^2 + 3x + 3 = 7x\sqrt{x+1}$.

2. In $\triangle ABC$, $m\angle C = 90°$, $AC = 12$ and $AB = 13$. Point M lies on $\overline{AC}$ and point N lies on hypotenuse $\overline{AB}$ such that $AM = MN = NB$. Compute AM.

3. If a, b, c and d are distinct numbers drawn from $\{1, 2, 3, 4, 5\}$, determine the least possible positive solution for x to the following system:

$$
\begin{aligned}
ax + by &= 1 \\
cx + dy &= 2
\end{aligned}
$$

1. In $2x^2 + 3(x+1) = 7x\sqrt{x+1}$ set $y = \sqrt{x+1}$, obtaining $2x^2 + 3y^2 = 7xy \rightarrow$

   $2x^2 - 7xy + 3y^2 = 0 \rightarrow (2x - y)(x - 3y) = 0 \rightarrow y = 2x$ or $y = \dfrac{x}{3}$. If $y = 2x$ we

   obtain $2x = \sqrt{x+1} \rightarrow 4x^2 - x - 1 = 0 \rightarrow x + \dfrac{1 = \sqrt{17}}{8}$. If $y = \dfrac{x}{3}$ we obtain

   $\dfrac{x}{3} = \sqrt{x+1} \rightarrow x^2 - 9x - 9 = 0 \rightarrow x + \dfrac{9 = 3\sqrt{13}}{2}$. Answer: $\boxed{\dfrac{9 + 3\sqrt{13}}{2}}$.

2. Draw a perpendicular from M meeting $\overline{AB}$ at P. Since

   $\triangle APM \sim \triangle ACB$, set $MP = 5x$, $AP = 12x$, and $AM = 13x$.

   Since $AM = MN$, then $\triangle MPN$ is also a 5-12-13 triangle,

   making $PN = 12x$. Since $MN = NB$, then $NB = 13x$,

   making $AB = 13 = 12x + 12x + 13x = 37x$. Thus, $x = \dfrac{13}{37}$

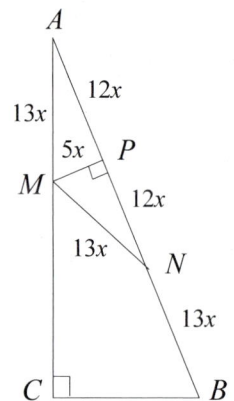

   $\rightarrow 13x = MN = \boxed{\dfrac{169}{37}}$.

3. Using determinants, $x = \dfrac{\begin{vmatrix} 1 & b \\ 2 & d \end{vmatrix}}{\begin{vmatrix} a & b \\ c & d \end{vmatrix}} = \dfrac{d - 2b}{ad - bc}$. Set $d - 2b = 1$, giving

   $(b, d) = (1, 3)$ or $(2, 5)$. Using $(1, 3)$ we obtain $x = \dfrac{\begin{vmatrix} 1 & 1 \\ 2 & 3 \end{vmatrix}}{\begin{vmatrix} a & 1 \\ c & 3 \end{vmatrix}} = \dfrac{3 - 2}{3a - c}$. We maximize the

   denominator by choosing $a = 5$ and $c = 2$ giving $\dfrac{1}{13}$. Using $(2, 5)$ we obtain

   $x = \dfrac{\begin{vmatrix} 1 & 2 \\ 2 & 5 \end{vmatrix}}{\begin{vmatrix} a & 2 \\ c & 5 \end{vmatrix}} = \dfrac{5 - 4}{5a - 2c}$. We maximize the denominator by choosing $a = 4$ and $c = 1$,

   giving $\dfrac{1}{18}$. The least positive solution for x is $\boxed{\dfrac{1}{18}}$.

ARML
2008

ARML 2008 took place on May 30 and 31, 2008 at four sites: the University of Nevada at Las Vegas, Penn State University, the University of Iowa, and the newest site, the University of Georgia. There were 42 teams in Division A and 85 teams in Division B for a total of 127 teams., including the alternate teams. Teams from Taiwan, Hong Kong, Colombia, Turkey, the Philippines, Bulgaria, and Vietnam competed in the ARML International Division. The Academy for the Advancement of Science and Technology (AAST), coached by Joe Holbrook, brought nine teams this year.

In the A division, there was a close competition for first place between a number of regions. San Francisco Bay Area A and Chicago A led the way on the team round with perfect scores of 40. With a perfect score on the Power Question, San Francisco had a 9 point lead going into the individual round, but other teams surged forward and when the dust had settled, New York City A and Phillips Exeter Red led with 154 points while Eastern Massachusetts A trailed by only one point. As usual, the relay round would determine the overall champion. The first relay question was difficult and with 8 points each, NYC A and Exeter seized a lead of 7 points over Mass A. On the final relay, NYC A got 8, Exeter got 6 and so by a mere two points, New York City A claimed the top position for the first time since 1995. In the B division, the Paradise Mall Hong Kong team was tops with 141 but it didn't win the International Division since Taiwan A, competing in Division A, won with a score of 148. In the B Division the Vermont All-Stars team was first among teams from the United States with a score of 122.

This year Oregon and Hong Kong sent teams to ARML for the first time and both did well. Several teams realigned and so New Mexico, Nevada, and Arizona combined to send the Desert Southwest team.

Paul Dreyer was awarded the Alfred Kalfus Founder's Award in recognition of his long and significant involvement with ARML. Paul participated in ARML in 1988-1990, missing the 1991 contest only because it coincided with his graduation from the North Carolina School of Science and Math. Paul helped coach the North Carolina team from 1992 to 1996 under his former coach and mentor, John Goebel. Since then he has served as the Director of Development and Western Site Coordinator. He has been an ARML problem writer since 1999. In 2008 he founded, organized, and ran a new contest called ARML Local.

Patricia Gabriel of Thomas Jefferson High School in Alexandria, VA and Mrs. Rechilda Villame of the Philippines were awarded the Samuel L. Greitzer Coach Awards. Ms. Gabriel has worked with the Thomas Jefferson math team since 1985 and has been the head coach for most of that time. Besides organizing TJ's participation in ARML, she has actively and energetically made it possible for the math students at Thomas Jefferson to participate in an amazing array of contests with great success. Despite being department chair she's often put more than 10 hours per week into the math team.

Mrs. Villame has been the Philippines ARML coach since 2000; she has worked tirelessly to prepare the team during the six hour, six days a week training session that the team takes part in for 5 weeks during the summer. She prepares problems and guides students deftly toward solutions. Her students know that her efforts and support have greatly helped them to improve.

Georgia ARML of Conyers, GA was awarded the Harry and Ruth Ruderman Award for winning the ARML Power Contest.

The following were awarded the Douglas Cameron Baker Memorial Award: Max Rosett of Utah and Nate Harmon of Chicago. Max single-handedly started the Utah ARML team and has been its guiding light. He taught the younger students, set the curriculum for meets, recruited new students, and helped with fundraising. Nate made a great ARML teammate because of his broad base of knowledge, ingenuity, problem-solving skills, diligence, and enthusiasm.

T–1. A square tile A is cut in half with a single straight cut. One of the pieces is joined to a square tile B of a size different from A, forming a rectangle of area 6. Compute the perimeter of that rectangle.

T–2. Sam, a ne'er-do-well, missed x problems on a test. Each problem is worth one point and x is a two-digit number. However, he correctly solved y problems where y consists of the digits of x reversed. To the nearest percent, his grade rounds to 24%. Compute y, the number of problems he solved correctly.

T–3. For a positive integer n, let $\langle n \rangle$ denote the closest integral perfect square to n, e.g., $\langle 71 \rangle = 64$ and $\langle 21 \rangle = 25$. Compute the smallest positive integer n such that $\langle 91 \rangle \cdot \langle 120 \rangle \cdot \langle 143 \rangle \cdot \langle 180 \rangle \cdot \langle n \rangle = 91 \cdot 120 \cdot 143 \cdot 180n$.

T–4. A rectangle with integer side lengths and an area of 99 is rotated 180° in its plane about one of its vertices, sweeping out a region of area R. Compute the smallest possible value for R.

T–5. If n has 60 positive factors, compute the largest number of positive factors that n^2 could have.

T–6. Let $O = (0,0)$ and $A = (5,0)$. For certain positive values of k, there exists $f(x) = ax^2$, $a > 0$, such that $m\angle QOA = 2m\angle POA$ where $P = (1, f(1))$, and $Q = (k, f(k))$. Compute all possible positive values of k.

T–7. Let S be the set of all complex ordered triple solutions to the following system:

$$
\begin{array}{ccccc}
x & + & yz & = & 7 \\
y & + & xz & = & 10 \\
z & + & xy & = & 10
\end{array}
$$

Let $\left(\hat{X}, \hat{Y}, \hat{Z} \right)$ be the coordinatewise sum of all ordered triples (x, y, z) in S. Compute $\hat{X}$.

T–8. In the figure at the right, a step is legal if it begins in any hexagon and moves to any adjacent hexagon with a different letter. Compute the number of distinct, directed paths of 2 legal steps. Note: Two paths are distinct if they do not visit the same hexagons in the same order.

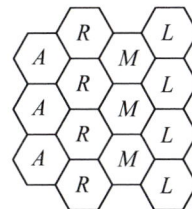

T–9. In the complex plane, z, z^2, z^3 form, in some order, three of the vertices of a non-degenerate square. Let a and b represent the smallest and largest possible areas of the squares, respectively. Compute the ordered pair (a, b).

T–10. The positive integers $a_1, a_2, a_3, \ldots, a_{72}$ form an increasing arithmetic sequence with $a_5 = 300$. If we remove 67 of these numbers, including a_3 through a_7, the resulting five integers form a geometric sequence. Compute the value of the largest of those five integers.

1. $8\sqrt{2}$

2. 29

3. 462

4. $99 + 101\pi$

5. 405

6. $k > 2$. The following is equivalent: $(2, \infty)$.

7. 7

8. 110

9. $\left(\dfrac{5}{8}, 10\right)$. The following is equivalent: $(.625, 10)$.

10. 1215

T–1. Given a large square of side a and a small square of side b, a rectangle can only be formed if $b = \dfrac{a}{2}$. Its area is $ab + b^2 =$ $a^2/2 + \left(a/2\right)^2 = (3/4)a^2 = 6 \rightarrow a^2 = 8 \rightarrow a = 2\sqrt{2}$.

The perimeter is $2a + 4b = 4a = \boxed{8\sqrt{2}}$.

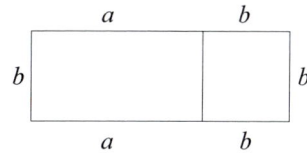

T–2. Let $x = 10A + B$ and $y = 10B + A$. The total number of points is $11A + 11B$ so we have the following:

$.235 \leq \dfrac{10B + A}{11B + 11A} < .245 \rightarrow 2.585(B + A) \leq 10B + A < 2.695(B + A)$. Simplifying gives

$A \leq 4.678B$ and $4.3097B < A$. The values that solve these inequalities are $B = 2$ and $A = 9$, so he solved $\boxed{29}$ problems and missed 92. Note: $\dfrac{29}{29 + 92} \approx .2397$.

Alternate solution: From $\dfrac{10B + A}{11A + 11B} \approx \dfrac{24}{100} \approx \dfrac{6}{25}$ we obtain $184B \approx 41A$. Thus

$A \approx \left(4\tfrac{20}{41}\right)B \rightarrow A \approx \dfrac{9}{2}B \rightarrow B = 2$ and $A = 9$.

T–3. $\langle 91 \rangle \cdot \langle 120 \rangle \cdot \langle 143 \rangle \cdot \langle 180 \rangle \cdot \langle n \rangle = 91 \cdot 120 \cdot 143 \cdot 180n \rightarrow 10^2 \cdot 11^2 \cdot 12^2 \cdot 13^2 \cdot \langle n \rangle = 91 \cdot 120 \cdot 143 \cdot 180n$. Canceling common factors yields $22\langle n \rangle = 21n$. Since 21 and 22 are relatively prime, n is a multiple of 22 and $\langle n \rangle$ is a multiple of $21^2 = 441$. Thus, $n \geq 441$ and $n = 22k$. The first multiple of 22 greater than 441 is 462. Since $22\langle 462 \rangle = 22 \cdot 21^2$ and $21 \cdot 462 = 21 \cdot 21 \cdot 22$, the answer is $\boxed{462}$.

T–4. Let $ABCD$ have integral sides p and q. Rotating rectangle $ABCD$ clockwise $180°$ about A gives the figure shown. The total area covered is equal to the semicircle whose radius is $\overline{AC}$ and the sum of the areas of triangles ABC and $C'D'A$. The two triangles combine to form a copy of $ABCD$, so their total area is 99. The area of the

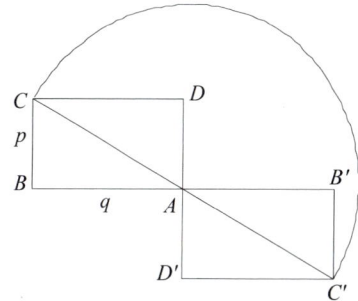

semicircle with radius $\overline{AC}$ is $\dfrac{\pi(AC)^2}{2} = \dfrac{\pi\left(p^2 + q^2\right)}{2}$ where

$p \cdot q = 99$. Since $p^2 + q^2$ is minimized when p and q are as close as possible, choose either $p = 9, q = 11$ or $p = 11, q = 9$ to obtain the smallest possible area. It is $\boxed{99 + 101\pi}$.

T–5. If $n = p_1^{\,a} p_2^{\,b} \ldots p_k^{\,c}$, then the number of factors of n equals $(a + 1)(b + 1)\ldots(c + 1)$ and the number of factors of n^2 equals $(2a + 1)(2b + 1)\ldots(2c + 1)$. Consider the following:

If $60 = 2 \cdot 30$, then $n = p_1 p_2^{\,29}$, $n^2 = p_1^{\,2} p_2^{\,58}$, and n^2 has $3 \cdot 59 = 177$ factors.

If $60 = 6 \cdot 10$, then $n = p_1^{\,5} p_2^{\,9}$, $n^2 = p_1^{\,10} p_2^{\,18}$ and n^2 has $11 \cdot 19 = 209$ factors. For $60 = 3 \cdot 20$,

n^2 has 195 factors, for $60 = 4 \cdot 15$, n^2 has 203 factors, and for $60 = 5 \cdot 12$, n^2 has 207 factors.

For $60 = 2 \cdot 5 \cdot 6$, $n = p_1 p_2{}^4 p_3{}^5$, $n^2 = p_1{}^2 p_2{}^8 p_3{}^{10}$ and n^2 has $3 \cdot 9 \cdot 11 = 297$ factors. For $60 = 2 \cdot 3 \cdot 10$, n^2 has 285 factors, for $60 = 2 \cdot 2 \cdot 15$, n^2 has 261 factors, and for $60 = 3 \cdot 4 \cdot 5$, n^2 has 315 factors. However, 60 could also equal $2 \cdot 2 \cdot 3 \cdot 5 \rightarrow n = p_1 p_2 p_3{}^2 p_4{}^4 \rightarrow$ $n^2 = p_1{}^2 p_2{}^2 p_3{}^4 p_4{}^8$ and here n^2 has $3 \cdot 3 \cdot 5 \cdot 9 = 405$ factors. Ans: $\boxed{405}$.

T–6. Note that $m\angle QOA$ and $m\angle POA$ lie in the interval $(0°, 90°)$. Since the tangent function is one-to-one on $0° < \theta < 90°$, then $m\angle QOA = 2m\angle POA$ if and only if $\tan\angle QOA = \tan 2\angle POA$.

We have $P = (1, a)$, $Q = (k, ak^2)$, $\tan\angle QOA = \dfrac{ak^2}{k} = ak$ and

$\tan\angle POA = a$. From $\tan\angle QOA = \tan 2\angle POA = \dfrac{2\tan\angle POA}{1 - \tan^2\angle POA}$,

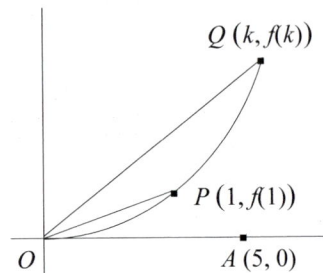

we obtain $ak = \dfrac{2a}{1 - a^2} \rightarrow k = \dfrac{2}{1 - a^2} \rightarrow a^2 = 1 - \dfrac{2}{k} \rightarrow a = \sqrt{1 - \dfrac{2}{k}}$. Thus, $1 - \dfrac{2}{k} > 0 \rightarrow \boxed{k > 2}$.

T–7. Subtracting (3) from (2) gives $y - z + xz - xy = 0 \rightarrow$

$(y - z)(1 - x) = 0$. Thus, $x = 1$ or $y = z$. If $x = 1$,

substituting into (1) and (2) yields $1 + yz = 7 \rightarrow yz = 6$ or

(1)	x	+	yz	=	7
(2)	y	+	xz	=	10
(3)	z	+	xy	=	10

$y + z = 10$. Therefore, y and z are distinct roots of the equation $t^2 - 10t + 6 = 0$, so $x = 1$ counts twice.

If $y = z$, then from (1) we have $x + y^2 = 7$ and from (2) we have $y + xy = 10 \rightarrow y^2(1 + x)^2 = 100$.

Substituting the first into the second yields $(7 - x)(x^2 + 2x + 1) = 100 \rightarrow x^3 - 5x^2 - 13x + 93 = 0$. The sum of the roots is 5, so the sum of the values of x satisfying the system is $1 + 1 + 5 = \boxed{7}$.

T–8. Consider the copies of the grid to the right. In the first, each cell is marked with the number of legal 1-step paths that end in the cell. This is just the number of adjacent cells with differing letters. In the second, note that the number of legal 2-step paths that terminate in a given cell is equal to the sum of the number of legal 1-step paths that terminate in

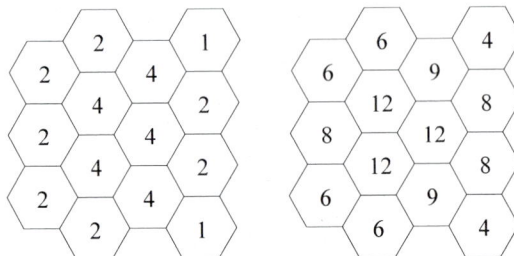

1-step paths   2-step paths

adjacent cells of a different letter. If we fill a cell in the right-hand grid with the sum of those adjacent cells' entries from the left-hand grid, we will have the number of legal 2-step paths that terminate there. Of course, we do not add in the number of legal one-step paths that come from a cell of the same letter. For example, we get a 9 in the upper M cell in the third column because its legal adjacent cells in the left-hand grid contain 4, 2, 2, and 1. The sum of the numbers in the cells in the right-hand grid gives the total number of legal 2-step paths. That sum is $\boxed{110}$.

T–9. Assume that a solution would look like the diagram at the right. If we think of z, z^2 and z^3 as vectors in the complex plane, then $z^2 - z = \overrightarrow{AB}$ and $z^3 - z = \overrightarrow{AD}$. $\overrightarrow{AB}$ and $\overrightarrow{AD}$ must have the same magnitude and that magnitude equals the side of the square. Also, since multiplication by i rotates by $90°$, $\left(\overrightarrow{AB}\right)i = \overrightarrow{AD}$ and $\left(\overrightarrow{AD}\right)(-i) = \overrightarrow{AB}$. Thus, the quotient of the two vectors equals either i or $-i$. These considerations underlie the following solution:

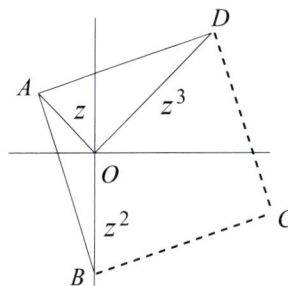

We will consider three cases, depending on which element of $\left\{z, z^2, z^3\right\}$ is between the other two in the square. In each case we will find possible values for z by setting the quotient of the adjacent sides, expressed as complex vectors, equal to $\pm i$. That means that as vectors, the ratio of side lengths is $|\pm i|$ and the angle between them is $\arg(\pm i) = \pm 90°$.

i) Let z be between z^2 and z^3. Then $\dfrac{z^3 - z}{z^2 - z} + = i \;\rightarrow\; z + 1 = \pm i \;\rightarrow\; z = -1 \pm i$. If $z = -1 + i$, $z^2 = -2i$ giving $\left|z^2 - z\right| = \sqrt{10}$, so the area is 10. If $z = -1 - i$, we also obtain an area of 10.

ii) Let z^2 be between z and z^3. Then $\dfrac{z^3 - z^2}{z^2 - z} = \pm i \;\rightarrow\; z + = i$. In this case $z^2 = -1$ and so $\left|z^2 - z\right| = |-1 \pm i| = \sqrt{2}$. The area of the square is 2.

iii) Finally, let z^3 lie between z and z^2. Then $\dfrac{z^3 - z}{z^3 - z^2} = \pm i \;\rightarrow\; \dfrac{z(z^2 - 1)}{z^2(z - 1)} = \pm i \;\rightarrow\; \dfrac{z + 1}{z} = \pm i$

$\dfrac{1}{z} = -1 \pm i \;\rightarrow\; z = -\dfrac{1}{2} \mp \dfrac{1}{2}i$. This gives $z^2 = \pm \dfrac{1}{2}i$, so the length of the diagonal of the square equals

$\left|z^2 - z\right| = \left|\dfrac{1}{2}i - \left(-\dfrac{1}{2} - \dfrac{1}{2}i\right)\right| = \left|\dfrac{1}{2} + i\right| = \sqrt{\dfrac{1}{4} + \dfrac{4}{4}} = \dfrac{\sqrt{5}}{2}$. The area is then $\left(\dfrac{\sqrt{5}}{2\sqrt{2}}\right)^2 = \dfrac{5}{8}$.

The minimum area is $\frac{5}{8}$ and the maximum is 10, so the answer is $\boxed{\left(\frac{5}{8},\ 10\right)}$. Graphs of examples of solutions to cases (i), (ii), and (iii) respectively are shown below from left to right:

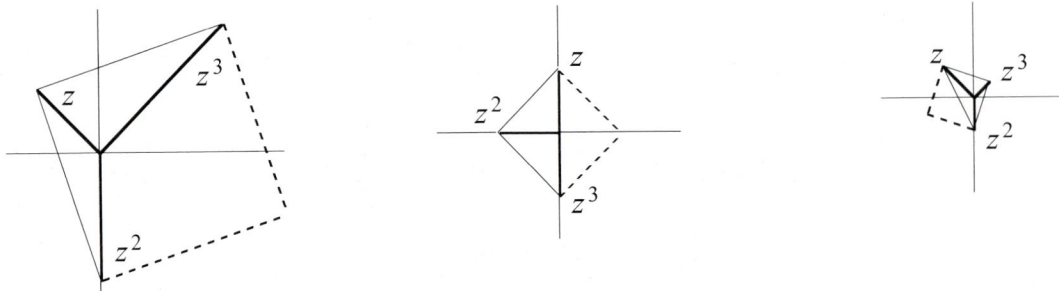

T–10. Call the common difference of the arithmetic sequence d, call a_n the first of the five terms forming the geometric sequence, and call r the common ratio. If a_n and a_{n+k} are consecutive terms of the geometric sequence, then the next term will be $r\left(a_{n+k}\right) = r\left(a_n + kd\right) = ra_n + rkd \pm a_{n=k} = rkd = a_{n+k+rk}$. The following term will be $r\left(a_{n+k+rk}\right) = r\left(a_{n+k} + rkd\right) = r\left(a_{n+k}\right) + r^2kd = ra_n + rkd + r^2kd = a_{n\pm k\pm rk\pm r^2k}$. Since there are k terms between the first two terms of the geometric sequence, rk terms between the second term a_{n+k} and the third term a_{n+k+rk} of the geometric sequence, and r^2k between the third and fourth terms, then the differences in the subscripts of the terms in the geometric sequence increase geometrically at the rate r as well. In what follows we will call the differences in the indices *gaps*. So the gap between a_n and a_{n+k} will be called k.

Let's see if we can find a solution for integral r. The smallest possible integral value for r is 2. If the difference between the subscripts of the first two terms of the geometric sequence is k, then we have the terms a_n, a_{n+k}, a_{n+3k}, a_{n+7k}, a_{n+15k}. The sum of the gaps between the first and fifth will be $k + 2k + 4k + 8k = 15k$. Since $15k$ must be less than 72, then $k < 5$. This prohibits us from having an initial term of a_1 or a_2 since for $k = 1, 2, 3,$ or 4, the second or third term of the geometric sequence would be between a_3 and a_7, and those terms were deleted. Thus our first term must be a_8 or larger. But this is impossible because if we trace the arithmetic sequence backwards from the initial term a_n of the geometric sequence, we would reach 0 at a_{n-k}. For example, if the first term of the geometric sequence is a_8 and if $k = 2$, then $a_{8+2} = a_{10} = 2a_8$. The common difference $d = \dfrac{a_{10} - a_8}{2} = \dfrac{2a_8 - a_8}{2} = \dfrac{a_8}{2}$.

Thus $a_6 = a_8 - 2d = a_8 - a_8 = 0$. If $r = 3$, the difference in indices between the first and fifth terms would be $k + 3k + 9k + 27k = 39k$, forcing k to be 1. If the initial term a_n of the geometric sequence has $n > 1$, we could trace the arithmetic sequence backwards and hit a negative value at $a_{n-k} = a_{n-1}$. For example, since $k = 1$, then $a_{n+1} = 3a_n$ and the common difference is $2a_n$. But since there is at least one term before a_n, $a_{n-1} = a_n - 2a_n = -a_n$ and that is impossible. On the other hand if $r = 3$ and if $n = 1$, then the third term of the geometric sequence is $a_{1=1=3} \pm a_5$, but a_5 was deleted. If $r \geq 4$, the gap between the first and the fifth term would be at least $1 = 4 = 16 = 64 \pm 81$ terms and that least amount exceeds 72 and is too large.

Since no integer value for r will work, we set $r = \dfrac{p}{q}$ where p and q are relatively prime integers. If a_{n+k} is the second term of the geometric sequence, the gaps between the subsequent terms, namely, rk, r^2k, and r^3k, must be integers. Since $\dfrac{kp^3}{q^3}$ is an integer, q^3 divides k. Thus, the gap between a_n and $a_{n\pm k}$ will be a multiple of q^3 and the gap between the fourth and the fifth terms of the geometric sequence, r^3k, will be a multiple of p^3. The only integral p and q that are relatively prime and satisfy $p^3 + q^3 \leq 71$ are $p = 3$ and $q = 2$. If $r = \dfrac{3}{2}$ and $k = 8$, then the four gaps are 8, 12, 18, and 27, and these sum to 65. Since the gaps sum to 65, the first term cannot be after a_7. This forces a first term of a_1 or a_2. Since $r = \dfrac{3}{2}$ and $k = 8$, we have $a_n + 8d = \dfrac{3}{2}a_n \rightarrow a_n = 16d$. If $n = 1$, then $300 \pm a_5 \pm a_{n=4} \pm 16d = 4d \pm 20 \rightarrow d = 15$. If $n = 2$, then $300 = a_{n+3} = 19d$, but that does not give an integral value for d so n can't be 2. So the first term of the geometric sequence, which we called a_n, is actually a_1. Since $a_5 = 300$ and $d = 15$, then $a_1 = 300 - 4 \cdot 15 = 240$. Since $a_1 = 240$, $r = \dfrac{3}{2}$ and the gaps are 8, 12, 18, and 27, we have $a_1 = 240$, $a_9 = 240\left(\dfrac{3}{2}\right) = 360$, $a_{21} = 360\left(\dfrac{3}{2}\right) = 540$,

$a_{39} = 540\left(\dfrac{3}{2}\right) = 810$, and finally, $a_{66} = 240\left(\dfrac{3}{2}\right)^4 = \boxed{1215}$.

Given a rectangle whose dimensions are $a \times b$, where a and b are integers, a *tiling* by rectangular tiles of dimensions $u_1 \times v_1, u_2 \times v_2$, etc., where all dimensions are integers, is an arrangement of tiles that fill the rectangle with no gaps and no overlaps. The edges of the tiles are parallel to the sides of the rectangle. For example, some of the ways to tile a 4×4 rectangle with 2×2 and 1×4 tiles would be to use four of either tile as shown by the left two diagrams or two of each as shown by the right two diagrams:

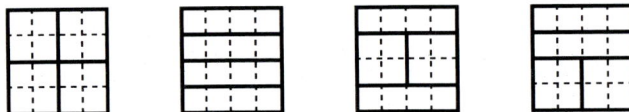

A $u \times v$ tile has a height of u and a width of v. The diagram shows a 2×3 tile on the left and a 3×2 tile on the right. Tiles cannot be rotated into different orientations and two $u \times v$ tiles are indistinguishable. As example of different tilings, there are two ways to tile a 1×3 rectangle with a 1×1 tile and a 1×2 tile—the 1×1 tile can go to the left or to the right of the 1×2 tile. Let $S(n)$ and $\left| S(n) \right|$ represent the set of tilings of a $1 \times n$ rectangle and the number of such tilings, respectively.

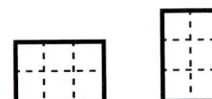

---

1.   a) Compute the number of ways a 1×4 rectangle can be tiled with 1×1 and 1×2 tiles.

       b) Give two different tilings of a 12×15 rectangle with combinations of 2×4 and 3×3 tiles.

       c) Prove that it is impossible to tile an 80×80 rectangle with tiles of sizes 3×11 and 4×15.

2.   a) For $n \in \{1, 2, \ldots, 10\}$, compute the number of ways to tile a $1 \times n$ rectangle with tiles of sizes 1×1 and 1×2. Give your answers in a table.

       b) Determine, with proof, a recursive formula for the number of ways to tile a $1 \times n$ rectangle with 1×1 and 1×2 tiles. Use the formula to compute the number of ways to tile a 1×17 rectangle.

3.   a) In a table, list all values of $n \le 40$ such that a $1 \times n$ rectangle can be tiled with 1×10 and 1×12 tiles. For each n, list a combination of 10's and 12's that work.

       b) Compute the number of values of n, $1000 \le n \le 2008$, for which a $1 \times n$ rectangle can be tiled with 1×10 and 1×12 tiles.

       c) Determine, with justification, a recursive formula for the number of ways to tile a $1 \times n$ rectangle with 1×2 and 1×3 tiles. Then compute the number of ways to tile a 1×17 rectangle.

4. For this question only, suppose that 1×1 tiles are gray and
    1×2 tiles are colored in two ways: the right half white and
    the left half black or vice-versa. Thus, there are two distinct
    types of 1×2 tiles.

    a) Using these colored tiles, determine the number of distinguishable tilings for a 1×17 rectangle.
    Explain the method used.

    b) Using these colored tiles, give an <u>explicit, closed-form</u> formula in terms of n for the number of
    distinguishable tilings of a $1 \times n$ rectangle. This is a non-recursive formula. Justify your formula.

5. Find, with justification, the number of different ways to tile an 8×8 rectangle using 2×2 and
    1×3 tiles. It is not necessary to use both types in a tiling.

For the rest of the problems, you may assume the following *Spanning Theorem:* A $1 \times n$ rectangle can be
tiled with tiles of sizes $1 \times u$ and $1 \times v$ if and only if there exist nonnegative integers t_1 and t_2 such that

$ut_1 + vt_2 = n$. Let $\langle u, v \rangle$ denote $\{ ut_1 + vt_2 \ : \ t_1, t_2 \text{ nonnegative integers} \}$. We express this theorem
compactly as follows:

A $1 \times n$ rectangle can be tiled with tiles of sizes $1 \times u$ and $1 \times v$ if and only if $n \in \langle u, v \rangle$.

We now consider a generalization of the Spanning Theorem:

6. a) Prove that if an $m \times n$ rectangle can be tiled with $u_1 \times v_1$ and $u_2 \times v_2$ tiles, then
    $$m \in \langle u_1, u_2 \rangle \text{ and } n \in \langle v_1, v_2 \rangle. \ (*)$$

    b) Give an example to show that the condition $m \in \langle u_1, u_2 \rangle$ and $n \in \langle v_1, v_2 \rangle$ is not sufficient to
    guarantee the existence of a tiling of an $m \times n$ rectangle with $u_1 \times v_1$ and $u_2 \times v_2$ tiles.

Because the generalized spanning condition (*) does not guarantee the existence of a tiling of a given rectangle using two given tiles, most of the rest of this power question is devoted to understanding when such a tiling is possible.

Below are two tilings of a 6×7 rectangle with combinations of 2×2 and 1×3 tiles:

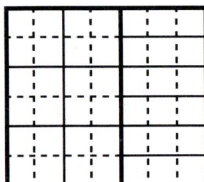   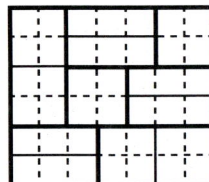

Tiling 1   Tiling 2

Notice that in Tiling 1, the 6×7 rectangle has been effectively subdivided into two smaller rectangles of dimensions 6×4 and 6×3, each of which is tiled with copies of a single tile. To divide Tiling 2 into sub-rectangles tiled with copies of a single tile would require seven sub-rectangles: one 4×2, two $2 \times 2's$, three $2 \times 3's$, and one 2×4. Call the *complexity* of a particular tiling the smallest number c, $c \geq 1$, of sub-rectangles, each tiled with copies of a single tile, into which a tiled rectangle can be divided. So Tiling 1 is of complexity 2 and Tiling 2 is of complexity 7.

In what follows, we will assume that no tile is a scaled copy of any other tile, that is, if one tile is $u_1 \times v_1$ and the other tile is $u_2 \times v_2$, we assume $\dfrac{u_1}{u_2} \neq \dfrac{v_1}{v_2}$.

7.   Under what conditions on u_1, v_1, u_2, v_2, m, and n does an $m \times n$ rectangle have a tiling of complexity 1 when $u_1 \times v_1$ and $u_2 \times v_2$ tiles are used? Justify your answer.

8.   Under what conditions on u_1, v_1, u_2, v_2, m, and n does an $m \times n$ rectangle have a tiling of complexity at most 2 when $u_1 \times v_1$ and $u_2 \times v_2$ tiles are used? Justify your answer.

138

Let R be an $m \times n$ rectangle, where m and n are <u>not</u> necessarily integers, that has been colored in a checkerboard pattern with squares of size $\frac{1}{2} \times \frac{1}{2}$, as in the diagram below, with $m \approx 3.2$ and $n \approx 4.8$.

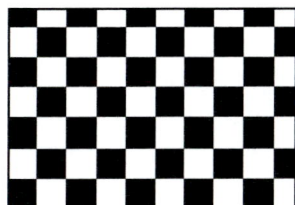

You may assume as a lemma that if a $u \times v$ tile is placed on R with edges parallel to the sides of the rectangle, and at least one of u and v is an integer, then the tile covers equal areas of black and white.

9. Prove that if R is tiled with two different kinds of tiles, where each kind of tile has at least one integral dimension, then at least one of m and n is an integer.

10. If u_1, v_1, u_2, v_2, m, and n are all positive integers, and if an $m \times n$ rectangle R can be tiled with tiles of dimensions $u_1 \times v_1$ and $u_2 \times v_2$, prove that it has a tiling with those tiles of complexity at most 2.

1.   a) There are $\boxed{5}$ ways. Using S for a 1×1 and D for a 1×2, they are: $SSSS$, SSD, SDS, DSS, DD.

b) There are many, one of which uses only 3×3 squares. Two others are shown below:

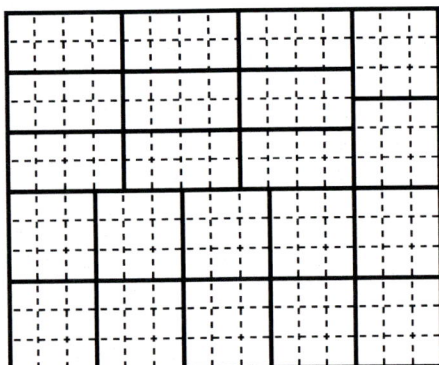

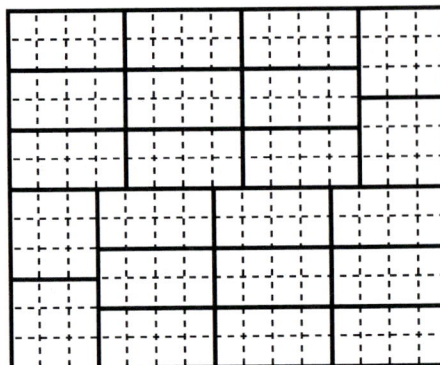

c)   Proof #1: The area of each kind of tile is divisible by 3, but the area of the rectangle is not.

Proof #2: Assume that it is possible to tile an 80×80 rectangle with 3×11 and 4×15 tiles. Looking across the top row, we would see j 3×11 tiles and k 4×15 tiles, where j and k are nonnegative integers. Because there are no gaps and no overlaps, $11j + 15k = 80$. But this Diophantine equation has no solutions in positive integers since from $j = 7 - k + \dfrac{3 - 4k}{11}$ we discover that j is a positive integer for $k \leq -2$.

2.   a) The numbers form the familiar sequence Fibonacci sequence where $F_{n+1} = F_n + F_{n-1}$.

N	1	2	3	4	5	6	7	8	9	10
Tilings	1	2	3	5	8	13	21	34	55	89

b) In general, there are F_{n+1} ways to tile a $1 \times n$ rectangle with 1×1 and 1×2 tiles.

Proof: Let $S(n)$ be the set of tilings of a $1 \times n$ rectangle, and let $\left| S(n) \right|$ be the number of elements of $S(n)$. Then $\left| S(1) \right| = F_2 = 1$ and $\left| S(2) \right| = F_3 = 2$, i.e., a 1×2 rectangle can be tiled with two 1×1 tiles or a single 1×2 tile. That establishes the base case. Assume that $\left| S(k) \right| \pm F_{k=1}$ for $k = 0, 1, \ldots, n$. Any tiling of a $1 \times (n + 1)$ rectangle is either a tiling of a $1 \times n$ rectangle followed by a 1×1 tile or a tiling of a $1 \times (n - 1)$ rectangle followed by a 1×2 tile. This observation allows us to partition $S(n + 1)$ into disjoint subsets, one of which is in 1:1 correspondence with $S(n)$ and the other with $S(n - 1)$. So $\left| S(n + 1) \right| = \left| S(n) \right| + \left| S(n - 1) \right|$, the recursive formula for the Fibonacci numbers.

Because $F_{18} = 2584$, we have $\left| S(17) \right| = \boxed{2584}$.

140

3.   a) The table below shows the combinations of 1×10 and 1×12 tiles that yield each result.

n	10	12	14	16	18	20	22	24	26	28	30	32	34	36	38	40
10's	1	0	np	np	np	2	1	0	np	np	3	2	1	0	np	4
12's	0	1	np	np	np	0	1	2	np	np	0	1	2	3	np	0

   b) In the table np stands for *not possible*. Note that for $n = 30, 32, 34, 36$, and 40, a $1 \times n$ rectangle is tileable. Note also that a 1×48 rectangle is tileable using four 1×12 tiles. By using 1×10 tiles we can therefore tile any rectangle where n is an even number greater than 38. Since for every even value of n, $1000 \le n \le 2008$, all $1 \times n$ rectangles are tileable, the number of values of n is $\dfrac{2008 - 1000}{2} = 1 \pm \boxed{505}$.

   c) Let $S(n)$ be the set of tilings of a $1 \times n$ rectangle with 1×2 and 1×3 tiles, and let $\left| S(n) \right|$ be the number of elements of $S(n)$. Notice that $\left| S(1) \right| = 0$ and $\left| S(2) \right| = \left| S(3) \right| = 1$. A 1×4 rectangle can only be tiled in one way using two 1×2 tiles, so $\left| S(4) \right| = 1$. To tile a 1×5 rectangle we either add a 1×3 tile to a rectangle ending in a 1×2 tile or 1×2 tile to a rectangle ending in a 1×3 tile, giving $\left| S(5) \right| = \left| S(3) \right| + \left| S(2) \right| = 2$. By an argument similar to that in (1a) we can show that $\left| S(n = 1) \right| \pm \left| S(n - 1) \right| = \left| S(n - 2) \right|$. Using this relation we can make a table:

n	1	2	3	4	5	6	7	8	9	10	11	12	13	14	15	16	17
$\left\| S(n) \right\|$	0	1	1	1	2	2	3	4	5	7	9	12	16	21	28	37	49

A 1×17 rectangle can be tiled in $\boxed{49}$ ways.

4.   a) As before, let $S(n)$ represent the set of all tilings of a $1 \times n$ strip, but this time using the coloring scheme described in the problem, and let $\left| S(n) \right|$ be the number of elements of $S(n)$. Reasoning as in problem 2, the elements of $S(n + 1)$ can be mapped onto the elements of $S(n)$ and of $S(n - 1)$, but this time the relation is many-to-one:

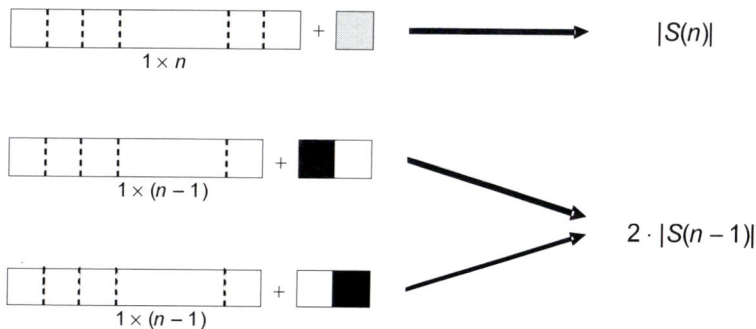

So $\left| S(n + 1) \right| = \left| S(n) \right| + 2\left| S(n - 1) \right|$ with $\left| S(1) \right| = 1$ and $\left| S(2) \right| = 3$. Using this recursive formula, $\left| S(17) \right| = \boxed{87381}$.

4b) Let S represent the 1×1 tile, R the 1×2 tile with the black right side, and L the 1×2 tile with the black left side. For $n = 1, 2, 3, 4$, we have the following tilings:

n	Tilings	No. of Tilings
1	S	1
2	SS, R, L	3
3	SSS, SR, RS, SL, LS	5
4	$SSSS$, SSR, SSL, SRS, SLS, RSS, LSS, RL, LR, RR, LL	11

Notice that if we triple the number of tilings we have the following pattern:

n	Three times the number of tilings	Formula
1	3	$2^2 - 1$
2	9	$2^3 \pm 1$
3	15	$2^4 - 1$
4	33	$2^5 + 1$

This suggests that the number of tilings of a $1 \times n$ rectangle is $|T(n)| \pm \dfrac{2^{n=1} = (-1)^n}{3}$.

Proof by induction:

The formula is clearly true for $n = 1$ and 2. Assume the formula holds for $n = k - 1$ and k, that is

that $\left| S(k-1) \right| = \dfrac{2^k + (-1)^{k-1}}{3}$ and $\left| S(k) \right| = \dfrac{2^{k+1} + (-1)^k}{3}$. Starting with a tiled $1 \times k$ rectangle,

we add a 1×1 tile to cover the $1 \times (k+1)$ rectangle, giving $\dfrac{2^{k+1} + (-1)^k}{3}$ ways to tile the

$1 \times (k+1)$ rectangle. Starting with a tiled $1 \times (k-1)$ rectangle, we can add either the R or L

1×2, giving $2 \left(\dfrac{2^k + (-1)^{k-1}}{3} \right) = \dfrac{2^{k+1} + 2(-1)^{k-1}}{3}$ ways tile a $1 \times (k+1)$ rectangle. The sum

equals $\dfrac{2^{k+1} + (-1)^k}{3} + \dfrac{2^{k+1} + 2(-1)^{k-1}}{3} = \dfrac{2^{k+2} + (-1)^k + 2(-1)^{k-1}}{3}$. If k is odd then

$(-1)^k + 2(-1)^{k-1} = 1 = (-1)^{k+1}$. If k is even then $(-1)^k + 2(-1)^{k-1} = -1 = (-1)^{k+1}$. Therefore,

we have shown that $\left| S(k=1) \right| \pm \dfrac{2^{k=2} = (-1)^{k=1}}{3}$ which was the desired result.

<u>Alternate derivation</u>: Let $\left|S(n)\right| = x^n$. From $\left|S(n+1)\right| = \left|S(n)\right| + 2\left|S(n-1)\right|$, we obtain

$x^{n+1} = x^n + 2x^{n-1}$ which, since $x \neq 0$, is equivalent to $x^2 - x - 2 = 0$ with roots $x = 2, -1$.

So the general solution to $\left|S(n+1)\right| = \left|S(n)\right| + 2\left|S(n-1)\right|$ is $\left|S(n)\right| = A \cdot 2^n + B(-1)^n$. To find

the particular solution that fits our initial conditions, let $n = 1$ and $n = 2$ to find $2A - B = 1$ and

$4A + B = 3$. Solving we obtain $A = 2/3$ and $B = 1/3$. Thus, $\left|S(n)\right| \pm \frac{2}{3} \cdot 2^n = \frac{1}{3}(-1)^n$.

<u>Alternate formula</u>: If the number of 1×2 tiles used in a tiling is k, then there are 2^k possible
orientations of those tiles. So we must separate $S(17)$ into disjoint subsets according to the number
of 1×2 tiles used in each tiling. Let $S(n, k)$ be the set of all tilings of a $1 \times n$ strip that use precisely
k 1×2 tiles. Each tiling in $S(n, k)$ uses $(n - 2k)$ 1×1 tiles; these two sets of tiles can be

rearranged in $\dfrac{(n-k)!}{(n-2k)!k!} = \dbinom{n-k}{k}$ ways before the orientation of 1×2 tiles is taken into account.

So $\left|S(n,k)\right| = \dbinom{n-k}{k} \cdot 2^k$. Then $\left|S(n)\right| = \sum_{k=0}^{\lfloor n/2 \rfloor} \left|S(n,k)\right| = \sum_{k=0}^{\lfloor n/2 \rfloor} \dbinom{n-k}{k} \cdot 2^k$. For $n = 17$, this

sum evaluates to 87381, which checks with our answer to (4a).

5. Call 2×2 tiles *squares* and 1×3 tiles *triominoes*. The 8×8 rectangle can be completely covered

with squares or by some combination of squares and triominoes. Because the height of each tile

divides the height of the rectangle, it is natural to break the problem down into cases according to

the number of horizontal *fault lines*, lines dividing the tiled rectangle into tiled sub-rectangles

without breaking any existing tile in the tiling. Consider the tiling shown below where three

horizontal fault lines divide the rectangle into four 2×8 rectangles:

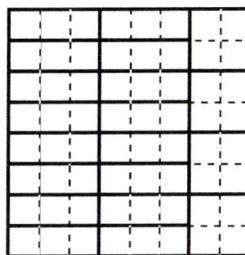

A 2×8 rectangle containing four triominoes and one square can be arranged in 3 ways or the
triominoes can be replaced with three squares, making 4 distinct 2×8 rectangles as shown:

If we imagine that the 8×8 rectangle consists of 4 rows of 2×8 strips, then there are 4^4 distinct
tilings of the 8×8 rectangle using the 2×8 strips. Each tiling has three horizontal fault lines.
Note that this count includes the all-squares case mentioned initially.

We can eliminate one horizontal fault line by replacing two adjacent 2×8 rectangles with one of two possible 4×8 rectangles with no horizontal fault lines as shown:

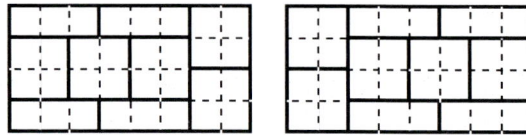

The 4×8 can either be at the top, on the bottom, or in the middle as shown below:

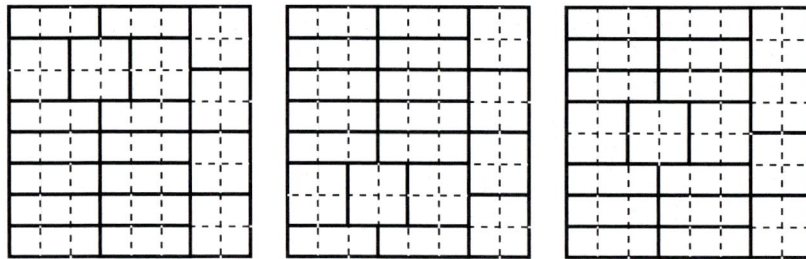

Two horizontal fault lines

In each of these cases, there are two possible orientations for the 4×8 rectangle, and four possibilities for each 2×8 rectangle as shown above, for a total of 32 tilings in each case, making 96 tilings in total.

There are two cases in which there is one horizontal fault line. On the left, the fault line divides the square into two 4×8 rectangles. In the middle, the fault line divides the square into 6×8 and 2×8 rectangles. In the left hand case, there are 2 possibilities for the orientation of each 4×8 sub-rectangle, for a total of 4 tilings. In the middle case there are 16 tilings since there are 2 ways to tile the 6×8 region, 4 ways to tile the 2×8 region, and the 6×8 can either be on top or bottom. In the case where there are no fault lines, shown on the right, there are 2 possibilities since the column of four squares can go on the left or right.

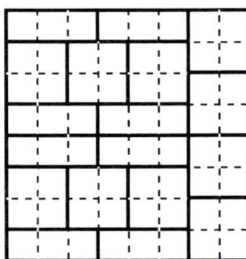

One horizontal fault line   One horizontal fault line   No horizontal fault lines

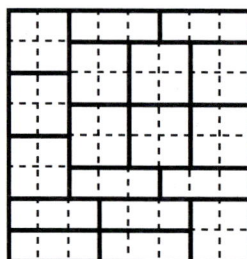

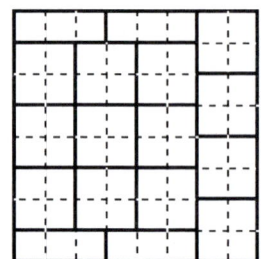

Therefore, the total number of tilings is $256 + 96 + 4 + 16 + 2 = \boxed{374}$.

144

6. a) Looking down the left side of the rectangle, we see a combination of j_1 $u_1 \times v_1$ tiles and j_2 $u_2 \times v_2$ tiles, where j_1 and j_2 are nonnegative integers. Then $(j_1)(u_1) + (j_2)(u_2) = m$ because there are no gaps or overlaps. Therefore, $m \in \langle u_1, u_2 \rangle$. Similarly, looking across gives nonnegative integers k_1 and k_2 such that $(k_1)(v_1) + (k_2)(v_2) = n$, so $n \in \langle v_1, v_2 \rangle$.

   b) A 20×16 rectangle cannot be tiled with tiles of size 3×4 and 5×3, even though $20 = 5 \cdot 3 + 1 \cdot 5 \in \langle 5, 3 \rangle$ and $16 = 1 \cdot 4 + 4 \cdot 3 \in \langle 3, 4 \rangle$. The reason is that the area of each kind of tile is divisible by 3, while the area of the rectangle is 320, which is not divisible by 3.

7. A tiling has complexity 1 if it can be completely tiled with copies of a single tile. This occurs if and only if both $u_1 \mid m$ and $v_1 \mid n$, or both $u_2 \mid m$ and $v_2 \mid n$.

   <u>Proof</u>: Suppose that the tile used is the $u_1 \times v_1$ tile. In that case, looking down the left edge we would see some integer number of tiles, say k, and looking across the top edge, we would see an integer number of tiles, say p. So $u_1 \cdot k = m$ and $v_1 \cdot p = n$, and therefore $u_1 \mid m$ and $v_1 \mid n$. If the tile used was the $u_2 \times v_2$ tile, an analogous argument shows $u_2 \mid m$ and $v_2 \mid n$. Conversely, if $u_1 \mid m$ and $v_1 \mid n$, then there exist integers k and p such that $u_1 \cdot k = m$ and $v_1 \cdot p = n$. Then we can make a strip of k tiles going down the left edge, forming a $u_1 \cdot k \times v_1 = m \times v_1$ rectangle. Note that p of those rectangles can be tiled horizontally to make an $m \times v_1 p = m \times n$ rectangle, thereby covering the $m \times n$ rectangle.

8. For any tiling at all to exist, $m \in \langle u_1, u_2 \rangle$ and $n \in \langle v_1, v_2 \rangle$. A tiling has complexity 2 if the rectangle can be divided into exactly two rectangles, each of which uses one of the two types of tiles. Such a tiling exists if and only if the foregoing condition holds along with either (a) $u_1 \mid m$ and $u_2 \mid m$ or (b) $v_1 \mid n$ and $v_2 \mid n$. We prove case (a); case (b) is analogous. Suppose the rectangle has a tiling of complexity 2. Then the rectangle can be divided into two sub-rectangles covered with copies of different tiles; call the dividing line the *fault line*. The fault line must be either horizontal or vertical; assume it is vertical. This leads to case (a), as we will show. Then we have rectangles R_1 of dimensions $m \times a$ and R_2 of dimensions $m \times b$ such that $a + b = n$ and a and b are integers. Assume without loss of generality that tile 1 is used for R_1 and tile 2 is used for R_2. By problem 7 applied to R_1, $u_1 \mid m$ and $v_1 \mid a$, giving $a = kv_1$ with $k \in \mathbf{Z}^+$. By problem 7 applied to R_2, $u_2 \mid m$ and $v_2 \mid b$, giving $b = pv_1$ with $p \in \mathbf{Z}^+$. Then $a + b = n \rightarrow kv_1 + pv_2 = n \rightarrow n \in \langle v_1, v_2 \rangle$. Conversely, if $u_1, u_2 \mid m$ and $n \in \langle v_1, v_2 \rangle$ then choose nonnegative integers k and p such that $v_1 k + v_2 p = n$. If either k or $p = 0$, then either $v_2 \mid n$ or $v_1 \mid n$ and by problem 7 we can tile the

entire rectangle with a single tile (complexity = 1), so assume that $k, p > 0$. By problem 7, we can create an $m \times v_1 k$ rectangle tiled entirely with $u_1 \times v_1$ tiles and an $m \times v_2 p$ rectangle tiled entirely with $u_2 \times v_2$ tiles. Then placing those rectangles next to each other creates an $m \times (v_1 k + v_2 p)$ rectangle which equals an $m \times n$ rectangle with a tiling of complexity exactly 2.

9.   If neither m nor n is an integer, then R does not contain equal amounts of black and white area.

Proof: Let $r = m - \lfloor m \rfloor$ and $s = n - \lfloor n \rfloor$, and separate R into four rectangles: an $\lfloor m \rfloor \times \lfloor n \rfloor$ rectangle R_1, an $r \times \lfloor n \rfloor$ rectangle R_2, an $\lfloor m \rfloor \times s$ rectangle R_3, and an $r \times s$ rectangle R_4.

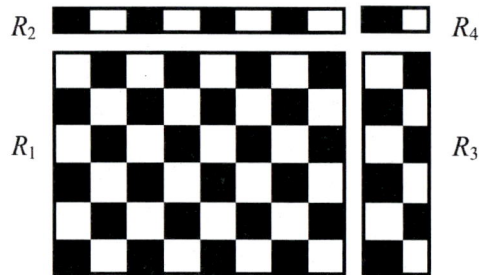

By the lemma, R_1, R_2, and R_3 each contain equal areas of white and black. R_4 does not. If $r, s > \frac{1}{2}$, then R_4 is entirely black; if $r < \frac{1}{2} < s$, then it contains $\frac{r}{2}$ black area and $\left(s - \frac{1}{2}\right) r$ white area, and $s - \frac{1}{2} \neq \frac{1}{2}$ since $s < 1$. If $\frac{1}{2} < r < s$, then it contains $\frac{1}{4}$ black area $+ \left(r - \frac{1}{2}\right)\left(s - \frac{1}{2}\right)$ black area for a total of $rs - \frac{1}{2}(r + s) + \frac{1}{2}$ black area, and $\frac{1}{2}\left(r - \frac{1}{2}\right) + \frac{1}{2}\left(s - \frac{1}{2}\right)$ white area $= \frac{1}{2}(r + s) - \frac{1}{2}$ white area. But if these are equal, then $rs - r - s + 1 = 0 \rightarrow (r - 1)(s - 1) = 0 \rightarrow r = 1$ or $s = 1$, neither of which is possible. On the other hand, by the lemma, every tile will cover equal areas of black and white. Therefore, no combination of those tiles can cover R.

146

10. A tiling of complexity 1 is a tiling that only uses one kind of tile, so either $u_1 \mid m$ and $v_1 \mid n$ or $u_2 \mid m$ and $v_2 \mid n$. So the problem is trivial if R can be tiled using only kind of tile. We prove that if R can *only* be tiled using both kinds of tiles, then R has a tiling of complexity 2. Consider a tiling T of the $m \times n$ rectangle with both $u_1 \times v_1$ and $u_2 \times v_2$ tiles. If only one kind of tile is used, we're done. If not, then scale the rectangle and tiling vertically by a factor of $\dfrac{1}{u_1}$ and horizontally by a factor of $\dfrac{1}{v_2}$, so that we now have a tiling T' of an $\dfrac{m}{u_1} \times \dfrac{n}{v_2}$ rectangle with tiles of size $1 \times \dfrac{v_1}{v_2}$ and $\dfrac{u_1}{u_2} \times 1$. By (8b), one of the dimensions of T' must be an integer, so either $\dfrac{m}{u_1}$ is an integer or $\dfrac{n}{v_2}$ is an integer or both; that is $u_1 \mid m$ or $v_2 \mid n$. An analogous argument shows that $u_2 \mid m$ or $v_1 \mid n$. But because there is no tiling of complexity 1, if $u_1 \mid m$ then v_1 does not divide n, so $u_2 \mid m$. Analogously, if $v_2 \mid n$ then $v_1 \mid n$ also.

The result of problem 10 proves the following surprising result: two tiles will only tile a given rectangle if either (a) one tile alone would suffice or (b) either the length or the width could be tiled with copies of a single tile. If you would have to use a combination of both kinds of tiles to make both the length and the width of the rectangle, then you cannot tile the rectangle with those tiles.

I–1. Line k is parallel to line j and $\angle 1$, $\angle 2$, $\angle 3$ and $\angle 4$ form, in that order, an increasing arithmetic sequence of angles with $m\angle 3 < 90°$. If $m\angle 1 = 50°$, compute the largest possible integer value for the measure of $\angle 4$.

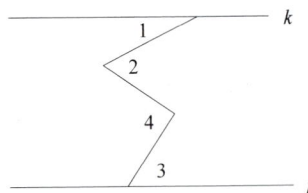

I–2. A positive integer with exactly four positive factors is called "quadly". Compute the least n for which each of n, $n + 1$, and $n + 2$ is quadly.

I–3. Find the sum of the squares of the solutions to $\left| x^2 - x + \dfrac{1}{2008} \right| = \dfrac{1}{2008}$.

I–4. Hexagon $ABCDEF$ is inscribed in circle O and $AB = CD = EF = 2BC = 2ED = 2AF$. If $AD = 8$, compute the perimeter of $ABCDEF$.

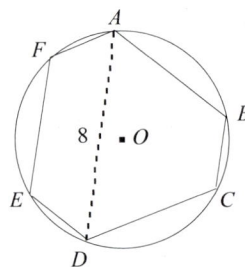

I–5. Rectangle $MNOP$ is gray on the backside, white on the front, and $MN = 2016$. It is folded along lines $\overline{AD}$ and $\overline{BC}$, producing rectangle $ABCD$. Assume $MA > BN$. In $ABCD$, the difference in the areas of the shaded regions equals the area of the non-shaded region of width x. The length of $\overline{MA}$ ranges between a and b with $a < b$. Compute the ordered pair (a, b).

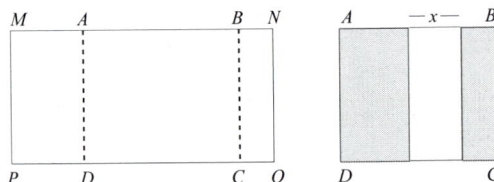

I–6. Let x be in radians with $0 < x < \dfrac{\pi}{2}$. If $\sin(2\sin x) = \cos(2\cos x)$, then $\tan x + \cot x$ can be written as $\dfrac{a}{b - \pi^c}$ where a, b, and c are positive integers. Compute the sum $a + b + c$.

I–7. The equation $\dfrac{\log_{12}\left(\log_8\left(\log_4 x\right)\right)}{\log_5\left(\log_4\left(\log_y\left(\log_2 x\right)\right)\right)} = 0$ has a solution for x when $1 < y < b$, $y \neq a$. Compute the ordered pair (a, b) where b is as large as possible.

I–8. For $k > 1$, let S_k denote the sum of the k consecutive integers starting with k. Compute the smallest value for k such that S_k is a perfect square.

1. 109

2. 33

3. $1\frac{501}{502}$ or the equivalent $\frac{1003}{502}$

4. 24

5. (504, 672)

6. 50

7. (2, 16)

8. 81

I–1.　The measures of the angles are $m\angle 1 \pm 50$, $m\angle 2 \pm 50 = d$, $m\angle 3 \pm 50 = 2d$, and $m\angle 4 \pm 50 = 3d$.

Since $\angle 3$ is acute, $50 + 2d < 90 \to d < 20$. Since $m\angle 4$ is to be an integer, choose $d = 19\frac{2}{3} = \frac{59}{3}$ as

the largest possible value of d. Thus, the largest possible integer value for $m\angle 4$ is $50 + 59 = \boxed{109}$.

Alternately, if $d < 20$, then $m\angle 4 = 50 + 3d < 50 + 60 = 110$, so $m\angle 4 = 109$.

It is interesting to note that it was not necessary to state that $\angle 4$ is the

last term in the arithmetic sequence. By drawing lines parallel to lines

k and m through the vertices of angles 2 and 4, one can see that

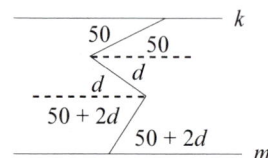

$m\angle 4 \pm d = (50 = 2d) \pm 50 = 3d$.

I–2.　If n is quadly, it must equal either p^3 or pq for distinct primes p and q. Checking p^3 we have the

following triples $(n, n + 1, n + 2)$: $(8, 9, 10)$, $(27, 28, 29)$, and $(125, 126, 127)$. We note that 9, 28, and 126

all fail to have exactly 4 factors. So we try numbers of the form $n = pq$ which lead to the triples $(6, 7, 8)$,

$(10, 11, 12)$, $(14, 15, 16)$, $(15, 16, 17)$, $(21, 22, 23)$, $(22, 23, 24)$, $(26, 27, 28)$, $(33, 34, 35)$, $(34, 35, 36)$. Note

that 7, 11, 16, 17, 23, 24, and 28 all fail to have exactly four factors. But $34 = 2(17)$ and $35 = 5(7)$ both

have exactly 4 factors, so the answer is $\boxed{33}$.

Had we asked for a much larger value of n, this method would not have been satisfactory. A deeper analysis

is called for. First, let $n = p^3$ where p is a prime greater than 3 since we know from the previous analysis

that $p = 2$ or 3 fails. Then $n + 1 = p^3 + 1$ cannot be quadly. The reason is that the even number $p + 1$ is a

factor of $p^3 + 1$, i.e., $p^3 = 1 \pm (p = 1)(p^2 - p = 1)$. This means that $p + 1$ has a factor of 2 and at least

one other prime factor, so by itself $p + 1$ has at least 4 factors. For example, if $p = 7$ then $p + 1$ has

factors 1, 2, 4, and 8. If $p = 5$, then $p + 1$ has factors 1, 2, 3, and 6. In addition, since $p^2 - p + 1 < p + 1$

for $p < 2$, $p^2 - p + 1$ adds at least one more factor and so $n \pm 1$ can't have exactly 4 factors. Thus we

restrict ourselves to numbers of the form $n = pq$. Here $n + 1$ must be even and have divisors 1, 2, r, and $2r$

for r prime, since if $n + 1$ were odd, one of n or $n + 2$ would be divisible by 4, generating a number with

more than 4 factors. Also note that one of $n, n + 1, n + 2$ must be a multiple of 3. So we restrict our search

to consecutive integers of the form $2q$ followed by $3p$ or $3p$ followed by $2q$. Since $2q$ is always the

middle number $n + 1$, $3p$ may equal n or $n + 2$. One can then confirm that $3 \cdot 11, 2 \cdot 17$, and $5 \cdot 7$ form

the least possible desired sequence. The next triple is $(85, 86, 87)$.

I–3.　There are two cases: (i) $x^2 - x + \frac{1}{2008} = \frac{1}{2008} \to x^2 - x = 0 \to x = 0$ or 1. In (ii) we have

$x^2 - x + \frac{1}{2008} = -\frac{1}{2008} \to x^2 - x + \frac{1}{1004} = 0$. To obtain the sum of the squares of the roots without

finding the roots, let the roots be p and q. We have $pq = \frac{1}{1004}$ and $p + q = 1 \to p^2 + 2pq + q^2 = 1$.

Thus, $p^2 + q^2 = 1 - \dfrac{1}{502} = \dfrac{501}{502}$. Since the sum of the squares of the roots of the other equation is 1, the

sum of the squares of all four roots is $1 + \dfrac{501}{502} = \boxed{1\dfrac{501}{502} = \dfrac{1003}{502}}$.

I–4.   Inscribe equilateral triangle AEC as shown. By Ptolemy's Theorem on inscribed quadrilateral $AEDC$, $AD \cdot EC = AE \cdot DC + ED \cdot AC$. Since $AE = EC = AC$, we have $AD \cdot EC = EC(DC + ED)$ giving $AD = ED + DC$. Thus the perimeter of $ABCDEF$ is $3 \cdot 8 = \boxed{24}$.

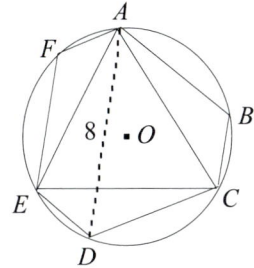

Alternate solution #1: Draw chord $\overline{CF}$. Since $m\overset{\frown}{AF} = m\overset{\frown}{DE}$, $\overline{AD} \parallel \overline{FE}$. Since $m\overset{\frown}{FE} = m\overset{\frown}{CD}$, $\overline{CF} \parallel \overline{DE}$. Thus $DEFP$ is a parallelogram, giving $DE = PF$ and $EF = DP$. Likewise $ABCP$ is a parallelogram, so $BC = AP$. Since $BC = DE = AF$ we have $8 = AD = AP + PD = BC + EF = DE + EF$. The perimeter is $3(DE + EF) = 24$.

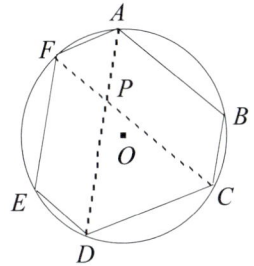

Alternate solution #2: Extend $\overline{AB}$ and $\overline{DC}$ to meet at G. $ABCDEF$ is equiangular since any two adjacent sides subtend a $240°$ angle, so the measure of each angle of the hexagon is $120°$. Thus, exterior angles $\angle CBG$ and $\angle BCG$ measure $60°$ so $\triangle BCG$ is equilateral, making $BG = CG = x$. Since $m\angle G = 60°$ and $AG = DG = 3x$, $\triangle AGD$ is equilateral, making $3x = 8$. The perimeter of the hexagon is $9x$ and that equals 24.

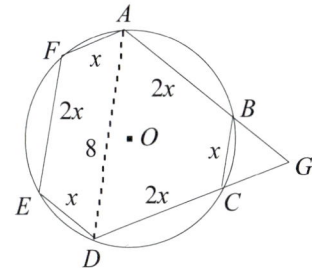

I–5.   From $2y + x + 2z = 2016$ and $y - z = x$, we obtain $3y + z = 2016$. If z decreases, then y increases implying that $3y$ approaches 2016. Thus, $y < \dfrac{2016}{3} = 672$. If z increases, y decreases and they approach each other. But since $y < z$, $4y < 2016$, making $y > \dfrac{2016}{4} = 504$. Thus, $504 < MA < 672$. Answer: $\boxed{(504, 672)}$.

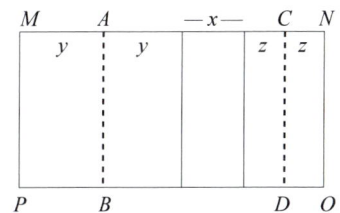

I–6.   If it were the case that $0 < 2\sin x < \dfrac{\pi}{2}$ and $0 < 2\cos x < \dfrac{\pi}{2}$, then we'd have $2\sin x = \dfrac{\pi}{2} - 2\cos x \;\rightarrow$

$(\sin x + \cos x)^2 = \left(\dfrac{\pi}{4}\right)^2 \;\rightarrow\; 1 + 2\sin x \cos x = \dfrac{\pi^2}{16}$. Thus $2\sin x \cos x = \dfrac{\pi^2 - 16}{16}$, but that's impossible since the product can't be negative if $\sin x$ and $\cos x$ lie in $\left(0, \frac{\pi}{2}\right)$. So, one of $2\sin x$ or $2\cos x$ must be

greater than $\frac{\pi}{2}$. It can't be $2\cos x$ because then $\cos(2\cos x) < 0$ while $\sin(2\sin x) > 0$.

So we must have $\frac{\pi}{2} < 2\sin x < \pi$ and $0 < 2\cos x < \frac{\pi}{2}$. For

$\sin(2\sin x)$ to equal $\cos(2\cos x)$, angles $2\sin x$ and $2\cos x$ must differ

by $\frac{\pi}{2}$ as shown in the unit circle at the right where $\beta = 2\sin x$ and

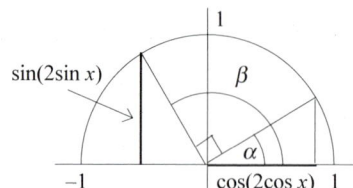

$\alpha = 2\cos x$. Thus, $2\sin x - 2\cos x = \frac{\pi}{2}$ → $(\sin x - \cos x)^2 = \left(\frac{\pi}{4}\right)^2$ → $1 - 2\sin x \cos x = \frac{\pi^2}{16}$ →

$\sin x \cos x = \frac{16 - \pi^2}{32}$. Since $\tan x + \cot x = \frac{\sin x}{\cos x} + \frac{\cos x}{\sin x} = \frac{1}{\sin x \cos x}$, then $\tan x + \cot x = \frac{32}{16 - \pi^2}$ and

$(a, b, c) = (32, 16, 2)$. Thus $a + b + c = \boxed{50}$.

I–7. The equation will have a solution for those values of x for which the numerator equals 0 and the denominator is defined but is not equal to 0.

i) The numerator is 0 if $\log_{12}\left(\log_8\left(\log_4 x\right)\right) = 0$ → $\log_8\left(\log_4 x\right) = 1$ → $\log_4 x = 8$ → $x = 4^8 = 2^{16}$.

ii) The denominator is not equal to 0 if $\log_5\left(\log_4\left(\log_y\left(\log_2 x\right)\right)\right) \ne 0$ → $\log_4\left(\log_y\left(\log_2 x\right)\right) \ne 1$ →

$\log_y\left(\log_2 2^{16}\right) \ne 4$ → $\log_y 16 \ne 4$ → $y \ne 2$. We are asked for a such that $y \ne a$. Clearly, $a = 2$.

iii) The denominator is defined if and only if $\log_4\left(\log_y\left(\log_2 x\right)\right) > 0$ → $\log_y\left(\log_2 2^{16}\right) > 1$ → $16 > y$.

We are asked for solutions for x when $1 < y < b$ and b is as large as possible. Thus $b = 16$. Ans: $\boxed{(2, 16)}$.

I–8. We have $S_k = k + (k + 1) + \cdots + (2k - 1) = \frac{k(3k - 1)}{2}$. Note that k and $3k - 1$ are relatively prime to

each other. For S_k to be a perfect square, either (i) both $\frac{k}{2}$ and $3k - 1$ are perfect squares or (ii) both k and

$\frac{3k - 1}{2}$ are perfect squares. In (i) we set $k = 2a^2$ and $3k - 1 = b^2$ for some positive integers a and b.

From $3k = 6a^2$, we obtain $6a^2 - 1 = b^2$ → $6a^2 - b^2 = 1$. Considering $6a^2 - b^2 = 1$ modulo 3, we

have $b^2 \equiv -1 \pmod 3$ which is impossible. In (ii) we set $k = a^2$ and $3k - 1 = 2b^2$ for some integers

a and b. From $3k = 3a^2$ we obtain $3a^2 - 1 = 2b^2$. It is clear that a must be odd because the difference

of an even number and 1 can't be even. Also, $a > 1$ since $k > 1$. Setting $a = 3, 5, 7,$ and 9, respectively,

we obtain $2b^2 = 26, 74, 146,$ and 242, respectively. The first solution occurs when $a = 9$, making

$b^2 = 121$ → $b = 11$. The smallest value of k for which S_k is a perfect square is $k = 9^2 = \boxed{81}$.

R1–1. *ABCD* is a parallelogram, *M* is the midpoint of $\overline{DC}$,

$AP = 65$, and $PM = 30$. Compute the largest possible

integer value for *AB*.

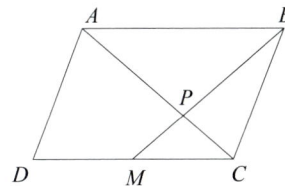

R1–2. Let T = TNYWR. If $x^2 + x + 1 = \dfrac{T}{x-1}$, compute the real value of x.

R1–3. Let T = TNYWR. In $\triangle ABC$, $AB = 3$, $AC = 4$, and

$BC = 5$. If the ratio of the area of $\triangle ABD$ to the area of

$\triangle ADC$ equals $\dfrac{1}{T}$, compute $\tan \angle BAD$.

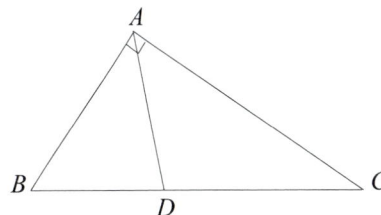

R2–1. Compute the smallest integer that equals both the sum of four consecutive positive integers and the product of three consecutive integers.

R2–2. Let T = TNYWR. Shown is a long snakelike figure of height 3 ending at $x = \dfrac{T}{2}$. Compute the perimeter of the figure.

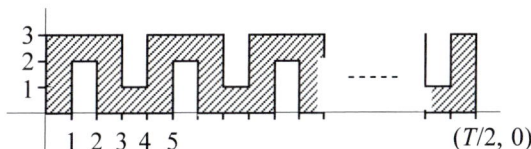

R2–3. Let T = TNYWR. Let f be a quadratic function with $f(1) = 112$ and $f(4) = T$. Compute $f(3) - f(2)$.

Relay #1:

R1–1. 124

R1–2. 5

R1–3. $\dfrac{4}{15}$ or the equivalent $.2\overline{6}$

Relay #2:

R2–1. 210

R2–2. 424

R2–3. 104

R1–1.   Since $ABCD$ is a parallelogram and $MC = \dfrac{1}{2}AB$,

$\triangle APB \sim \triangle CPM$ with a scale factor of $2:1$. Since $PM = 30$, then $PB = 60$. By the triangle inequality theorem on triangle APB, $AP + PB > AB \rightarrow 60 + 65 > AB$. The largest possible integral value of AB is therefore $\boxed{124}$.

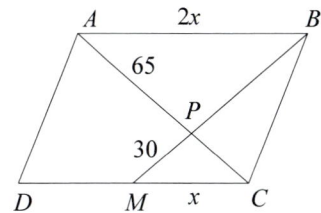

R1–2. $T = 124$. From $x^2 + x + 1 = \dfrac{T}{x-1}$ we obtain $(x-1)(x^2+x+1) = T \rightarrow x^3 - 1 = T$.

Thus $x^3 = T + 1 \rightarrow x^3 \pm 124 = 1 \pm 125$, so $x = \boxed{5}$.

R1–3. $T = 5$. Since the ratio of the area of $\triangle ABD$ to the area of

$\triangle ADC$ equals $\dfrac{1}{T}$, then $\dfrac{.5(AB)(AD)\sin\theta}{.5(AD)(AC)\sin(90°-\theta)} = \dfrac{1}{T}$.

Canceling AD and substituting gives $\dfrac{3\sin\theta}{4\cos\theta} = \dfrac{1}{T} \rightarrow$

$\tan\theta = \dfrac{4}{3T}$. Thus, $\tan\angle BAD = \boxed{\dfrac{4}{15}}$.

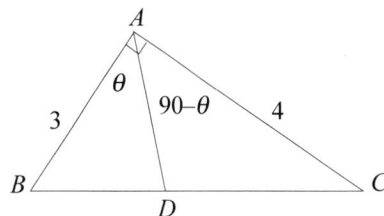

R2–1.   Since $n = k + (k+1) + (k+2) + (k+3) = 4k + 6$, the sum of four consecutive positive integers is at least 10 and cannot be a multiple of 4. Thus, the product of the three consecutive integers cannot be a multiple of 4. The smallest possible case is $5 \cdot 6 \cdot 7 = 210$. Setting $4k + 6 = 210 \rightarrow k = 51$, giving $51 + 52 + 53 + 54 = 210$. Answer: $\boxed{210}$.

R2–2. $T = 210$. The top horizontal segments add to a length of $T/2$ as do the bottom horizontal segments. The two end vertical segments equal 3 each. The other vertical segments have a

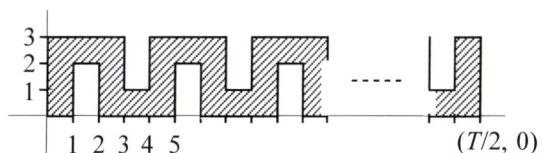

length of 2 and there are $T/2 - 1$ of those. The total perimeter $P = 6 + 2(T/2) + 2(T/2 - 1) = 2T + 4$. Thus $P = 2(210) + 4 = \boxed{424}$.

R2–3. $T = 424$. Let $f(x) = ax^2 + bx + c$. Then $f(4) - f(1) = (16a + 4b + c) - (a + b + c) = 15a + 3b$

while $f(3) - f(2) = (9a + 3b + c) - (4a + 2b + c) = 5a + b$. Thus, for any quadratic function,

$\dfrac{f(4) - f(1)}{3} = f(3) - f(2)$. Here, $f(3) - f(2) = \dfrac{T - 112}{3} = \dfrac{424 - 112}{3} = \boxed{104}$.

155

1. Find the smallest positive prime factor of $1 + 2 \cdot 2008 + 2008^2$.

2. Let T = TNYWR. Square $ABCD$ has an area of 49. Point P lies inside the square so that the area of $\triangle PCD$ is $2T$. Compute the distance from P to $\overline{AB}$.

3. Let T = TNYWR. Simplify $\dfrac{\sqrt{2^{30+2T}} \cdot \sqrt{2^{-10-T^2}}}{\sqrt{4^{T+5}}}$.

4. Let T = TNYWR. In the complex plane, points z_1, z_2, z_3, and z_4 are the vertices of a square whose center is at the origin. The sides of the square are parallel to the coordinate axes and the side length is T. Compute the product $z_1 \cdot z_2 \cdot z_3 \cdot z_4$.

5. Let T = TNYWR. Compute the value of K such that $\log_{2T}(4T)$, $\log_{\sqrt{2}} 8$, and $\log_3 9^{K-T}$ are consecutive terms of a geometric sequence.

6. Let T = TNYWR. Compute the number of integers x that satisfy the following system of inequalities: $x^2 > x + 6$ and $|x| < T^2$.

7. Let T = TNYWR. A large fruit basket has an unlimited supply of apricots, raisins, mangoes, and lemons. Compute the smallest value of K so that any selection of K pieces of fruit has at least one of the following: i) 1001 apricots, ii) 2008 raisins, iii) 220 mangoes, or iv) T lemons.

8. Let M be the sum of the digits of the number you received from position 7 and let N be the sum of the digits of the number you received from position 9. Define the sequence $a_1, a_2, a_3, \ldots$ by $a_1 = M$, $a_2 = N$, and for $k \geq 3$, $a_k \pm a_{k-1} = 2a_{k-2}$. Compute the smallest value of k such that $a_k > 2008$.

156

15.   A cube has a surface area of A and a volume of $8A$. Find the length of an edge of the cube.

14.   Let T = TNYWR. Find the smallest positive value of b so that the ellipse defined

     by $\dfrac{x^2}{T} + \dfrac{y^2}{b^2} = 1$ is similar to the ellipse defined by $\dfrac{x^2}{9} + \dfrac{y^2}{27} = 1$.

13.   Let T = TNYWR. Find the sum of the reciprocals of the three roots of the equation

     $x^3 - Tx^2 = 10x \pm 12$.

12.   Let T = TNYWR. Find the least common multiple of 10, 25, and $6T$.

11.   Let T = TNYWR. Let x be in radians. If $f(x) = \sin\left(\dfrac{2x}{T}\right)$, $g(x) = \cos\left(\dfrac{Tx}{2008}\right)$, and

     $h(x) = \tan\left(\dfrac{x}{2T}\right)$, let the periods of f, g, and h be p, q, and r respectively.

     Compute $\max \{p, q, r\}$.

10.   Let T = TNYWR. A circle is centered at the origin and has area T. Let $A = (2006,0)$,

     $B = (2008,0)$, and let $C = (x,y)$ be a point on the circle such that the area of $\triangle ABC$ is 2.

     Compute the smallest possible value of x.

9.   Let T = TNYWR and let $K = T^2$. Let S be the increasing sequence of four-digit numbers with

     distinct digits chosen from the set $\{1, 3, 5, 7, 9\}$. Find the Kth term of S.

8.   Let M be the sum of the digits of the number you received from position 7 and let N be the sum of

     the digits of the number you received from position 9. Define the sequence $a_1, a_2, a_3, \ldots$

     by $a_1 = M$, $a_2 = N$, and for $k \geq 3$, $a_k = a_{k-1} + 2a_{k-2}$. Compute the smallest value of k

     such that $a_k > 2008$.

1. 7

2. 3

3. $\sqrt{2}$

4. 1

5. 10

6. 193

7. 3419

----

15. 48

14. 4

13. $\dfrac{5}{6}$

12. 50

11. 100π

10. $-4\sqrt{6}$

9. 7953

8. 9

1. $2008^2 + 2 \cdot 2008 + 1 = (2008 + 1)^2 = 2009^2 = (7 \cdot 7 \cdot 41)^2$. Ans: $\boxed{7}$.

2. Area of $PDC = \dfrac{1}{2} x \cdot 7 = 2T \rightarrow x = \dfrac{4T}{7}$. $PE = 7 - x = 7 - \dfrac{4T}{7}$.

   Since $T = 7$, $PE = 7 - 4 = \boxed{3}$.

   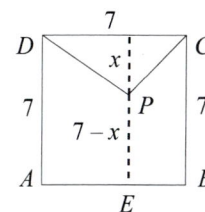

3. $\dfrac{\sqrt{2^{30=2T}} \cdot \sqrt{2^{-10-T^2}}}{\sqrt{4^{T=5}}} \pm \dfrac{2^{T=15} \cdot 2^{-5-T^2/2}}{2^{T=5}} \pm 2^{(-T^2/2)=5}$. Since $T = 3$ we have $2^{-9/2+5} = \boxed{\sqrt{2}}$.

4. Without loss of generality, let $z_1 = \dfrac{T}{2} + \dfrac{T}{2}i$, $z_2 = -\dfrac{T}{2} + \dfrac{T}{2}i$, $z_3 = -\dfrac{T}{2} - \dfrac{T}{2}i$,

   and $z_4 = \dfrac{T}{2} - \dfrac{T}{2}i$. Then $\left(z_1 \cdot z_4\right)\left(z_2 \cdot z_3\right) = \left(\dfrac{T^2}{4} + \dfrac{T^2}{4}\right)\left(\dfrac{T^2}{4} + \dfrac{T^2}{4}\right) = \dfrac{T^4}{4}$.

   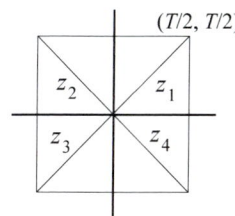

   Since $T = \sqrt{2}$, then $\dfrac{T^4}{4} = \boxed{1}$.

5. $\log_{\sqrt{2}} 8 = 6$ and $\log_3 3^{(2K-2T)} = 2K - 2T$. So $\dfrac{2K - 2T}{6} = \dfrac{6}{\log_{2T}(4T)} \rightarrow K = \dfrac{18}{\log_{2T}(4T)} + T$.

   Since $T = 1$, $K = \dfrac{18}{\log_2 4} + 1 = 9 + 1 = \boxed{10}$.

6. $x^2 - x - 6 > 0 \rightarrow (x - 3)(x + 2) > 0 \rightarrow x < -2$ or $x > 3$. $|x| < T^2 \rightarrow -T^2 < x < T^2$. Since $T = 10$,

   $-100 < x < 100$. Thus, $x \in \{-99, -98, \ldots -4, -3, 4, 5, \ldots, 98, 99\}$. There are $(-3 - -99 + 1)$ plus

   $(99 - 4 + 1) = 97 + 96$ integers in the set. Total: $\boxed{193}$.

7. If we have chosen 1000 apricots, 2007 raisins, 219 mangoes, and $T - 1$ lemons, then the next piece of fruit

   chosen will give us one of 1001 apricots, 2008 raisins, 220 mangoes, or T lemons. Thus, the smallest value of

   K is $1000 + 2007 + 219 + T - 1 + 1 = 3226 + T$. Since $T = 193$, $K = 3226 + 193 = \boxed{3419}$.

   ----

15. Let x be the edge of the cube. Then $6x^2 = A$ and $x^3 = 8A \rightarrow \dfrac{x^3}{6x^2} = \dfrac{8A}{A} \rightarrow \dfrac{x}{6} = 8$. Thus, $x = \boxed{48}$.

14. The ellipses will be similar if $\dfrac{T}{b^2} = \dfrac{9}{27} = \dfrac{1}{3}$, giving $b^2 = 3T$. They will also be similar if $\dfrac{T}{b^2} = \dfrac{27}{9} = 3$,

   giving $b^2 = \dfrac{T}{3}$. The latter gives the smaller value for b. Thus, since $T = 48$, $b^2 = 16 \rightarrow b = \boxed{4}$.

13. The roots of the equation $-12x^3 = 10x^2 - Tx = 1 \pm 0$ are the reciprocals of the roots of the equation $x^3 - Tx^2 = 10x - 12 \pm 0$. The sum of the roots of the first equation is $-\dfrac{10}{-12} = \boxed{\dfrac{5}{6}}$. In this problem the value of T is irrelevant.

12. The least common multiple of $2 \cdot 5$, $5 \cdot 5$, and $2 \cdot 3 \cdot T$ must contain factors of 2, 5, 5, and could contain a factor of 3, depending on the value of T. Since $T = 5/6$, the question asks for the LCM of $2 \cdot 5$, $5 \cdot 5$, and 5 and that is $\boxed{50}$.

11. The period of f is $\dfrac{2\pi}{\dfrac{2}{|T|}} = \pi|T|$, the period of g is $\dfrac{2\pi}{\dfrac{|T|}{2008}} = \dfrac{4016\pi}{|T|}$, the period of h is $\dfrac{\pi}{\dfrac{1}{2|T|}} = 2\pi|T|$.

   Thus, we need only compare the periods of g and h to find the largest. Setting $\dfrac{4016\pi}{|T|} = 2\pi|T|$ gives

   $T^2 = 2008 \to T \approx 45$. If $T > 45$, then $\dfrac{4016\pi}{T}$ is the larger and if $T > 45$, then $2\pi T$ is the larger. Since $T = 50$, $2\pi T = \boxed{100\pi}$ is larger.

10. Since $\pi r^2 = T$, then $r^2 = \dfrac{T}{\pi}$. Since $AB = 2$, the height y of $\triangle ABC$ equals 2, giving $r^2 - x^2 = 2^2 \to \dfrac{T}{\pi} - 4 = x^2$. Since $T = 100\pi$, $x^2 = 96 \to$ the smallest possible value of x is $\boxed{-4\sqrt{6}}$.

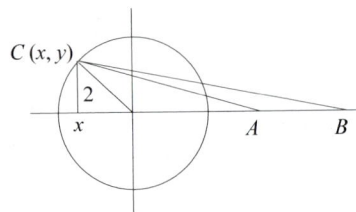

9. Since $K = T^2$, $K = 96$. If we choose one of the five numbers as the digit in the thousands place, then we can choose the other 3 digits in ${}_4C_3 = 4$ ways and they can be arranged to make 3! different five-digit numbers. Thus, there are 4! = 24 five-digit numbers starting with each digit in turn. The 96th term is therefore the last term of the sequence with a thousands digit of 7. It will be $\boxed{7953}$.

8. Position 7 sends 3419 to position 8 so $M = 17$. Position 9 sends 7953 to position 8, so $N = 24$. Thus,

   $a_1 = 17$, $a_2 = 24$, $a_3 = 24 + 2 \cdot 17 = 58$, $a_4 = 58 + 2 \cdot 24 = 106$, $a_5 = 106 + 2 \cdot 58 = 222$,

   $a_6 = 222 + 2 \cdot 106 = 434$, $a_7 = 434 + 2 \cdot 222 = 878$, $a_8 = 878 + 2 \cdot 434 = 1746$,

   $a_9 = 1746 + 2 \cdot 878 = 3502 > 2008$, so a_k is first greater than 2008 for $k = \boxed{9}$.

   Note: more generally, we have $a_1 \pm M$, $a_2 \pm N$, $a_3 \pm N = 2M$, $a_4 \pm 2M = 3N$, $a_5 \pm 6M = 5N$,

   $a_6 = 10M + 11N$, $a_7 = 22M + 21N$, $a_8 = 42M + 43N$, $a_9 = 86M + 85N, \ldots$. Since the coefficients of

   M and N are nearly equal, compute $\dfrac{2008}{M+N} = \dfrac{2008}{41} \approx 48.975$. Since $43(N+M) < 2008$ and

   $85(M+N) > 2008$, the desired term is a_9.

160

1. In $\triangle ABC$, points P_1 and P_2 trisect $\overline{AB}$, points $Q_1, \ldots, Q_6$ divide $\overline{BC}$ into seven equal parts, and points $R_1, \ldots, R_8$ divide $\overline{AC}$ into nine equal parts. The segments $\overline{AQ_1}, \ldots, \overline{AQ_6}$, $\overline{BR_1}, \ldots, \overline{BR_8}$, $\overline{CP_1}$, and $\overline{CP_2}$ divide $\triangle ABC$ into K disjoint regions. Compute K.

2. The graph of $y^2 + \sqrt{\left(25 - x^2\right)\left(5 - x\right)^2} = y\left(\sqrt{25 - x^2} + \sqrt{\left(5 - x\right)^2}\right)$ divides the xy-plane into a number of regions, one of which has finite area A. Compute A.

3. *ABCDEF* and *ABMNOP* are regular hexagons of side length 1. Compute the area of quadrilateral *PNCE*.

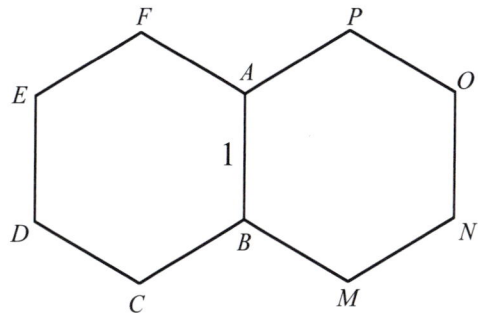

1. The 6 lines to $\overline{BC}$ partition $\triangle ABC$ into 7 regions. The 8 lines to $\overline{AC}$ create 9 new regions for each line to $\overline{BC}$. Thus, after these two sets of lines are drawn, $\triangle ABC$ is divided into 63 regions. Each of the 2 lines to $\overline{AB}$ crosses the 6 lines from A and the 8 lines from B, so each creates $6 + 8 + 1 = 15$ new regions, provided that there are no triple intersections, i.e., no cases where the lines to $\overline{AB}$, $\overline{BC}$, and $\overline{AC}$ are concurrent. For each triple intersection we lose a region. If the number of triple intersections is T, the overall number of regions is $7 \cdot 9 + 15 \cdot 2 - T = 93 - T$. Ceva's Theorem allows us to compute T. Without loss of generality, assume that the sides of ABC are 3, 7, and 9 in length and that the interior segments intersect the sides at points that are spaced 1 unit apart. Thus, the values of r, q, and p will be integers with $r \in \{1, 2\}$, $q \in \{1, 2, 3, 4, 5, 6, 7, 8\}$ and $p \in \{1, 2, 3, 4, 5, 6\}$.

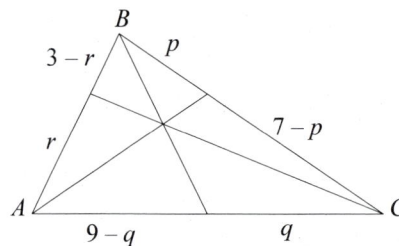

Ceva's Theorem states that three interior lines drawn from the vertices are concurrent if and only if $\left(\dfrac{3-r}{r}\right)\left(\dfrac{9-q}{q}\right)\left(\dfrac{7-p}{p}\right) = 1$. For each ordered triple (r, q, p) satisfying that equation, our line segments are concurrent and we lose a region. If $r = 1$ we have $\left(\dfrac{9-q}{q}\right)\left(\dfrac{7-p}{p}\right) = \dfrac{1}{2}$ and if $r = 2$, we have $\left(\dfrac{9-q}{q}\right)\left(\dfrac{7-p}{p}\right) = 2$. In either case, note that $\dfrac{9-q}{q}$ simplifies to $8, \dfrac{7}{2}, 2, \dfrac{5}{4}, \dfrac{4}{5}, \dfrac{1}{2}, \dfrac{2}{7}$, and $\dfrac{1}{8}$ respectively, and $\dfrac{7-p}{p}$ simplifies to $6, \dfrac{5}{2}, \dfrac{4}{3}, \dfrac{3}{4}, \dfrac{2}{5}$, and $\dfrac{1}{6}$ respectively. Since the values of $\dfrac{9-q}{q}$ contain no multiples of 3 while many of the values of $\dfrac{7-p}{p}$ do, we can only obtain a product of 2 or $\dfrac{1}{2}$ for values of $\dfrac{7-p}{p}$ that do not contain a multiple of 3. Thus, $p = 2$ or 5. If $p = 2$ and $r = 2$, then $\dfrac{9-q}{q} \cdot \dfrac{7-2}{2} = 2 \rightarrow \dfrac{9-q}{q} = \dfrac{4}{5}$, true for $q = 5$, giving $(r, q, p) = (2, 5, 2)$. If $p = 2$ and $r = 1$, $\dfrac{9-q}{q} \cdot \dfrac{7-2}{2} = \dfrac{1}{2} \rightarrow \dfrac{9-q}{q} = \dfrac{1}{5}$ and there is no value of q giving that. If $p = 5$ and $r = 1$, then $\dfrac{9-q}{q} \cdot \dfrac{7-5}{5} = \dfrac{1}{2} \rightarrow$ $\dfrac{9-q}{q} = \dfrac{5}{4}$, true for $q = 4$, giving $(r, q, p) = (1, 4, 5)$. There is no value of q that gives a product of 2. We have two solutions: $(r, q, p) = (2, 5, 2)$ or $(1, 4, 5)$. Thus there are two instances where the cevians are concurrent, making $T = 2$, and the number of regions equals $93 - 2 = \boxed{91}$.

2. $y^2 + \sqrt{(25 - x^2)(5 - x)^2} = y\left(\sqrt{25 - x^2} + \sqrt{(5 - x)^2} \right) \rightarrow$

$y^2 - \left(\sqrt{25 - x^2} + \sqrt{(5 - x)^2} \right) y + \sqrt{(25 - x^2)}\sqrt{(5 - x)^2} = 0$.

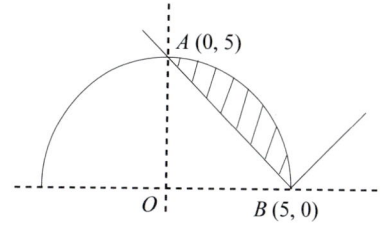

This factors as $\left(y - \sqrt{25 - x^2} \right)\left(y - \sqrt{(5 - x)^2} \right) = 0$. Since $\sqrt{(5 - x)^2} = |x - 5|$ we have

$\left(y - \sqrt{25 - x^2} \right)\left(y - |x - 5| \right) = 0 \rightarrow y = \sqrt{25 - x^2}$ or $y = |x - 5|$. The graph is shown above.

The region with finite area is the segment AB of a circle with radius 5. Its area is the

area of sector AOB − the area of $\triangle AOB = \dfrac{1}{4} \cdot 25\pi - \dfrac{1}{2} \cdot 5 \cdot 5 = \boxed{\dfrac{25\pi}{4} - \dfrac{25}{2}}$.

3. Since $\overline{EP}$ and $\overline{FA}$ intersect at their midpoint G, and
$\overline{CN}$ and $\overline{BM}$ intersect at their midpoint H, then
$\triangle EFG \cong \triangle PAG \cong \triangle CBH \cong \triangle NMH$. Let x be the
area of each. Let y be the area of $\triangle EDC$ and $\triangle PON$;
let z be the area of $EGABC$ and $NHBAP$. Thus, the

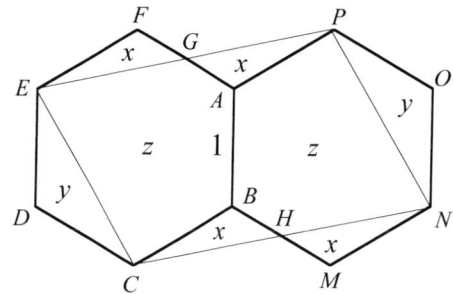

area of $PNCE = 2z + 2x$. Since the area of each hexagon is $x + y + z$, the area of $PNCE$ equals

the area of the hexagons minus $2y$. Each hexagon can be broken up into 6 equilateral triangles of

side 1 whose area is $\dfrac{1^2\sqrt{3}}{4}$ and the area y of $\triangle EDC$ equals $\dfrac{1}{2} \cdot 1 \cdot 1 \cdot \sin 120° = \dfrac{1}{2} \cdot \dfrac{\sqrt{3}}{2}$. This

gives $2\left(6 \cdot \dfrac{1^2\sqrt{3}}{4} \right) - 2 \cdot \dfrac{1}{2} \cdot \dfrac{\sqrt{3}}{2} = \boxed{\dfrac{5\sqrt{3}}{2}}$.

Don Barry, head author from 1995 to 2008, is on the left.

Marty Badoian, Vice President of ARML and a long-time coach, is on the right.

ARML
LOCAL
2008

This contest is designed to offer schools an opportunity to either practice for ARML or to take part in a contest similar to ARML at a local site. A team consists of up to 6 students. The local site administrator downloads the problems on the date of the contest, administers the test, corrects the problems, and emails back the team's results. The answers to all problems are numerical, there are no proofs to correct.

ARML Local consists of four parts, none of which allowed calculators in 2008.

The <u>Team Round</u> consists of 10 questions. The team of students works together for 40 minutes to find the answers to the problems.

The <u>Theme Round</u> takes 60 minutes and consists of around ten questions based on a common topic. Unlike the Power Question at ARML, the Theme Round does not involve proof. The reason for this is that it would be impossible to ensure consistency of grading across so many different sites.

The <u>Individual Round</u> consists of 10 questions given in pairs with 10 minutes allowed for each pair.

The <u>Relay Rounds</u> depart from the approach used at ARML to some degree by taking advantage of the fact that teams consist of 6 members. First of all, there are three rounds not two. Secondly, the first relay is for three teams of two, the second is for two teams of three, and the third is for one team of all six students. The times allotted for the relays are 6, 8, and 10 minutes respectively.

More information about the contest is available at http://arml.com/arml_local/

1. Compute the smallest six-digit number with distinct digits that is a multiple of 11.

2. The set of points (x,y) such that $|x-3| \le y \le 4 - |x-1|$ defines a region in the xy-plane. Compute the area of this region.

3. Let r and s be the solutions to $2x^2 - 3x = 11$. Compute the value of $\left(4r^3 - 4s^3\right)(r-s)^{-1}$.

4. A regular octagon with sides of length 1 has 20 diagonals. Compute the sum of the <u>squares</u> of the lengths of these diagonals.

5. Two points are chosen randomly from the border of a 3 x 3 square grid. Compute the probability that the line segment between the two points intersects at most three of the 1 x 1 subsquares. In the examples shown to the right, $\overline{AB}$ and $\overline{BC}$ each intersect three subsquares and $\overline{AC}$ intersects five.

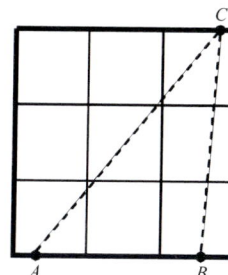

6. Given that $\log_{10} 2 \approx 0.3010$, $\log_{10} 3 \approx 0.4771$, $\log_{10} 5 \approx 0.6990$, and $\log_{10} 7 \approx 0.8451$ compute the leftmost digit in the base-10 representation of 5^{200}.

7. A circle with radius 5 and center (a,b) is tangent to the lines $y = 6$ and $y = 0.75x$. Compute the largest possible value of $a + b$.

8. A deck of seven cards numbered 0 to 6 are shuffled randomly and the following game is played. A card is turned face-up. If the card is a zero, the player loses. If the card is $k > 0$, then the next k cards in the deck are discarded facedown (or all of the cards, if fewer than k remain). The process is repeated until either a zero is turned face-up (a loss) or all of the cards are either turned up or discarded (a win). Compute the probability that the player wins.

9. Fifty light switches, labeled 1 to 50, are all initially set to off. Consider the 50-step process that proceeds as follows. On step k, if k is prime, then every light switch labeled with a multiple of k is switched from on to off, or vice versa. If k is not prime, do nothing. Compute the number of light switches that are on at the end of the process.

10. A pocketless, frictionless, rectangular billiard table with corners $ABCD$ has side le1 $AB = 3$ feet and $BC = 8$ feet. A particle is fired from corner A at a random angle i1 table. When the particle hits a wall, it leaves the wall at the same angle. Consider statement: "The probability that the particle hits at least k walls prior to hitting $\overline{AB}$ the first time is at least ½." Compute the maximum integer value for k such that th statement is true.

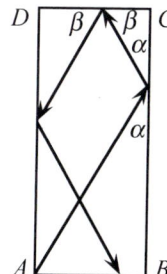

1. Noting that 1023 is a multiple of eleven, all six-digit numbers of the form $1023xy$ will be multiples of eleven if and only if $x = y$. Accordingly, one should next look at numbers of the form $1024xy$. Using a well-known test for divisibility by eleven, $1024xy$ is a multiple of eleven provided $1 + 2 + x = 0 + 4 + y$ or $x = y + 1$. Therefore, the smallest multiple of eleven with distinct digits is $\boxed{102465}$.

2. The graphs of the two functions $y = |x - 3|$ and $y = 4 - |x - 1|$ are shown to the right. The region is a rectangle with side lengths of $\sqrt{2}$ and $3\sqrt{2}$. Therefore, the area is $\boxed{6}$.

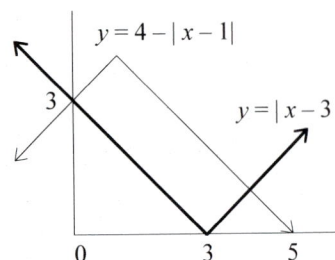

3. Rewriting the equation as $2x^2 - 3x - 11 = 0$, the product of the roots rs is $-11/2$ and the sum of the roots $r + s$ is $3/2$. Thus,

$$\left(4r^3 - 4s^3\right)(r - s)^{-1} = 4\left(r^3 - s^3\right)(r - s)^{-1} = 4(r - s)\left(r^2 + rs + s^2\right)(r - s)^{-1} =$$

$$4\left(r^2 + 2rs + s^2 - rs\right) = 4\left((r + s)^2 - rs\right) = 4\left((3/2)^2 + 11/2\right) = 4(31/4) = \boxed{31}.$$

4. By symmetry, we are interested in $8 \cdot AD^2 + 8 \cdot AC^2 + 4 \cdot AE^2$. If F and G are the bases of the perpendiculars dropped from B and C to $\overline{AD}$, then $AF = CG = \sqrt{2}/2$ and

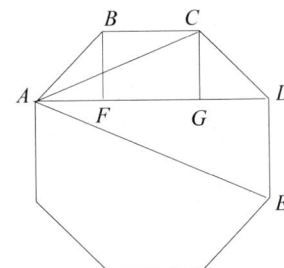

$$AC^2 = CG^2 + (AF + FG)^2 =$$

$$\left(\sqrt{2}/2\right)^2 + \left(1 + \sqrt{2}/2\right)^2 = 2 + \sqrt{2}. \text{ Similarly,}$$

$$AD^2 = (AF + FG + GD)^2 = \left(1 + \sqrt{2}\right)^2 = 3 + 2\sqrt{2} \text{ and}$$

$$AE^2 = AD^2 + DE^2 = \left(3 + 2\sqrt{2}\right) + 1 = 4 + 2\sqrt{2} \text{ making}$$

$$8AC^2 + 8AD^2 + 4AE^2 = 8\left(2 + \sqrt{2}\right) + 8\left(3 + 2\sqrt{2}\right) + 4\left(4 + 2\sqrt{2}\right) = \boxed{56 + 32\sqrt{2}}.$$

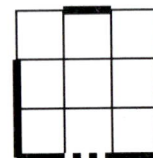

5. By symmetry and reflections/rotations, one can assume that the first point chosen lies either on the bottom left or bottom middle segment of the exterior. In both of those cases, the segments from the first point to two-thirds of the points on the boundary, highlighted in the graphic to the right, intersect at most three 1 by 1 sub-squares. Hence, the answer is $\boxed{\dfrac{2}{3}}$.

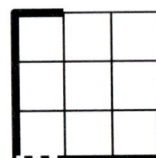

Bottom Left   Bottom Middle

6. $\log_{10} 5^{200} = 200 \log_{10} 5 \approx 200(0.6990) = 139.8$. Therefore, we know that 5^{200} has 140 digits. Also, since $\log_{10} 6 = \log_{10} 2 + \log_{10} 3 \approx 0.7781 < 0.8 < 0.8451 \approx \log_{10} 7 < 0.8451$, we know the leftmost digit is $\boxed{6}$.

7. As the circle is tangent to the line $y = 6$, the y-coordinate of the center C must be either 1 or 11. However, to maximize $a + b$ the center should be above the line $y = 6$ and to the right of the line $y = 0.75x$. Let P be the point of tangency of the circle with the line $y = 0.75x$. As the radius PC is perpendicular to the line $y = 0.75x$, its slope must be $-4/3$, and since $PC = 5$, we know that the point P has the coordinates $(a - 3, 11 + 4) = (a - 3, 15)$. Since $15 = 0.75(a - 3)$, then $a = 23$, the center of the circle is at $(23,11)$, and the sum of the coordinates is $\boxed{34}$.

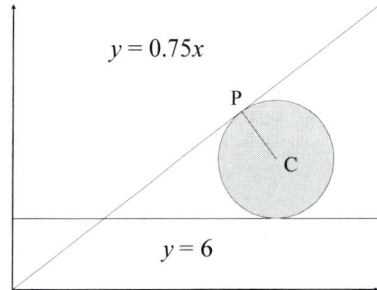

8. There are $7! = 5040$ possible shuffles of the cards. The easiest set to count is the arrangements of cards that lead to a loss. For example, any deck with 0 as the top card is a loser. We will denote it by 0xxxxxx. Another loser is a deck that has 1 as the top card and 0 as the third card. We will denote it by 1x0xxxx. The losing configurations are 0xxxxxx, 1x0xxxx, 1x2xx0x, 1x3xxx0, 2xx0xxx, 2xx1x0x, 3xxx0xx, 3xxx1x0, 4xxxx0x, and 5xxxxx0. The number of shuffles for each configuration are, respectively: $6!$, $5!$, $4!$, $4!$, $5!$, $4!$, $5!$, $4!$, $5!$, and $5!$, which sum to 1416, so the probability of winning is $1 - \dfrac{1416}{5040} = \boxed{\dfrac{151}{210}}$.

9. The switches that are on are those that correspond to numbers that have exactly one or three prime factors. The primes less than 50 are 2, 3, 5, 7, 11, 13, 17, 19, 23, 29, 31, 37, 41, 43, and 47. There are 15 of those. Now 4, 8, 16, 32, 9, 27, 25, and 49 are all powers of one prime. There are 8 of those, and 30 and 42 are products of three primes. The total number of on switches is $\boxed{25}$.

10. One can view the path of the particle as a straight line through a series of reflections of the billiard table. In the diagram to the right, one can see that the probability the particle hits at least k walls is $\dfrac{\tan^{-1}\left(\dfrac{16}{3(k - 1)}\right)}{\pi / 2}$. The first time that $\dfrac{\tan^{-1}\left(\dfrac{16}{3(k - 1)}\right)}{\pi / 2}$ drops below $\dfrac{1}{2}$ is when $\tan^{-1}\left(\dfrac{16}{3(k - 1)}\right) < \dfrac{\pi}{4}$, which implies that $\dfrac{16}{3(k - 1)} < 1$.

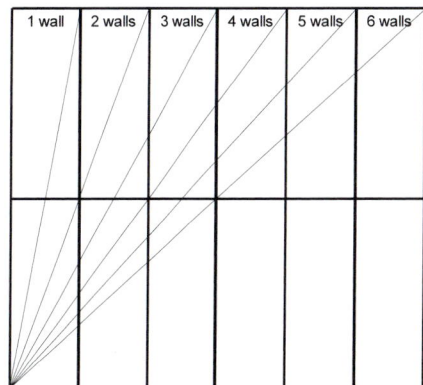

This occurs when $k = 7$, so the largest value of k for which the statement is true is $\boxed{6}$.

The following notation and definitions are assumed for this round:

An integer a divides b if there is another integer c such that $ac = b$. Note that this definition allows for a and/or b to be negative, and for b to be zero.

Two integers, a and b are *congruent modulo m* if m divides $a - b$. The notation for this is $a \equiv b \pmod{m}$. Alternately, a and b are congruent modulo m if there is some integer k such that $a = km + b$.

Two positive integers are *relatively prime* if their greatest common divisor is 1. For a positive integer n, $\varphi(n)$ denotes the number of positive integers less than or equal to n that are relatively prime to n. Euler's Theorem states that if n is a positive integer and a is another positive integer relatively prime to n, then $a^{\varphi(n)} \equiv 1 \pmod{n}$.

Part 1: Linear Ciphers

A cryptographic system (or cryptosystem, for short) is a means of encoding and decoding a message. A common cryptosystem for text, called a *substitution cipher*, is as follows:

1. Convert each letter into a number using the key below

A	B	C	D	E	F	G	H	I	J	K	L	M	N	O	P	Q	R	S	T	U	V	W	X	Y	Z
0	1	2	3	4	5	6	7	8	9	10	11	12	13	14	15	16	17	18	19	20	21	22	23	24	25

2. For a number x, apply some encryption function $e(x)$ to encode the number.

3. Reduce $e(x)$ to its *residue* modulo 26, that is, find the number y, $0 \le y \le 25$, such that $y \equiv e(x) \pmod{26}$.
4. Convert y to the corresponding letter.

The message **ARML LOCAL** would convert to **0-17-12-11 11-14-2-0-11**. If $e(x) = x + 13$, the residues of $e(x)$ modulo 26 would be **13-4-25-24 24-11-14-13-24**, and the resulting encrypted text would be **NEZY YBPNY**. This encryption method is called ROT-13 (for rotate 13). Note that $e(e(x)) \equiv x \pmod{26}$, so to decrypt a message encoded using ROT-13, one just applies the same method again.

Consider a more general form of encryption function: $e(x) = ax + b$, where a and b are integers. These are called *affine* (or *linear*) substitution ciphers. ROT-13 is an affine cipher with $a = 1$ and $b = 13$.

We will define an encryption function as *valid* if no two characters are encrypted to the same value. That is, an encryption function is valid if $x \ne y$, then $e(x) \not\equiv e(y) \pmod{26}$.

1. The encryption function $e(x) = 4x$ is not valid. What are two distinct letters which, when converted to numbers x and y as in step 1 above, have $e(x) \equiv e(y)(\mathrm{mod}\,26)$?

For Questions 2–3, consider the encryption function $e_1(x) = 5x + 4$.

2. Find all letters that do not change when encoded by $e_1(x)$.

3. A function $d(x)$ is the *decryption function* for an encryption function $e(x)$ if $d(e(x)) \equiv x(\mathrm{mod}\,26)$ for all values of x. If $d(x) = ax + b$ is a decryption function for $e_1(x)$, compute the ordered pair (a, b) where $0 \le a, b \le 25$.

4. Compute the number of integer values of a, $0 \le a \le 25$, for which $e(x) = ax$ is a valid encryption function.

5. Compute the number of ordered pairs (a, b), with $0 \le a, b \le 25$, for which $e(x) = ax + b$ is a valid encryption function such that $e(e(x)) \equiv x(\mathrm{mod}\,26)$ for all x, $0 \le x \le 25$.

Use the text below for problems 6 and 7.

"ASDQD JQD ASQDD HXWYV BI MXDV: MXDV, YJRWDY MXDV, JWY VAJAXVAXTV"

ODWCJRXW YXVQJDMX

The text above is a famous historical quote encoded using a linear cipher. The author's name, given in italics and encoded using the same cipher, follows the quote. All you know about the original text is that the first and second most frequently used letters in the original text along with the letters in the name of the author are E and I, respectively.

6. If $e_2(x) = ax + b$ is the valid encryption function used for the above quote, compute the ordered pair (a, b) where $0 \le a, b \le 25$.

7. If you decipher the entire text, you will also be able to identify the speaker of the quote. Who is it? Spelling counts, so be careful.

Part 2: Public Key Cryptography

Another, more advanced encryption method, is called the Rivest-Shamir-Adelman (RSA) algorithm. It works as follows.

1. Choose two prime numbers p and q. Let $n = pq$ with $\varphi(n) = (p-1) \times (q-1)$.

2. Pick an *encrypting key e* that is relatively prime to n.

3. Find a value d such that $ed \equiv 1 \left(\bmod \varphi(n) \right)$. This is a *decrypting key.*

4. Encrypt any numeric message k, $0 < k < n$, by finding the residue of $k^e \left(\bmod n \right)$. Call this residue r. This is the encrypted message.

5. To decrypt the encrypted message, find the residue of $r^d \left(\bmod n \right)$.

$$r^d \equiv \left(k^e \right)^d \left(\bmod n \right) \quad \text{and then} \quad k^{ed} = k^{1+m\varphi(n)} \text{ for some integer } m$$

$$k^{1+m\varphi(n)} = k \times k^{m\varphi(n)} \equiv k \times 1^m = k \left(\bmod n \right) \text{ (by Euler's Theorem)}$$

In practice, p and q are large (100-digit) prime numbers, so e and d may also be quite large. Therefore, computing the residue of k^e is potentially a time consuming process. Naively, one could compute the residue of k^e by first computing $\underbrace{k \cdot k \cdot k \cdot \ldots \cdot k}_{e-1 \text{ times}}$, requiring $e-1$ multiplications. However, if one can store the results of intermediate calculations, k^e can be computed much faster using a method called *binary exponentiation.*

Let $\left(b_m b_{m-1} \ldots b_0 \right)_2$ be the binary (base-2) representation of e with $b_m = 1$.

Compute k^e as follows:

    Start with $C = k$.

    For $j = 1$ to m

        Replace C with C^2.
        If $b_{m-j} = 1$ then replace C with $C \times k$.
    Next j

The result is k^e.

For example, if $e = 6$, then $6 = (110)_2$, and to compute k^6 we first square k to get k^2, multiply the result by k since $b_1 = 1$, getting k^3, then squaring the result again to get k^6. In short, a way of representing this series of calculations is $k \to k^2 \to k^3 \to k^6$. The naïve method for computing k^6, namely $k \times k \times k \times k \times k \times k$, would require five multiplication operations, while the binary exponentiation method requires only three.

For a positive integer x, let $m(x)$ be the number of multiplication operations to compute k^x using binary exponentiation. So, for example, $m(6) = 3$.

8.   Consider the set S of all three-digit, base-10, positive integers. Let a and b be the minimum and maximum values of $m(x)$ over all x in S. Compute the ordered pair (a, b).

9.   Computing k^{15} using the binary exponentiation method requires six multiplications ($k \to k^2 \to k^3 \to k^6 \to k^7 \to k^{14} \to k^{15}$). There is, however, a way to compute k^{15} using products of previously computed powers of k that requires only five multiplications. The sequence of calculations can be represented as $k \to k^a \to k^b \to k^c \to k^d \to k^{15}$ where a, b, c, and d are in increasing order and represent the intermediate powers of k calculated. Compute the ordered 4-tuple (a, b, c, d).

10.   Consider an implementation of RSA where $n = 33$, $\varphi(n) = 20$, and $e = 13$. You receive an encrypted message 2, which is the residue of $k^{13} \pmod{33}$ for some k, where $0 \le k \le 32$. Compute k. Hint: Find d first!

1. Any two letters that differ by 13 in the coding above map to the same letter under this code, as $4(x + 13) = 4x + 52 \equiv 4x \pmod{26}$. Therefore, any of the following pairs are correct: A and N, B and O, C and P, D and Q, E and R, F and S, G and T, H and U, I and V, J and W, K and X, L and Y, or M and Z.

2. For a letter with corresponding number x to not change when encoded, $5x + 4 \equiv x \pmod{26}$. Accordingly $4x \equiv -4 \pmod{26} \rightarrow 4x \equiv 22 \pmod{26}$. This holds for $x = 12$ and 25, corresponding to the letters $\boxed{\text{M and Z}}$.

3. $d(e_1(x)) = d(5x + 4) = a(5x + 4) + b = 5ax + (4a + b)$. In order for $d\big(e(x)\big) \equiv x \pmod{26}$, then $5a \equiv 1 \pmod{26}$ and $4a + b \equiv 0 \pmod{26}$. Noting that $21 \times 5 = 105 = 4 \times 26 + 1$, $a = 21$. Therefore, $4(21) + b \equiv 0 \pmod{26} \rightarrow b \equiv -84 \pmod{26} \rightarrow b = 20$, so the ordered pair $(a, b) = \boxed{(21, 20)}$.

4. In order for $e(x) = ax$ to be a valid encryption function, a and 26 must be relatively prime. All odd numbers less than 26 (except 13) are relatively prime to 26, so the answer is $\varphi(26) = \boxed{12}$.

5. $e(e(x)) = e(ax + b) = a(ax + b) + b = a^2 x + (ab + b)$. In order for an encryption function to be its own decryption function, $a^2 \equiv 1 \pmod{26}$ and $(a + 1)b \equiv 0 \pmod{26}$. From the first equation, a must be congruent to either -1 or $+1 \pmod{26}$, corresponding to the values $a = 1$ and $a = 25$. If $a = 1$, then $2b \equiv 0 \pmod{26}$, so b must be congruent to either 0 or 13 (mod 26). If $a \equiv -1 \pmod{26}$, then $(a + 1)b \equiv 0 \pmod{26}$ for all values of b, so the total number of ordered pairs is $\boxed{28}$.

6. By doing a frequency count of the ciphertext, one discovers D and X are the first and second most frequently used letters in the ciphertext. Therefore, $e_2(4) \equiv 3 \pmod{26}$ and $e_2(8) \equiv 23 \pmod{26}$, as 4, 3, 8, and 23 are the numbers corresponding to $E, D, I,$ and X, respectively. If $e_2(x) = ax + b$, then $4a + b \equiv 3 \pmod{26}$ and $8a + b \equiv 23 \pmod{26}$. Subtracting one equation from the other, we obtain $4a \equiv 20 \pmod{26}$ giving $a = 5$ or 18, but we can discard $a = 18$ as it would not be a valid encryption function. Thus, $4(5) + b \equiv 3 \pmod{26} \rightarrow b \equiv -17 \pmod{26} \rightarrow b \equiv 9 \pmod{26}$, so the solution is $\boxed{(5, 9)}$.

7.   Coming up with the entire plaintext to ciphertext table using the encryption function from the previous problem or determining the decryption function $d_2(x) = 21x + 19$, one determines that the historical figure is $\boxed{\text{BENJAMIN DISRAELI}}$. The quote is

"THERE ARE THREE KINDS OF LIES: LIES, DAMNED LIES, AND STATISTICS".

8.   The key thing to notice by reading through the algorithm is that the number of multiplications that take place to compute k^x is the exponent of the highest power of 2 less than or equal to x corresponding to the "Replace C with C^2" step, plus the number of ones in the base-2 representation of x, minus one corresponding to the "If $b_{m-j} = 1$ then replace C with $C \times k$" step. On the low side, $128_{10} = 1000000_2$ and so $m(128) = 7$. Every three-digit number x less than 128 has at least three ones in its binary representation so for these x, $m(x) > 7$. On the high end, several three digit numbers greater than 512 have 9 ones in their binary representation. The largest is $991_{10} = 1111011111_2$ giving $m(991) = 17$. The answer is $\boxed{(7, 17)}$.

9.   One method requiring only five multiplications is $k \rightarrow k^2 \rightarrow k^3 \rightarrow k^5 \rightarrow k^{10} \rightarrow k^{15}$, so a solution is $\boxed{(2, 3, 5, 10)}$. Also correct are $\boxed{(2, 4, 5, 10), \ (2, 3, 6, 12), \text{ and } (2, 3, 6, 9)}$.

10.   One should first find a value d such that $ed \equiv 1(\bmod \varphi(n)) \rightarrow 13d \equiv 1(\bmod 20) \rightarrow d \equiv 17(\bmod 20)$. Therefore, $2^{17} \equiv k(\bmod 33)$. At first glance, this looks like an onerous amount of work since $2^{17} = 131072$, but the residue of 2^{17} modulo 33 can be calculated fairly quickly using binary exponentiation.

$$2^2 \equiv 4(\bmod 33)$$
$$2^4 \equiv 4^2 \equiv 16(\bmod 33)$$
$$2^8 \equiv 16^2 \equiv 256 \equiv 25(\bmod 33)$$
$$2^{16} \equiv 25^2 \equiv 625 \equiv 31(\bmod 33)$$
$$2^{17} \equiv 2 \times 31 \equiv 62 \equiv 29(\bmod 33)$$

The answer is $\boxed{29}$.

1. An unfair coin is flipped twice. The probability of getting two Heads is 0.81. Compute the probability of flipping the coin twice and getting two Tails.

2. A hexagon has integral side lengths and a perimeter of 78 units. The lengths of the sides form an arithmetic progression. All side lengths but one are prime. Compute the length of the longest side.

3. The Fibonacci sequence F_n is defined by $F_0 = F_1 = 1$, $F_k = F_{k-1} + F_{k-2}$ for $k \geq 2$. For $k \leq 2$, define $T_k = F_{k-2} + F_k + F_{k+2}$. Compute T_{10}.

4. Compute the number of 4-digit numbers whose digits sum to 7.

5. The bases of two 50-foot long poles are 39 feet apart. Pole A is standing vertical. Pole B is leaning so that the top of the pole is 25 feet from Pole A. Compute the distance in feet from the midpoint of Pole B to the base of Pole A.

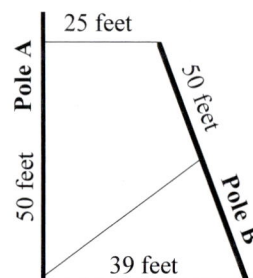

6. Compute the tens digit of $11^{12^{13}}$.

7. The shortest leg of a right triangle with integral side lengths is 18. Find the difference between the largest and smallest possible area of this triangle.

8. Compute the smallest positive integer value of a such that the set $\left\{\sqrt{a}, \sqrt{a+1}, \sqrt{a+2}, \ldots, \sqrt{a+2008}\right\}$ contains exactly three integers.

9. Compute the smallest positive <u>degree</u> value of α for which $k\sin(\theta - \alpha) = \sqrt{3}\sin\theta + \cos\theta$ for some positive value k and all values of θ.

10. Compute the four complex solutions of $(x-1)^4 + (x-5)^4 + 14 = 0$.

176

1. Pr(HH) = 0.81. Since the flips are independent, Pr(HH) = Pr(H)^2, so Pr(H) = 0.9 and Pr(T) = 0.1

    giving Pr(TT) = Pr(T)^2. Thus Pr(TT) = $\boxed{0.01 = \dfrac{1}{100}}$.

2. The average of the side lengths is 13. Since the lengths are in arithmetic progression, we know the

    two middle side lengths are $13 - \dfrac{d}{2}$ and $13 + \dfrac{d}{2}$, where d is the arithmetic difference. Since all

    sides are integral, d is even. Since at most one of the sides is not prime, the sides of the polygon

    must be odd. This forces d to be a multiple of 4. The smallest side is $13 - \dfrac{5d}{2}$ which must be at

    least 1, which implies that $d \le 4.8$. The only positive multiple of 4 less than 4.8 is 4, so the

    longest side is $13 + \dfrac{5d}{2} = 13 + \dfrac{20}{2} = \boxed{23}$.

3. $T_k = F_{k-2} + F_k + F_{k+2} = F_{k-2} + \left(F_{k-2} + F_{k-1}\right) + \left(F_k + F_{k+1}\right)$
    $= 2F_{k-2} + F_{k-1} + F_k + F_{k+1} = 2F_{k-2} + F_{k-1} + F_k + \left(F_{k-1} + F_k\right)$
    $= 3F_{k-2} + 3F_{k-1} + F_k = 4F_k \rightarrow T_{10} = 4F_{10} = 4(89) = \boxed{356}$.

4. Write the four digit number as $\underline{abcd}$, where $a + b + c + d = 7$. Since $a \ge 1$ and $b, c, d \ge 0$, we

    can consider a different problem where $a = a^* + 1$, and $a^*, b, c, d \le 0$, $a^* + b + c + d = 6$. This

    problem can be solved using stars-and-bars (6 stars, 3 bars), so the total number of four-digit

    numbers with digits summing to 7 is $\dbinom{9}{3} = \dfrac{9 \times 8 \times 7}{6} = \boxed{84}$.

5. Let A and B be the bottoms of the two poles, and let C and M be
    the top and midpoint of Pole B, respectively. Let D and N be the
    intersections of the perpendiculars to $\overline{AB}$ through C and M,
    respectively. Since $AD = 25$, $DB = 14$ and because M is the
    midpoint of $\overline{CB}$, then $DN = NB = 7$. Since MNB is a right
    triangle, $MN = 24$. As $AN = AD + DN = 32$, then

    $AM = \sqrt{24^2 + 32^2} = \boxed{40}$.

    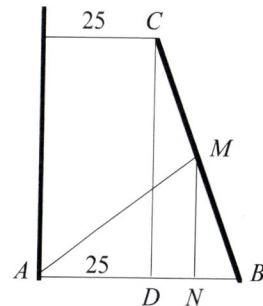

6. Observe that $11^x = (10 + 1)^x = 10^x + \binom{x}{1}10^{x-1} + \cdots + \binom{x}{x-1}10 + 1$. The only term in the binomial expansion that will impact the tens digit is the next to last one, which is equal to $10x$. Therefore, the tens digit of 11^x is equal to the units digit of x. The units digits of 12^x cycle 2, 4, 8, 6, 2, ... cycling every four powers of two, so the units digit of 12^{13} and therefore, the tens digit of $11^{12^{13}}$ is $\boxed{2}$.

7. Let x be the length of the hypotenuse of the triangle and b the length of the other leg. Then $18^2 = x^2 - b^2 = (x - b)(x + b)$. Note that $18^2 = 2^2 \times 3^4$. Since $x - b$ and $x + b$ have the same parity, they must both be even. Therefore, $x - b = 2 \times 3^m$ and $x + b = 2 \times 3^n$ with $m + n = 4$, $m < n$. This gives two possible cases, $n = 3$ and $n = 4$. When $n = 3$, then $x - b = 6$ and $x + b = 54$, leading to the solution $x = 30$, $b = 24$ and an area of 216. When $n = 4$, then $x - b = 2$ and $x + b = 162$, leading to the solution $x = 82$, $b = 80$ and an area of 720. The difference between these two areas is $\boxed{504}$.

8. Let $f(a)$ be the number of integers in the set. This function has a few interesting properties. For one thing, $f(a) - f(a + 1) = 0$ unless a is a perfect square and $a + 2009$ is not, in which case $f(a + 1) = f(a) - 1$. Or a is not a perfect square and $a + 2009$ is, in which case $f(a + 1) = f(a) + 1$. To find the first value of a for which $f(a) = 4$ and $f(a + 1) = 3$, we note that the last perfect square for which $f(a) = 5$ is $a = 249^2$ since $253^2 = 249^2 + 2008$. Since $f\left(250^2\right) = 4 \rightarrow f\left(250^2 + 1\right) = 3$, the answer is $250^2 + 1 = \boxed{62501}$.

9. $\sqrt{3}\sin\theta + 1\cos\theta = 2\left(\frac{\sqrt{3}}{2}\sin\theta + \frac{1}{2}\cos\theta\right) = 2\left(\cos 30^\circ \sin\theta + \sin 30^\circ \cos\theta\right)$

$= 2\left(\sin\left(\theta + 30^\circ\right)\right) = 2\left(\sin\left(\theta - 330^\circ\right)\right)$. The smallest positive degree value for α is $\boxed{330^\circ}$.

10. Let $y = x - 3$. Then $(x - 1)^4 + (x - 5)^4 + 14 = (y + 2)^4 + (y - 2)^4 + 14 = 2y^4 + 48y^2 + 46$

$= 2\left(y^2 + 23\right)\left(y^2 + 1\right)$ This equals zero when $y = \sqrt{23}i$, $-\sqrt{23}i$, i, or $-i$ giving

$\boxed{x = 3 + \sqrt{23}i,\ 3 - \sqrt{23}i,\ 3 + i,\ 3 - i}$.

R1-1.   Compute the value $\sqrt{10\sqrt{80\sqrt{10\sqrt{80\sqrt{\cdots}}}}}$.

R1-2.   Let $T = TNYWR$. Two cars, starting at the same spot, simultaneously begin driving north and east at $3T$ and $4T$ kilometers per hour, respectively. After an hour, the two cars turn directly at each other. Compute the distance in kilometers from the starting point to the point where the two cars collide.

R2-1.   The side lengths of a triangle are 3π, $2e$, and x. Compute the smallest integral value of x.

R2-2.   Let $T = TNYWR$. Compute $\dfrac{\left(T^{4\log_{10}5}\right)\left(\left(T^2\right)^{\log_{10}4}\right)}{T}$.

R2-3.   Let $T = TNYWR$. Set S has exactly T subsets including itself and the empty set. How many of these subsets have exactly 2 or 3 elements?

R3-1.   Compute the number of single-digit prime numbers that divide

$$2^{2008} + 3^{2008} + 4^{2008} + 5^{2008}$$ evenly.

R3-2.   Let $T = TNYWR$. Compute the integer b such that $(103)_b = (68)_b \times (T)_b$ where $(x)_b$ denotes the number x written in base b.

R3-3.   Let $T = TNYWR$. Compute the number of positive divisors of $2^{12} \cdot T$.

R3-4.   Let $T = TNYWR$. A rhombus with area T has one diagonal of length 13. Compute the length of the other diagonal.

R3-5.   Let $T = TNYWR$. If $f(x) = x^2 + Tx$, compute the sum of all of the values of x such that $f(x) = f(f(x))$.

R3-6.   Let $T = TNYWR$. A ten-sided die with the numbers 1 through 10 on the faces is rolled twice, getting numbers x and y. Compute the probability that $x + y + T \le 10$.

R1–1. Let $x = \sqrt{10\sqrt{80\sqrt{10\sqrt{80\sqrt{\cdots}}}}} \rightarrow x^2 = 10\sqrt{80\sqrt{10\sqrt{80\sqrt{\cdots}}}} \rightarrow$

$\dfrac{x^2}{10} = \sqrt{80\sqrt{10\sqrt{80\sqrt{\cdots}}}} \rightarrow \dfrac{x^4}{100} = 80\sqrt{10\sqrt{80\sqrt{\cdots}}} \rightarrow x^4 = 8000x \rightarrow x^3 = 8000$.

Thus, $x = \boxed{20}$.

R1 – 2. Assuming both cars start at the origin, after an hour, the cars are at the positions $(0, 3T)$ and $(4T, 0)$, at which point they are $5T$ km apart and then travel along the line $y = 3T - \dfrac{3}{4}x$. The cars close at a combined speed of $7T$ km per hour and collide at a point 3/7ths of the way along the segment. The coordinates of this point are $(12T/7, 12T/7)$, so the distance from the origin is

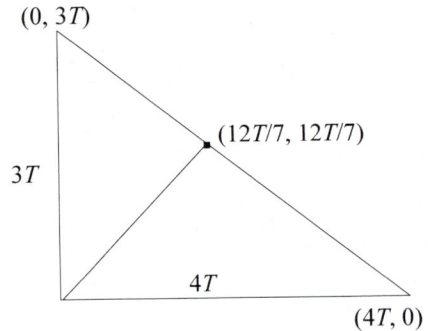

$\sqrt{2\left(\dfrac{12T}{7}\right)^2} = \left(\dfrac{12T}{7}\right)\sqrt{2}$. Since $T = 20$, the answer is $\boxed{\dfrac{240\sqrt{2}}{7}}$.

R2–1. $3\pi \approx 3(3.1416) = 9.4248$, $2e \approx 2(2.7183) = 5.4366$. Therefore, $x \geq 3\pi - 2e \approx 3.9882$. The smallest integral value of x is $\boxed{4}$.

R2–2. From $\dfrac{\left(T^{4\log_{10}5}\right)\left(\left(T^2\right)^{\log_{10}4}\right)}{T} = T^{4\log_{10}5 + 2\log_{10}4 - 1}$ we obtain

$T^{\log_{10}625 + \log_{10}16 - 1} = T^{\log_{10}10000 - 1} = T^3$. As $T = 4$, the answer is $\boxed{64}$.

R2–3. In order for the question to make sense, T should equal 2^m for some integer m, in which case the answer is $\dbinom{m}{2} + \dbinom{m}{3}$. Thankfully, $T = 64 = 2^6$, so the answer is

$\dbinom{6}{2} + \dbinom{6}{3} = 15 + 20 = \boxed{35}$.

180

R3–1.   Two of the terms are odd, two are even, so two divides the number. Even powers of an integer k are congruent to 0 mod 3 if k is a multiple of 3, and 1 otherwise. Since there are three terms congruent to 1 mod 3 and a fourth congruent to 0 mod 3, the sum is congruent to 0 mod 3. To determine divisibility by 5, look at the unit digits of each term, they are 6, 1, 6, and 5, respectively. Their sum is 18, so $2^{2008} + 3^{2008} + 4^{2008} + 5^{2008}$ is not divisible by 5. Since $5 \equiv -2 \pmod 7$ and $4 \equiv -3 \pmod 7$, $2^{2008} \equiv 5^{2008} \pmod 7$ and $3^{2008} \equiv 4^{2008} \pmod 7$. The powers of 2 mod 7 cycle: 2, 4, 1, 2, 4, 1, ... and the powers of 4 mod 7 cycle 4, 2, 1, 4, 2, 1, ... so $2^{2008} \equiv 2 \pmod 7$ and $4^{2008} \equiv 4 \pmod 7$. Hence, the sum is congruent to $2 + 4 + 4 + 2 = 12 \equiv 5 \pmod 7$. Therefore, two single-digit primes divide the sum $2^{2008} + 3^{2008} + 4^{2008} + 5^{2008}$ evenly. The answer is $\boxed{2}$.

R3–2. $b^2 + 3 = (6b + 8)T \rightarrow b^2 - 6bT + (3 - 8T) = 0$. Since $T = 2$, then $b^2 - 12T - 13 = 0$, giving $(b + 1)(b - 13) = 0 \rightarrow \boxed{b = 13}$.

R3–3.   Let $T = 2^k j$, where j is odd. For each divisor d of j there are $13 + k$ divisors of $2^{12}T$ corresponding to each value $2^i d$, $0 \le i \le 12 + k$. In this case, T is odd and prime. Thus $2^{12} \times 13$ has $\boxed{26}$ positive divisors.

R3–4.   The area of a rhombus is half the product of the lengths of the two diagonals. Since the area is 26, the other diagonal has length $\boxed{4}$.

R3–5. $f(f(x)) - f(x) = f(x^2 + Tx) - f(x) = (x^2 + Tx)^2 + T(x^2 + Tx) - (x^2 + Tx)$
$$= x^4 + 2Tx^3 + (T^2 + T - 1)x^2 + (T^2 - T)x$$
The sum of the roots of this function is $-2T = \boxed{-8}$. Note: when $T = 2$, the above factors as $x(x + 1)(x + 3)(x + 4)$)

R3–6.   The number of ways to represent k as the sum of two integers between 1 and 10 is $10 - |k - 11|$. There are 100 possible rolls, and $3 + 2 + 1 = 6$ are greater than or equal to 18 since $T = -8$. The answer is $\boxed{\dfrac{3}{50} = 0.06}$.

Team Round:

1. 102465   2. 6   3. 31   4. $56 + 32\sqrt{2}$ 5. $\dfrac{2}{3}$

6. 6   7. 34   8. $\dfrac{151}{210}$ 9. 25   10. 6

Theme Round:

1. There are 13 possible answers: A and N, B and O, C and P, D and Q, E and R, F and S, G and T, H and U, I and V, J and W, K and X, L and Y, or M and Z.

2. M and Z   3. (21, 20)   4. 12   5. 28   6. (5, 9)

7. BENJAMIN DISRAELI   (Spelling counts!)   8. (7, 17)

9. Any of (2, 3, 5, 10), (2, 4, 5, 10), (2, 3, 6, 9), or (2, 3, 6, 12).

10. 29

Individual Round:

1. 0.01   2. 23   3. 356   4. 84

5. 40   6. 2   7. 504   8. 62501

9. 330   10. $3 + i\sqrt{23}$, $3 + i$

Relay Round:

Relay 1:   1. 20   2. $\dfrac{240\sqrt{2}}{7}$

Relay 2:   1. 4   2. 64   3. 35

Relay 3:   1. 2   2. 13   3. 26   4. 4   5. −8   6. $\dfrac{3}{50}$

The Stretch Method

Inscribings Right Triangular

Random
Walks in Trees

Three's a Charm!

The Game of Yahtzee

ARML Power Contest
2004 - 2008

Electing a Candidate

The Algebra
of
Electrical Circuitry

Mathematical Billiards

Triangular Trigonometry

The ARML Power Contest provides a group problem-solving situation similar to the power question found at the ARML Competition. Each year the contest consists of two rounds, one problem set in November and the other in February. The mathematics level of the contest problems is geared so that students in an honors class, in a math club, or on a math team can have a unique problem solving and mathematical writing experience. There is no limit to the size of the team, but the time for solving the problem set is limited to 45 minutes. Coaches receive the contest materials at least one week prior to the start of the test period and may schedule the contest anytime during the designated two and a half weeks. After completing the contest, the solutions are mailed back and are then graded using a forty-point rubric. Scores for the two rounds are totaled and recognition and awards are given to the top ten scoring teams.

Right Triangular Inscribings

The Problems

In all the problems in this contest, $\triangle ABC$ is a <u>right triangle</u> with a

hypotenuse $\overline{AB}$ and, by convention, $AB = c$, $BC = a$, and $AC = b$.

Part 1 Inscribed Semicircles

1. A semicircle with center O and diameter $\overline{DC}$ *(on $\overline{AC}$)* is

inscribed in $\triangle ABC$. $\overline{AB}$ is tangent to the semicircle at E.

Determine the radius of the semicircle in terms of a and b.

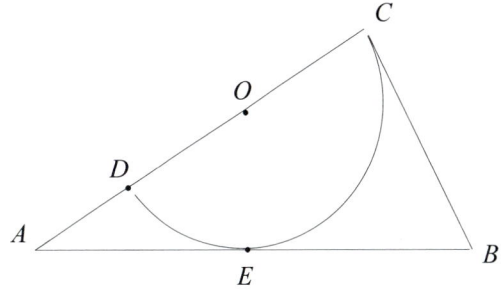

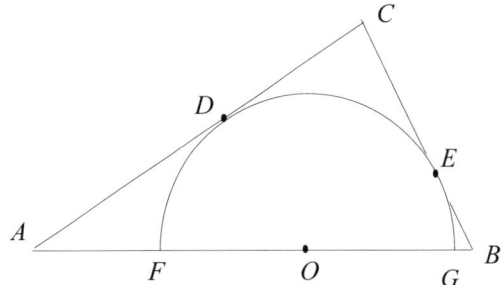

2. A semicircle with center O and diameter $\overline{FG}$ *(on $\overline{AB}$)* is

inscribed in $\triangle ABC$. $\overline{AC}$ is tangent to the semicircle at D

and $\overline{BC}$ is tangent to the semicircle at E. Determine the

radius of the semicircle in terms of a and b.

3. Two semicircles, S_1 and S_2, are inscribed in **isosceles** right

triangle $\triangle ABC$ and tangent to each other at D (on

hypotenuse $\overline{AB}$). $\overline{AC}$ is tangent to S_1 at E and $\overline{BC}$ is

tangent to S_2 at F.

a) Given any point D, describe how to construct S_1 and S_2.

b) Prove the sum of the radii of S_1 and S_2 is constant

(independent of the placement of *D)*.

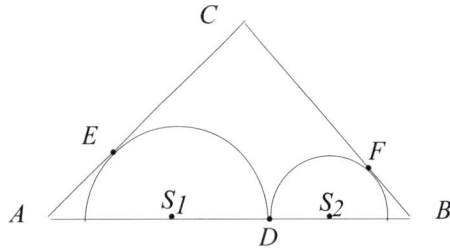

Part 2 Inscribed Circles

4. In about 300 B.C., a Greek geometer stated that $r = \dfrac{a+b-c}{2}$, relating the sides of $\triangle ABC$ to the radius, r, of

its inscribed circle. In 250 A.D., a Chinese mathematician came up with a different expression, $r = \dfrac{ab}{a+b+c}$.

Whose formula is correct? Justify your answer.

185

5. A circle with radius r is inscribed in right triangle $\triangle ABC$ with integer sides. Prove r must also be an integer.

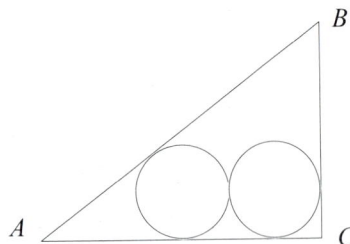

6a. Two congruent, tangent circles are "inscribed" in $\triangle ABC$ with $AC = 4$ and $BC = 3$, and both are tangent to $\overline{AC}$. $\overline{AB}$ is tangent to one circle and $\overline{BC}$ is tangent to the other. Find the length of the radii of the circles.

6b. A string of n congruent, tangent circles are "inscribed" in $\triangle ABC$ with $AC = 4$ and $BC = 3$, and are all tangent to $\overline{AC}$. $\overline{AB}$ is tangent to the circle on one end of the string of circles and $\overline{BC}$ is tangent to the circle on the other end. Find the length of the radii of the circles in terms of n.

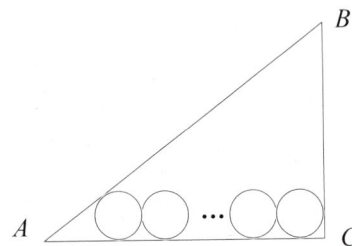

7a. Two congruent, tangent circles are "inscribed" in $\triangle ABC$ with $AC = 4$ and $BC = 3$, and are both tangent to $\overline{AB}$. $\overline{AC}$ is tangent to one circle and $\overline{BC}$ is tangent to the other. Find the length of the radii of the circles.

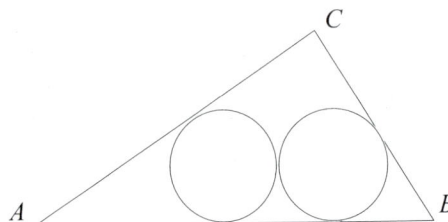

7b. A string of n congruent, tangent circles are "inscribed" in $\triangle ABC$ with $AC = 4$ and $BC = 3$, and are all tangent to $\overline{AB}$. $\overline{AC}$ is tangent to the circle on one end of the string of circles and $\overline{BC}$ is tangent to the circle on the other end. Find the length of the radii of the circles in terms of n.

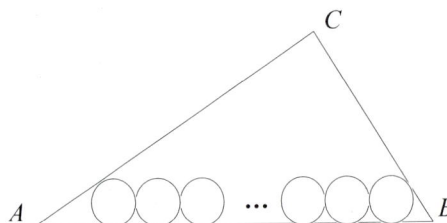

8. A string of n tangent circles are "inscribed" in $\triangle ABC$ with $AC = 4$ and $BC = 3$, and are all tangent to $\overline{AB}$ and $\overline{AC}$. If the first circle is the incircle and the nth circle is the circle closest to vertex A, find the length of the radii of the nth circle in terms of n.

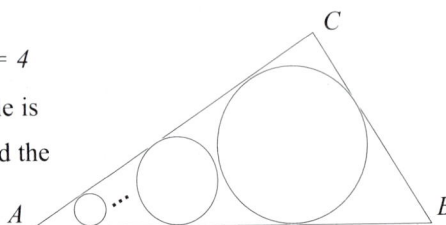

186

Part 3 Incircles

9a. In $\triangle ABC$ let $\overline{CD}$ be the altitude to the hypotenuse. If r_1, r_2, and r_3 are the radii of the incircles of triangles ABC, ADC, and BDC, respectively, prove $CD = r_1 + r_2 + r_3$.

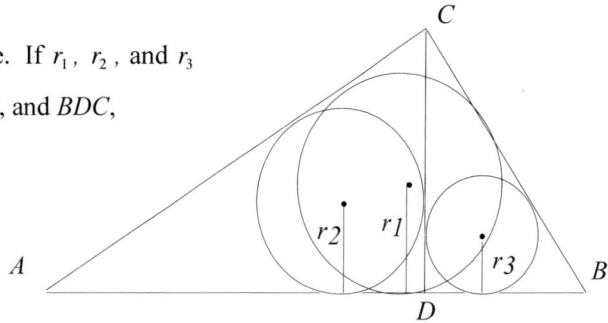

9b. Prove: $r_1^2 = r_2^2 + r_3^2$.

9c. Prove that the line connecting R and S, the incenters of $\triangle ADC$ and $\triangle BDC$, is perpendicular to the angle bisector of angle C.

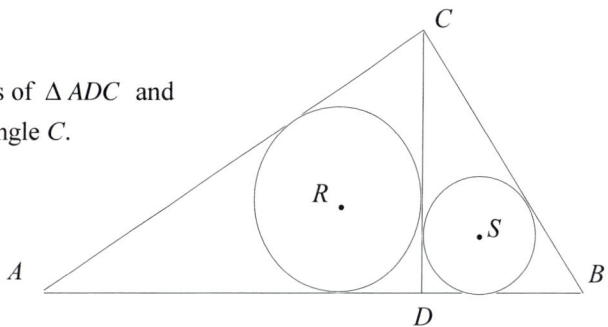

9d. R and S are the incenters of right triangles ADC and BCD and lines CR and CS intersect $\overline{AB}$ at P and Q, respectively. Prove $AC = AQ$ and $BC = BP$.

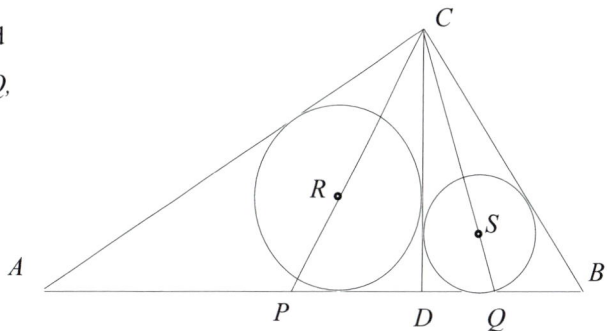

9e. Prove the incenter of $\triangle ABC$, point I, is also the circumcenter of $\triangle PQC$.

9f. If $AC = 4$ and $BC = 3$, find the area of quadrilateral $CRIS$.

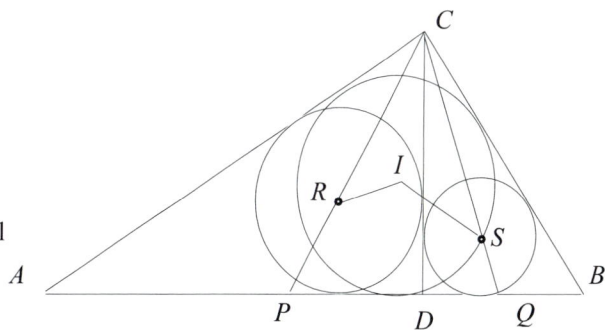

187

The Solutions

1. $\triangle AOE \sim \triangle ABC$

$$\frac{AO}{AB} = \frac{OE}{BC}$$

$$\frac{b-r}{c} = \frac{r}{a} \Rightarrow ab - ar = cr \Rightarrow ab = cr + ar$$

$$r = \frac{ab}{a+c} = \frac{ab}{a + \sqrt{a^2 + b^2}}$$

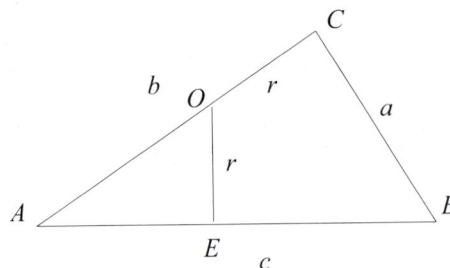

2. $\triangle AOD \sim \triangle OBE$

$$\frac{AD}{OE} = \frac{OD}{BE}$$

$$\frac{b-r}{r} = \frac{r}{a-r} \Rightarrow (b-r)(a-r) = r^2 \Rightarrow ab - br - ar + r^2 = r^2$$

$$r = \frac{ab}{a+b}$$

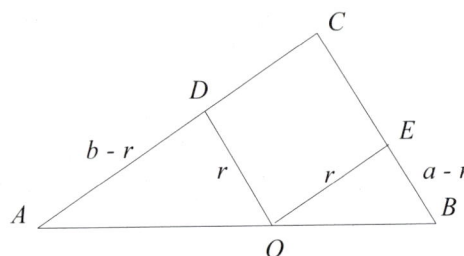

3. a) From D construct a perpendicular to $\overline{AB}$. This line will interest $\overline{AC}$, $\overline{BC}$, or point C.

Case 1 The perpedicular intersects $\overline{AC}$ at G. Bisect $\angle AGD$ and the intersection of this bisector with $\overline{AB}$ is point S_1. Extend $\overrightarrow{DG}$ and $\overrightarrow{BC}$ to intersect at point H. Bisect $\angle DHB$ and the intersection of this bisector with $\overline{AB}$ is point S_2.

Case 2 Same as case 1, interchanging A for B.

Case 3 The bisectors of $\angle ACD$ and $\angle BCD$ intersect $\overline{AB}$ at S_1 and S_2.

4. Both are correct!

$$b - r + a - r = c$$
$$a + b - c = 2r$$
$$\frac{a + b - c}{2} = r$$

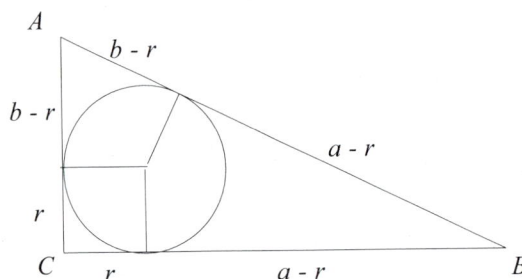

Area of $\triangle ABC = \frac{1}{2}ab$

Area of $\triangle ABC = \frac{1}{2}ar + \frac{1}{2}br + \frac{1}{2}cr$

$$ab = ar + br + cr$$

$$r = \frac{ab}{a+b+c}$$

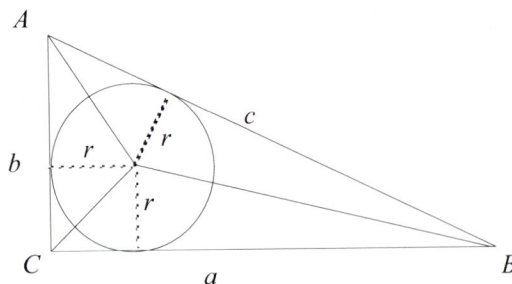

188

5. If a right triangle has integer sides, then a, b, and c form a Pythagorean triple with $a = 2mn$, $b = m^2 - n^2$, and $c = m^2 + n^2$, where m and n are relatively prime integers. From problem 4, $r = \dfrac{ab}{a+b+c}$. Therefore,

$$r = \frac{2mn(m^2 - n^2)}{2mn + m^2 - n^2 + m^2 + n^2} = \frac{2mn(m-n)(m+n)}{2mn + 2m^2} = m+n, \text{ an integer.}$$

6a. <u>Lemma</u> From problem 4, $r = \dfrac{ab}{a+b+c}$. Therefore, in a 3-4-5 triangle,

$r = \dfrac{(3)(4)}{3+4+5} = 1$ and if the radius of a circle inscribed in any triangle similar to a 3-4-5 triangle equals r, then the sides of the triangle are $3r$, $4r$, and $5r$.

Therefore, $4r + 2r = 4$ and so $r = \dfrac{2}{3}$.

6b. Using the above lemma, $2r(n-1) + 4r = 4$

$$2rn - 2r + 4r = 4$$
$$2rn + 2r = 4$$
$$r = \frac{4}{2n+2}.$$

7a. Again using the above lemma, $3r + 4r = 5$ and so $r = \dfrac{5}{7}$.

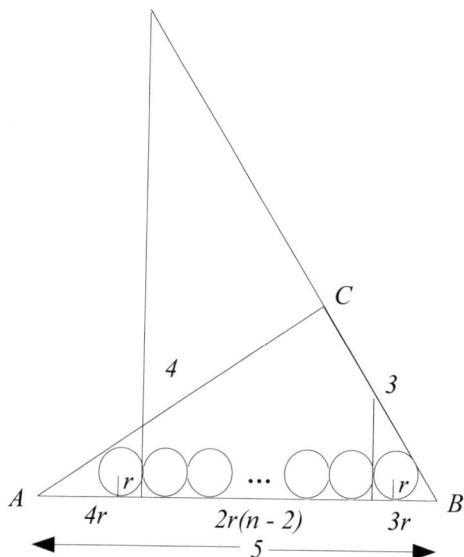

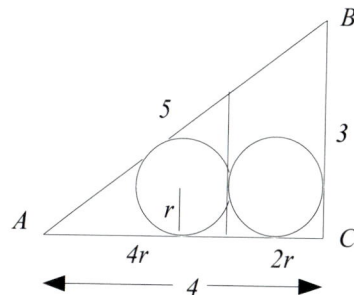

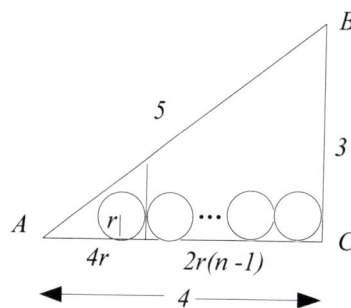

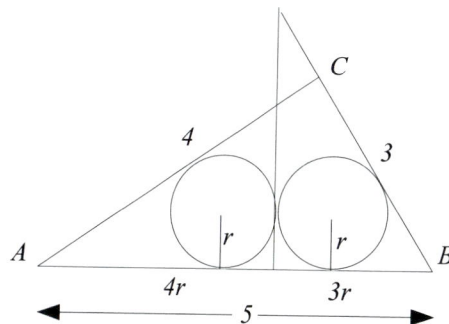

7b. Using the above lemma again,

$$4r + 2r(n - 2) + 3r = 5$$
$$4r + 2nr - 4r + 3r = 5$$
$$2nr + 3r = 5$$

and so, $r = \dfrac{5}{3 + 2n}$.

8. The angle bisector, *AI*, goes through the centers of all the *n* circles and the *n* radii divide $\triangle AID$ into similar triangles. $DI = 1$, $AD = 3$ and so $AI = \sqrt{10}$.

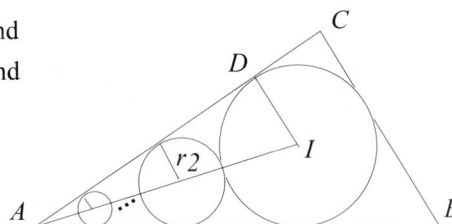

$$\frac{\text{radius}}{\text{hypotenuse}} = \frac{1}{\sqrt{10}} = \frac{r_2}{\sqrt{10} - 1 - r_2}$$

$$\sqrt{10}\, r_2 = \sqrt{10} - 1 - r_2$$

$$\sqrt{10}\, r_2 + r_2 = \sqrt{10} - 1$$

$$r_2\left(\sqrt{10} + 1\right) = \sqrt{10} - 1$$

$$r_2 = \frac{\sqrt{10} - 1}{\sqrt{10} + 1}$$

Since each similar triangle has the same scale factor, $r_3 = \left(\dfrac{\sqrt{10} - 1}{\sqrt{10} + 1}\right)\left(\dfrac{\sqrt{10} - 1}{\sqrt{10} + 1}\right)$ and $r_n = \left(\dfrac{\sqrt{10} - 1}{\sqrt{10} + 1}\right)^{n-1}$.

9a. $\triangle ABC \sim \triangle ACD$ with a scale factor of $\dfrac{c}{b}$. Therefore, $\dfrac{r_1}{r_2} = \dfrac{c}{b}$

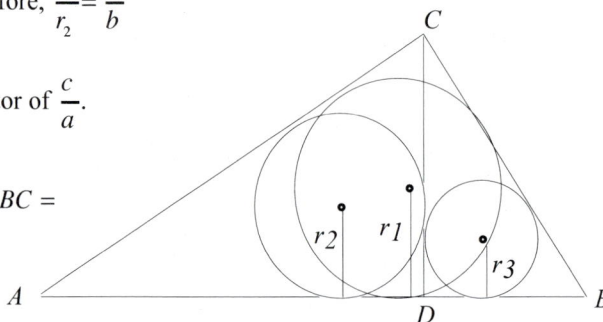

and so $b = \dfrac{r_2 c}{r_1}$. $\triangle ABC \sim \triangle CBD$ with a scale factor of $\dfrac{c}{a}$.

Therefore, $\dfrac{r_1}{r_3} = \dfrac{c}{a}$ and so $a = \dfrac{r_3 c}{r_1}$. The area of $\triangle ABC =$

$\frac{1}{2}(base)(height)$ or $(inradius)(semiperimeter) =$

$$\frac{1}{2}c\,(CD) = (r_1)\left(\frac{a + b + c}{2}\right)$$

$$= \frac{r_1}{2}\left(\frac{r_3 c}{r_1} + \frac{r_2 c}{r_1} + c\right) = \frac{r_1}{2}\left(\frac{r_3 c}{r_1} + \frac{r_2 c}{r_1} + \frac{r_1 c}{r_1}\right) = \frac{1}{2}c(r_1 + r_2 + r_3).\ \text{ So } CD = r_1 + r_2 + r_3.$$

9b. From 9a, $r_2 = \dfrac{r_1 b}{c}$ and $r_3 = \dfrac{r_1 a}{c}$. Therefore, $r_2{}^2 + r_3{}^2 = \left(\dfrac{r_1 a}{c}\right)^2 + \left(\dfrac{r_1 b}{c}\right)^2 = \dfrac{r_1{}^2}{c^2}(b^2 + a^2) = \dfrac{r_1{}^2}{c^2}(c^2) = r_1{}^2$.

9c. $\angle BAC = \angle BCD = \alpha$ and $\angle ABC = \angle ACD = 90 - \alpha$.

Therefore, in $\triangle ACV$, $\angle A = \dfrac{\alpha}{2}$ and $\angle C = 90 - \alpha + \dfrac{\alpha}{2}$

and so $\angle V = 90$. Also, in $\triangle BCU$, $\angle B = \dfrac{90 - \alpha}{2}$ and

$\angle C = \alpha + \dfrac{90 - \alpha}{2}$ and so $\angle U = 90$. Therefore, I is the

orthocenter of $\triangle CRS$ and CT is the other altitude. But I is also the incenter of $\triangle ABC$ and so CT is the bisector of $\angle ACB$. Therefore, the bisector of $\angle ACB$ is perpendicular to side RS of $\triangle CSR$.

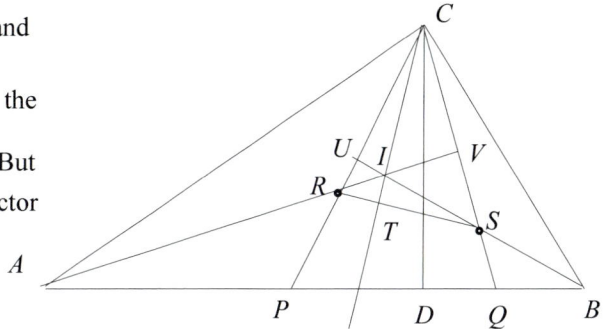

9d. From 9c, $\angle ACQ = 90 - \alpha + \dfrac{\alpha}{2} = 90 - \dfrac{\alpha}{2}$. In $\triangle QBC$, $\angle B = 90 - \alpha$ and $\angle C = \dfrac{\alpha}{2}$ and, therefore, by the

Exterior Angle Theorem, $\angle AQC = 90 - \alpha + \dfrac{\alpha}{2} = 90 - \dfrac{\alpha}{2}$. Therefore, $\triangle ACQ$ is isosceles and $AC = AQ$.

Using similar reasoning, $\angle BCP = \alpha + \dfrac{90 - \alpha}{2} = \dfrac{\alpha + 90}{2}$, In $\triangle PAC$, $\angle A = \alpha$ and $\angle C = \dfrac{90 - \alpha}{2}$ and,

therefore, by the Exterior Angle Theorem, $\angle BPC = \alpha + \dfrac{90 - \alpha}{2} = \dfrac{\alpha + 90}{2}$. Therefore, $\triangle BPC$ is isosceles and

$BC = BP$.

9e. Because $\triangle BCP$ is isosceles, BU, the bisector of $\angle B$, is also the perpendicular bisector of side PC. Because $\triangle ACQ$ is isosceles, AV, the bisector of $\angle A$, is also the perpendicular bisector of side QC. Therefore, I, the incenter of $\triangle ABC$, is now also the intersection of the perpendicular bisectors of $\triangle PQC$, is, therefore, the circumcenter of $\triangle PQC$.

9f. $\triangle AIB \sim \triangle ARC \sim \triangle BSC$ with scale factors $5: 4: 3$. Therefore, their areas have scale factors $25: 16: 9$.

Since the inradius is 1, the area of $\triangle AIB$ is $\dfrac{5}{2}$.

Therefore, the area of $\triangle ARC$ is $\left(\dfrac{16}{25}\right)\left(\dfrac{5}{2}\right) = \dfrac{8}{5}$ and

the area of $\triangle BSC$ is $\left(\dfrac{9}{25}\right)\left(\dfrac{5}{2}\right) = \dfrac{9}{10}$. And so the

area of $CRIS$ is $6 - \dfrac{5}{2} - \dfrac{8}{5} + \dfrac{9}{10} = 1$.

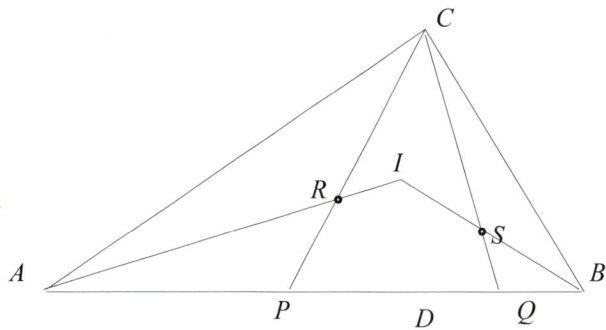

Algebra of Electrical Circuitry

The Background

The elements in this algebra are electrical switches. A switch can be <u>open</u> (represented by 0), with no electricity flowing through it, or <u>closed</u> (represented by 1), showing electricity flowing through it. Diagram 1 shows a simple electrical circuit consisting of a battery ($||||$), a light ($\bigcirc$), and a switch ($A \blacktriangledown$). If the switch is open, the light will be off (0) and if the switch is closed, the light will be lit (1).

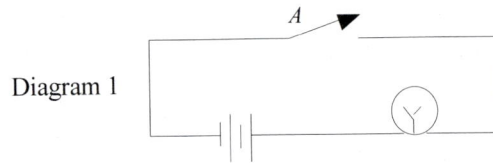

Diagram 1

Diagram 2 shows that two switches can be combined in a circuit in two distinct ways, either in parallel or in series.

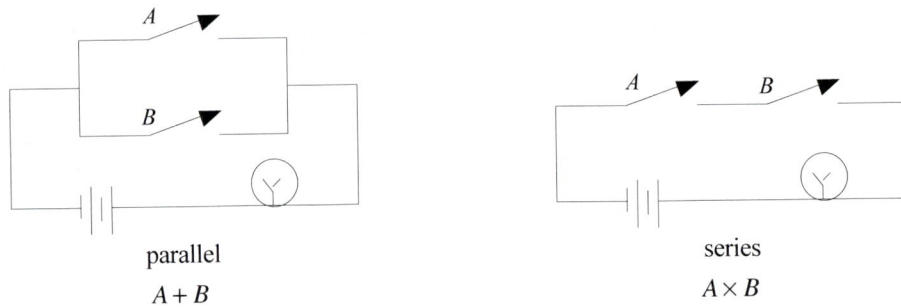

parallel

$A + B$

series

$A \times B$

Diagram 2

As indicated above, we will use the addition symbol (+) to indicate two switches in parallel and the multiplication symbol ($\times$) to indicate two switches in series. As in complex number algebra, $A \times B$ is often written as AB.

Parentheses may be necessary in representing some circuits as shown in Diagram 3. Both are a combination of three switches in parallel and series. The left diagram is $(A + B) \times C$, while the right is $A + (B \times C)$ or simply $A + BC$.

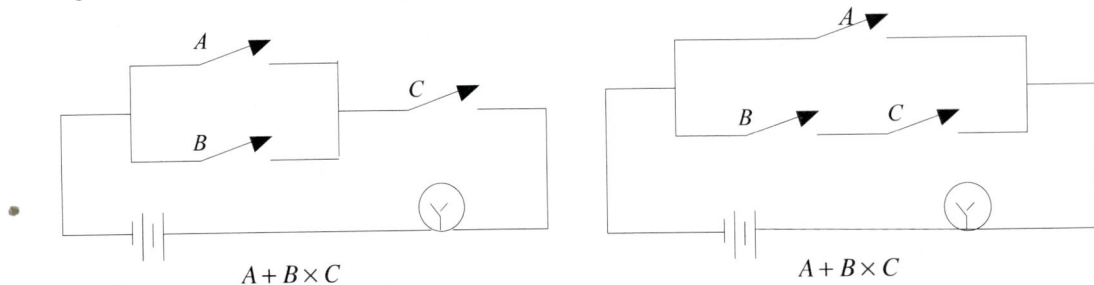

$A + B \times C$

$A + B \times C$

Diagram 3

192

The following diagrams are "Proofs Without Words" of some of the basic laws of this algebra showing equivalent circuits.

1. Commutative Laws

a)

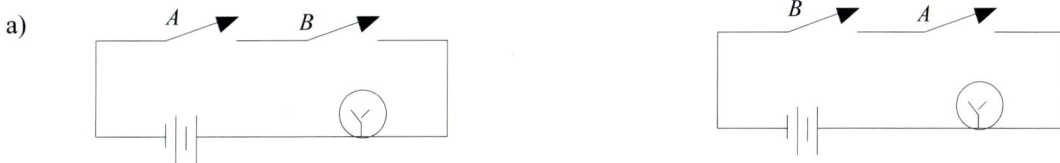

$$A \times B = B \times A$$

b)

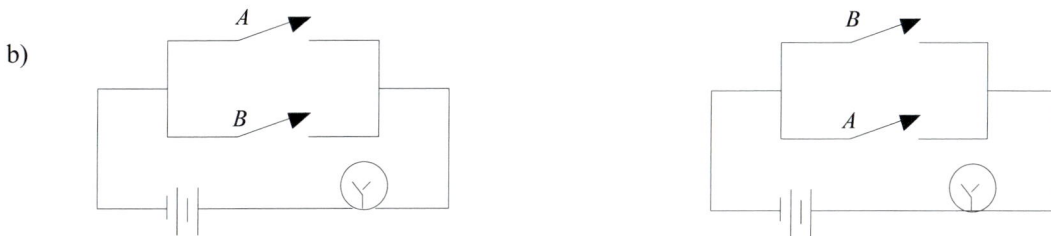

$$A + B = B + A$$

2. Associative Laws

a)

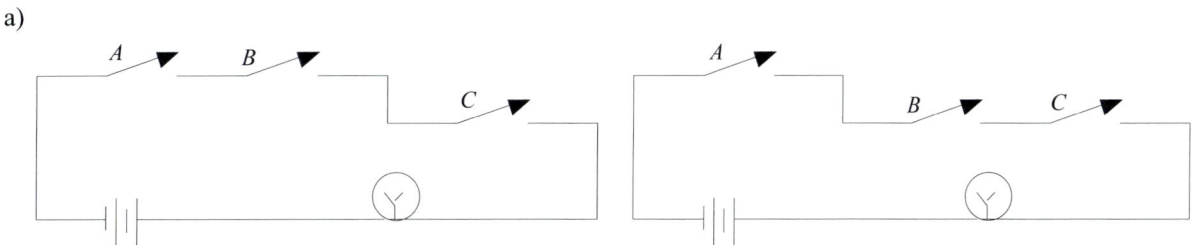

$$((A \times B) \times C = A \times (B \times C)$$

b)

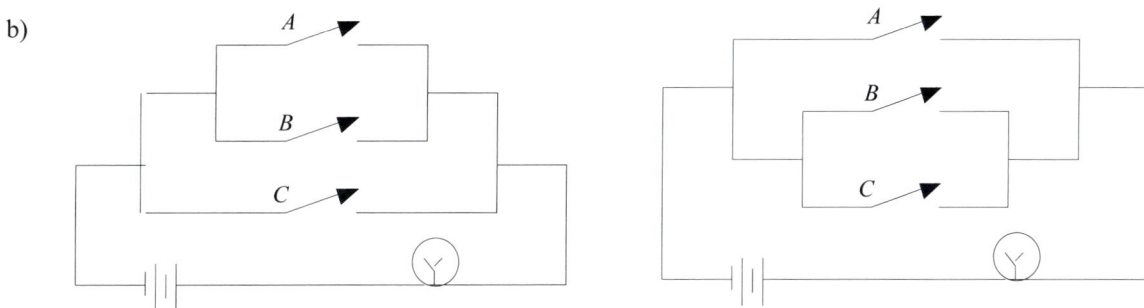

$$(A + B) + C = A + (B + C)$$

193

3/4. Idempotent and Complement Laws

Sometimes two switches are simultaneously both open or both closed and are designated with the same letter. If two switches are always in opposite states, i.e., when one is open, the other is closed and vice versa, they are called complements and will be designated as A and A'.

a)

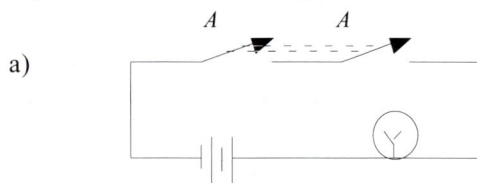

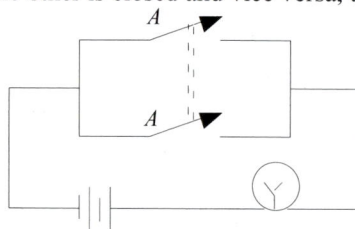

$$A \times A = A$$

$$A + A = A$$

b)

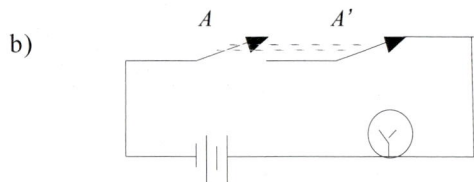

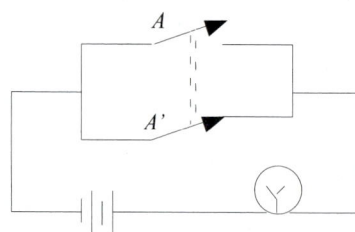

$$A \times A' = 0$$

$$A + A' = 1$$

5. Distributive Laws

a)

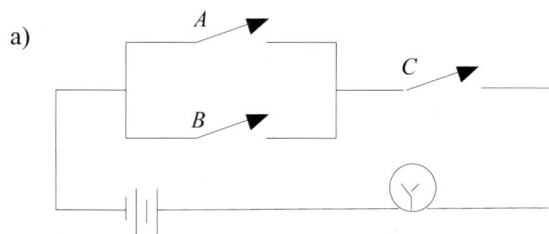

$$(A + B) \times C = (A \times C) + (B \times C)$$

(If C is closed and either A or B or both A and B are closed, the light will be lit in both circuits.)

b)

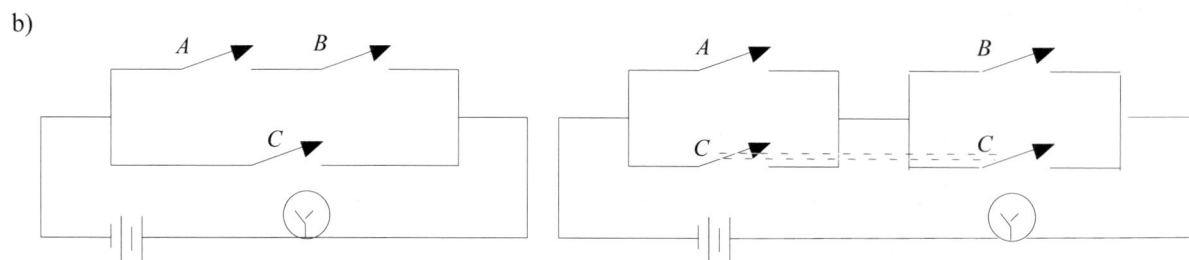

$$(A \times B) + C = (A + C) \times (B + C)$$

(If C is closed and/or if both A and B are closed, the light will be lit in both circuits.)

6. Identity Laws

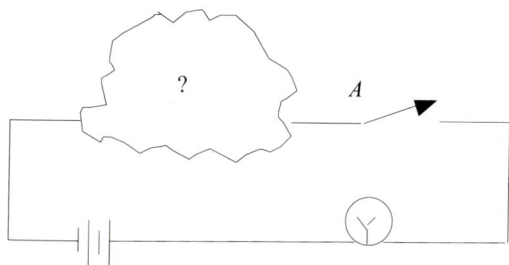

The cloud represents an unknown set of switches in series with switch A. Either electricity flows through this set (1) or it doesn't (0). Therefore,

a) $1 \times A = A$ (the light depends on switch A)

b) $0 \times A = 0$ (the light will always be off)

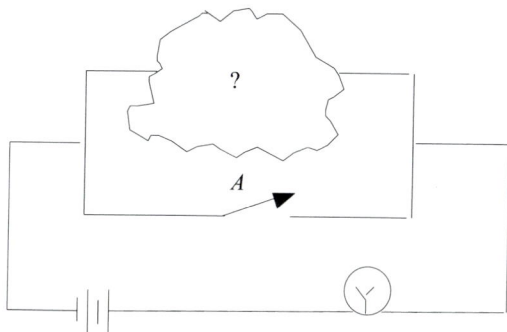

The cloud represents an unknown set of switches in parallel with switch A. Either electricity flows through this set (1) or it doesn't (*0*). Therefore,

c) $1 + A = 1$ (the light will always be on)

d) $0 + A = A$ (the light depends on switch A)

7. Absorption Laws

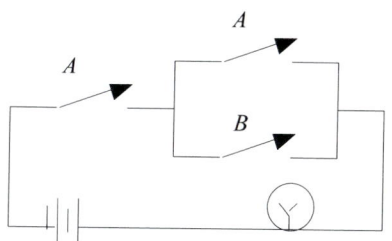 = 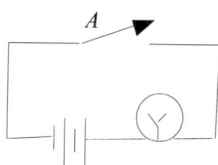 =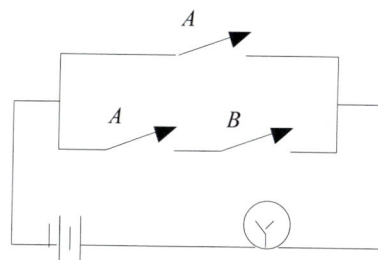

a) $A \times (A + B) = A$ *b)* $A + (A \times B) = A$

8. Involution (Double Complement) Law

$$\left(A'\right)' = A$$

9. DeMorgan's Laws

a) $(A + B)' = A' \times B'$ *b)* $(A \times B)' = A' + B'$

10. Principle of Duality: With the exception of the Involution Law, all of the above laws come in dual pairs: each member of the pair can be obtained from the other by interchanging "$+$" and "$\times$" and then "0" and "1".

This algebra is known as Boolean algebra, named for George Boole (1815 - 1864), the first professor of mathematics at Queens College, Cork, Ireland and author of <u>Mathematical Analysis of Logic</u> and <u>Laws of Thought</u>.

The Problems

1. Simplifying Circuits

For each of the following sets of switches,

   i) Write the Boolean algebra expression which describes it.

   ii) Using the Boolean algebra laws, simplify your expression. A Boolean expression is simplified if it is equivalent to the original and has the fewest number of switches possible. Two Boolean expressions are equivalent if one can be derived from the other using the laws of Boolean algebra. Be sure to show the steps of your simplification; obvious steps may be omitted. The bracketed number by each diagram represents the number of switches in the simplified circuit.

   iii) Draw the simplified circuit. (No need to draw the battery and light. Switch levers can be omitted.)

   For example,

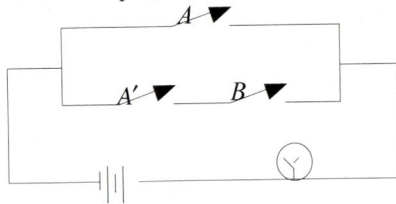

   i) $A + A'B$

   ii) $A + A'B = (A + A')(A + B)$

   $= 1(A + B)$

   $= (A + B)$

   iii) Simplified circuit:

   (In both circuits the lights are lit when A is closed and when A is open and B is closed.)

a) [2]

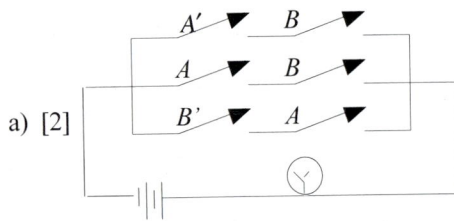

b) [2]

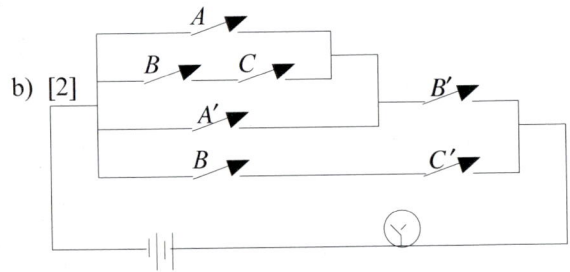

c) [3]

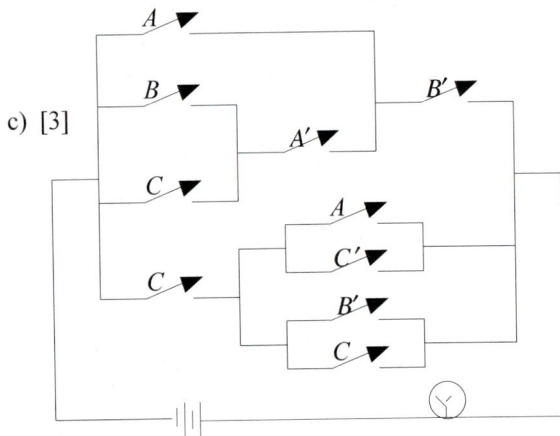

d) [4]

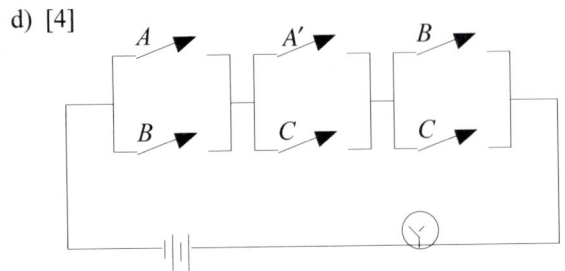

196

2. Designing Circuits

For each of the following problems create the simplest circuit which will satisfy the given constraints.

(Show your work!)

a)

switches				light
A	B	C	D	Ⓨ
1	1	0	0	1
0	1	1	0	1
0	1	0	0	1

(This first line means that the light will be on when switches A and B are closed and switches C and D are open.)

In the other thirteen combinations of switch states the light will be off.

b)

switches				light
A	B	C	D	Ⓨ
0	0	1	1	0
1	0	0	1	0
0	0	0	1	0

In the other thirteen combinations of switch states the light will be on.

c)

switches				light
A	B	C	D	Ⓨ
1	0	0	0	1
1	0	0	1	1
1	1	0	1	1
0	1	0	1	1
0	1	1	1	1

switches				light
A	B	C	D	Ⓨ
1	0	1	1	0
1	0	1	0	0
1	1	0	0	0
1	1	1	0	0
0	1	1	0	0

In the other six combinations of switch states it does not matter whether the light is on or not!

197

d) All guests are required to wear green to the Annual St. Patrick's Day Party. However, the green is limited to green socks, a green tie, a green jacket, or a green hair ribbon and limited to the following conditions:

i) A green jacket must be worn if a green tie is worn.

ii) Green socks and green jacket may be worn together only if a green tie or green ribbon is worn.

iii) If either a green jacket and a green ribbon are worn or green socks are not worn, then a green tie must be worn.

The bouncer has created a simple switch box to determine whether or not a potential guest should be admitted. He just flicks the four slide switches to yes or no and if the green light goes on the person is allowed to enter.

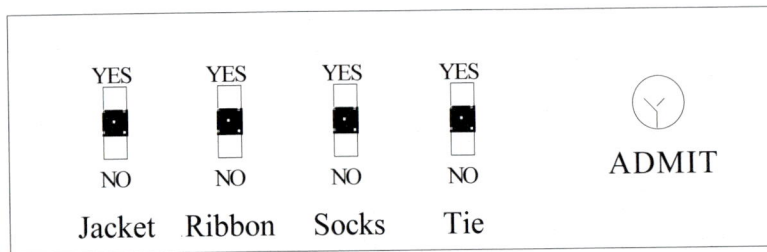

Design the simplified circuitry for this box. (Use *j, r, s,* and *t* for your variables.)

3. Other binary operators

a) The notion of *"exclusive or"* is very important in computer science. It means "either *A* or *B* but not both". The symbol, $\oplus$, is often used to represent the *exclusive or* function. It is defined as

$$A \oplus B = AB' + A'B$$

Simplify the following expressions:

i) $\left(A \oplus B\right)' \oplus \left(AB\right)'$ ii) $\left(A \oplus B \oplus AB\right)'$

b) Generally Boolean algebras have two binary operators (+ and ×) and one unary operator (') but a single binary operator called a Sheffer stroke (|) is all that is needed. A Sheffer stroke is sometimes called binary rejection, and can be thought of as *"neither A nor B"* or just *"NOR"*.
Symbolically it is defined as *A | B = A'B' = (A + B)'*. Determine an expression equivalent to each of the following but using only Sheffer strokes as the binary operator:

i) A' ii) AB iii) $A + B$

198

4.   Other Boolean Applications

a) In <u>Set Theory,</u> the elements of Boolean algebra become sets, 1 signifies "is in the set" and 0 signifies "is not in the set".

$A + B$ becomes $A \cup B$, the *union* of sets A and B and $A \times B$ becomes $A \cap B$, the *intersection* of sets A and B. A' becomes $\overline{A}$, the *complement* of A, i.e. not in set A.. The *empty set*, $\varnothing$, and the *universal set*, $\bigcup$, take on the roles of the identity elements 0 and 1.

i) A new binary operator, *difference*, is defined as $A - B = A \cap B'$. Prove the following set theory theorem using the above definitions and the laws of Boolean algebra:

$$A - (B \cup C) = (A - B) \cap (A - C)$$

ii) Show the above theorem is true using Venn Diagrams.

iii) A is a *subset* of B (symbolically, $A \subset B$) can be defined as $A \subset B$ is equivalent to $A \cup B = B$.

.Prove the following set theory theorem using the above definitions and the laws of Boolean algebra:

$$((A \cup B) \cap C) \subset (A \cup (B \cap C))$$

iv) Show the above theorem is true using Venn Diagrams.

b) In <u>Logic Theory,</u> the elements of Boolean algebra become simple statements that are true or false,

$p + q$ becomes $p \vee q$, i.e. $p\ OR\ q$ and $p \times q$ becomes $p \wedge q$, i.e. $p\ AND\ q$. The unary operator p' becomes $\sim p$, i.e. *NOT p*. *FALSE* and *TRUE* take on the roles of the identity elements 0 and 1.

i) A new binary operator, *implication*, is defined as $p \rightarrow q = \sim p \vee q$. It is often read as *"If p then q"*.

Prove the following logic theorem, called the *Law of Contrapositive*, using the above definitions and the laws of Boolean algebra:

$$p \rightarrow q\ =\ \sim q \rightarrow \sim p$$

ii) Another important law of logical reasoning is the *Law of Syllogism*, which states, "If p implies q is true and q implies r is true, then p implies r must also be true." Symbolically this law is written as:

$$((p \rightarrow q)\ \wedge\ (q \rightarrow r))\ \rightarrow\ (p \rightarrow r).$$

Prove this theorem is always true using the laws of Boolean algebra.

199

iii) Using the two laws of logic above, determine the conclusion that can be drawn from using ALL the statements in this logic puzzle of Louis Carroll, the author of <u>Through the Looking Glass</u> (or <u>Alice in Wonderland)</u>:

> The only animals in my house are cats.
>
> Every animal that loves to gaze at the moon is suitable for a pet.
>
> When I detest an animal, I avoid it.
>
> No animals are carnivores unless they prowl at night.
>
> No cat fails to eat mice.
>
> No animals ever like me except those in my house.
>
> Kangaroos are not suitable for pets.
>
> Only carnivores eat mice.
>
> I detest animals that do not like me.
>
> Animals that prowl at night always love to gaze at the moon

c) In <u>Number Theory</u>, the elements, a, b, of Boolean algebra become the factors of some positive *square-free* integer N. The $lcm(a,b)$, the least common multiple of a and b, becomes $a + b$ and $a \times b$ becomes $gcf(a,b)$, the greatest common factor of a and b. The unary operator a' becomes $\frac{N}{a}$. The numbers 1 and N take on the roles of the identity elements 0 and 1, respectively.

If $N = 210$, using the above definitions, find the value of $\left((6' + 15)(6 + 15')(6' + 15')\right)'$

(Be sure to show your work.)

The Solutions

1a. $A'B + AB + B'A$

$(A' + A)B + B'A$

$B + B'A$

$(B + B')(B + A)$

$(B + A)$

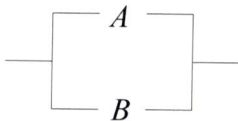

1b. $(A + BC + A')B' + BC'$

$(1)B' + BC'$

$(B' + B)(B' + C')$

$B' + C'$

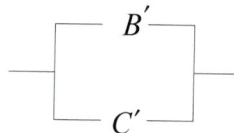

1c. $(A + (B + C)A')B' + C(A + C' + B' + C)$

$((A + B + C)(A + A'))B' + C(1)$

$(A + B + C)B' + C$

$AB' + B'C + C$

$AB' + C$

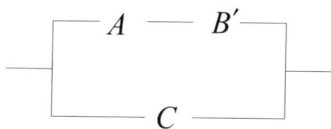

1d. $(A + B)(A' + C)(B + C)$

$(AA' + AC + BA' + BC)(B + C)$

$(AC + A'B + BC)(B + C)$

$ABC + ACC + A'BB + A'BC + BCB + BCC$

$AC + A'B + BC + A'A$

$(A + B)C + (A + B)A'$

$(A + B)(A' + C)$

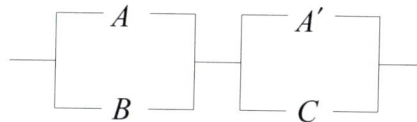

2a. $ABC'D' + A'BCD' + A'BC'D'$

$BD'(AC' + A'C + A'C')$

$BD'(AC' + A'(C + C'))$

$BD'(AC' + A')$

$BD'((A + A')(C' + A'))$

$BD'(C' + A')$

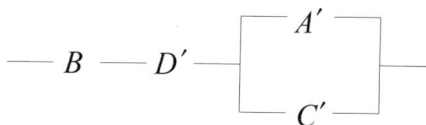

2b. $(A'B'CD + AB'C'D + A'B'C'D')'$

$(B'D(A'C + AC' + A'C'))'$

$(B'D(A'(C + C') + AC'))'$

$(B'D(A' + AC'))'$

$(B'D((A' + A)(A' + C')))'$

$(B'D(A' + C'))'$

$(B'D)' + (A' + C')'$

$B + D' + AC$

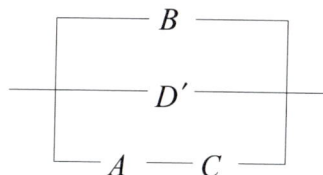

2c. It's difficult to write the initial algebraic statement as in problems 2a and 2b because we really don't know what the other six conditions should be set at. Is it best if they are all light the bulb, none of them light the bulb, or a combination? To help us out of this dilemma, the situation can be represented with a Vetch diagram (also called a Karnaugh map), a Venn diagram type drawing which can be used more than three sets. Each of the sixteen possibilities for the states of the four switches is represented by one of the cells in the grid. The two top rows represent the states when switch A is closed, the bottom rows when A is open. The two middle rows represent a closed switch C and the outer rows an open switch C. The first two columns, a closed switch B and the right two columns an open switch B. The two middle columns a close switch D and the outer two columns an open switch D.

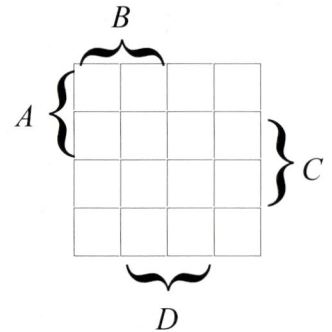

First place five ones representing the five states of the switches when the light is lit:

Then place the five zeros representing the five states of the switches when the light is off:

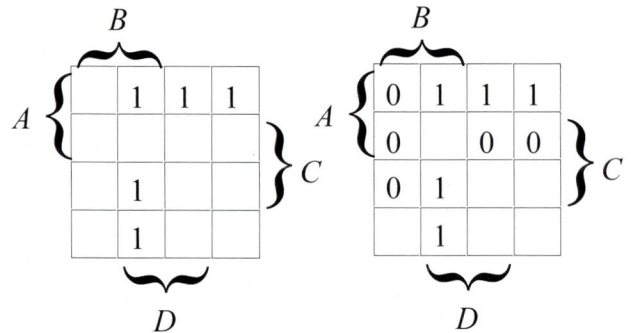

Finally in the remaining cells place a one or a zero, trying to make blocks of four squares (2x2, 1x4, or 4x1) with all ones or all zeros and/or maximizing symmetry:

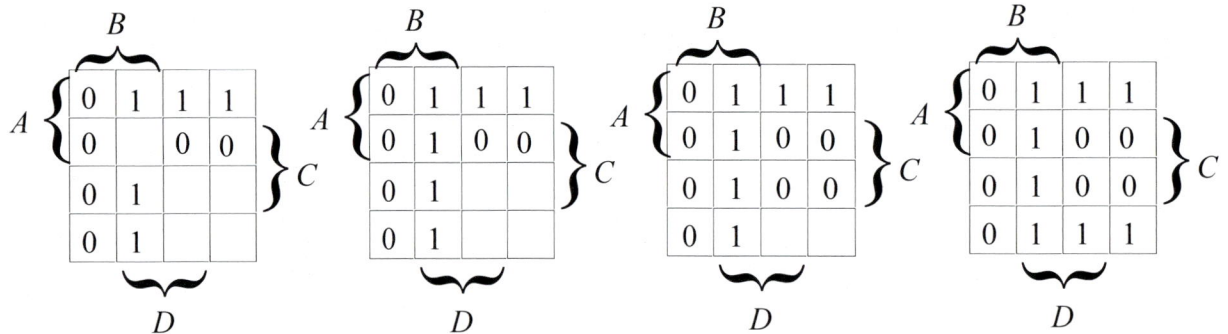

Now the algebraic statement can be written:

$$ABC'D + ABCD + A'BCD + A'BC'D + AB'C'D + AB'C'D' + A'B'C'D + A'B'C'D'$$
$$BD(AC' + AC + A'C + A'C') + B'C'(AD + AD' + A'D + A'D')$$
$$BD\big(A(C'+C) + A'(C+C')\big) + B'C'\big(A(D+D') + A(D+D')\big)$$
$$BD(A+A') + B'C'(A+A')$$
$$BD + B'C'$$

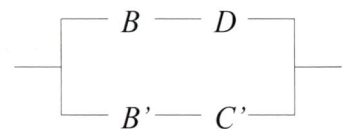

2d)

There are sixteen total possibilities:

J	R	S	T
1	1	1	1
1	1	1	0
1	1	0	1
1	1	0	0
1	0	1	1
1	0	1	0
1	0	0	1
1	0	0	0
0	1	1	1
0	1	1	0
0	1	0	1
0	1	0	0
0	0	1	1
0	0	1	0
0	0	0	1
0	0	0	0

Statement (i) eliminates four of them:

J	R	S	T
1	1	1	1
1	1	1	0
1	1	0	1
1	1	0	0
1	0	1	1
1	0	1	0
1	0	0	1
1	0	0	0
~~0~~	~~1~~	~~1~~	~~1~~
0	1	1	0
~~0~~	~~1~~	~~0~~	~~1~~
0	1	0	0
~~0~~	~~0~~	~~1~~	~~1~~
0	0	1	0
~~0~~	~~0~~	~~0~~	~~1~~
0	0	0	0

Statement (ii) eliminates another:

J	R	S	T
1	1	1	1
1	1	1	0
1	1	0	1
1	1	0	0
1	0	1	1
~~1~~	~~0~~	~~1~~	~~0~~
1	0	0	1
1	0	0	0
~~0~~	~~1~~	~~1~~	~~1~~
0	1	1	0
~~0~~	~~1~~	~~0~~	~~1~~
0	1	0	0
~~0~~	~~0~~	~~1~~	~~1~~
0	0	1	0
~~0~~	~~0~~	~~0~~	~~1~~
0	0	0	0

Statement (iii) eliminates five more:

J	R	S	T
1	1	1	1
~~1~~	~~1~~	~~1~~	~~0~~
1	1	0	1
~~1~~	~~1~~	~~0~~	~~0~~
1	0	1	1
~~1~~	~~0~~	~~1~~	~~0~~
1	0	0	1
~~1~~	~~0~~	~~0~~	~~0~~
~~0~~	~~1~~	~~1~~	~~1~~
0	1	1	0
~~0~~	~~1~~	~~0~~	~~1~~
~~0~~	~~1~~	~~0~~	~~0~~
~~0~~	~~0~~	~~1~~	~~1~~
0	0	1	0
~~0~~	~~0~~	~~0~~	~~1~~
~~0~~	~~0~~	~~0~~	~~0~~

The resulting algebraic statement is:

$$JRST + JRS'T + JR'ST + JR'S'T + J'RST' + J'R'ST'$$
$$JT\left(RS + RS' + R'S + R'S'\right) + J'ST'\left(R + R'\right)$$
$$JT\left(R(S + S') + R'(S + S')\right) + J'ST'$$
$$JT\left(R + R'\right) + J'ST'$$
$$JT + J'ST'$$

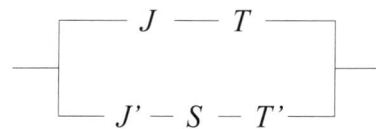

203

3a.i)
$$\left(A \oplus B\right)' \oplus \left(AB\right)'$$
$$(AB' + A'B)' \oplus (AB)'$$
$$(AB' + A'B)'(AB) + (AB' + A'B)(AB)' \quad \dagger$$
$$(AB')'(A'B)'(AB) + (AB' + A'B)(A' + B')$$
$$(A' + B)(A + B')(AB) + AB' + A'B$$
$$\left(A'B' + AB\right)(AB) + AB' + A'B$$
$$(AB) + AB' + A'B$$
$$A(B + B') + A'B$$
$$A + A'B$$
$$(A + A')(A + B)$$
$$A + B$$

3a.ii)
$$\left(A \oplus B \oplus AB\right)'$$
$$\left((AB' + A'B) \oplus AB\right)'$$
$$\left(AB' + A'B\right)(AB)' + \left(AB' + A'B\right)'(AB)' \quad \text{same as } (\dagger)' \text{ above.}$$
$$(A + B)'$$
$$A'B'$$

3b. By experimenting with the new symbol and it's definition:

   i) $A \mid A = (A + A)' = A'$

   ii) $(A \mid A) \mid (B \mid B) = A' \mid B' = AB$

   iii) $(A \mid B) \mid (B \mid A) = A'B' \mid B'A' = \left(A'B'\right)' = A + B$

4a.i) $A - (B \cup C) = (A - B) \cap (A - C)$
$$A \cap (B \cup C)' = (A \cap B') \cap (A \cap C')$$
$$A(B + C)' = AB' \times AC'$$
$$AB'C' = AB'C'$$

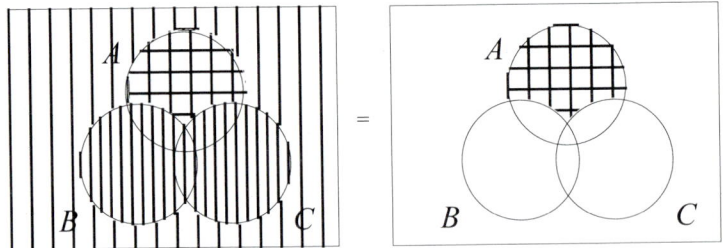

4a.iii) $\left((A \cup B) \cap C\right) \subset \left(A \cup (B \cap C)\right)$
$$(A + B)C \subset (A + BC)$$
$$(A + B)C \cup (A + BC) = (A + BC)$$
$$(AC + BC) + (A + BC) = (A + BC)$$
$$A + BC = A + BC$$

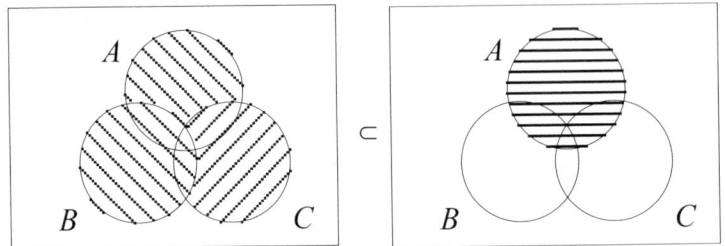

4b.i)
$$p \to q = \sim q \to \sim p$$
$$\sim p \vee q = \sim(\sim q) \vee \sim p$$
$$\sim p \vee q = q \vee \sim p$$

4b.ii)
$$\left((p \to q) \wedge (q \to r)\right) \to (p \to r)$$
$$\left((p' + q) \times (q' + r)\right)' + (p' + r)$$
$$(p' + q)' + (q' + r)' + p' + r$$
$$pq' + qr' + p' + r$$
$$(p + p')(q' + p') + (q + r)(r' + r)$$
$$q' + p' + q + r$$
$$1 + p' + r$$
$$1$$

4b.iii) Change all sentences to if ...then statements and represent symbolically:

If an animal is in my house, then it is a cat.	h → c
If an animal loves to gaze at the moon, then it is suitable for a pet.	g → s
If I detest an animal, then I avoid it.	d → a
If an animal is carnivorous, then it prowls at night.	r → p
If an animal is a cat, it eats mice.	c → e
If an animal likes me, then it is in my house.	l → h
If an animal is a kangaroo, then it is not suitable for a pet	k → ~s
If an animal eats mice, then it is carnivorous.	e → c
If an animal does not like me, then I detest it.	~l → d
If an animal prowls at night, then it loves to gaze at the moon.	p → g

Now start combining pairs of sentences together using the Law of Syllogism and the Law of Contrapositive

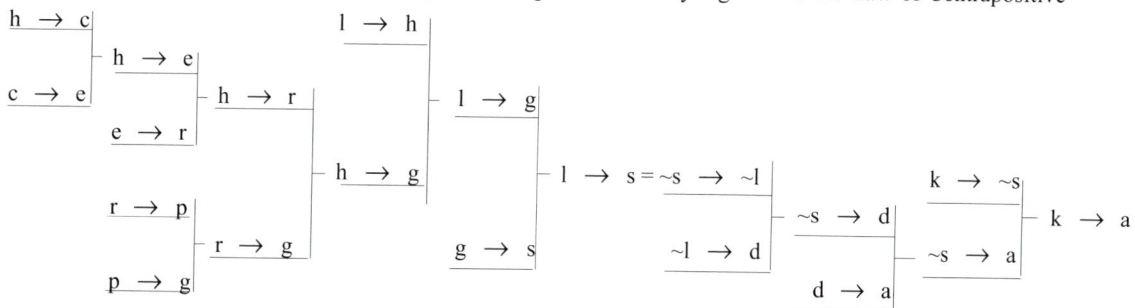

Therefore, the conclusion is "if it is a kangaroo, I avoid it." or simply "I avoid kangaroos!"

4c.iii) Method 1 – Do Boolean algebra with symbols and then translate into number theory representation.

$$\left((6'+15)(6+15')(6'+15')\right)'$$

$$\left((6\cdot6'+6'\cdot15'+15\cdot6+15\cdot15')(6'+15')\right)'$$

$$\left((6'\cdot15'+15\cdot6)(6'+15')\right)'$$

$$\left((6'\cdot6'\cdot15'+6'\cdot15\cdot6+15'\cdot6'\cdot15'+15'\cdot15\cdot6)\right)'$$

$$\left(6'15'+6'15'\right)'$$

$$\left(6'15'\right)'$$

$$6+15$$

$$lcm(6,15)$$

$$30$$

Method 2 – Translate into number theory first:

$$6'=\frac{210}{6}=35 \quad \text{and} \quad 15'=\frac{210}{15}=14$$

$$\left((6'+15')(6+15')(6'+15')\right)'$$

$$gcf\left(gcf\left(lcm(35,15),\ lcm(6,14)\right),\ lcm(35,14)\right)'$$

$$\left(gcf\left(gcf(105,42),\ 70\right)\right)'$$

$$\left(gcf(21,70)\right)'$$

$$(7)'$$

$$\frac{210}{7}=30$$

Triangular Trigonometry

The Problems

Part A. Proofs from Pictures

1. Make a copy of the diagram at the right on your answer sheet. Circle O is a unit circle, centered at O, with secant line $\overline{DE}$ containing point O. Lines $\overrightarrow{EG}$ and $\overrightarrow{DG}$ are tangent to the circle at points F and A, respectively. $\overline{EG} \perp \overline{DG}$ and $\overline{CB} \perp \overline{OA}$. If the measure of $\angle COA = \theta$, label the lengths of the sides of all the right triangles in the figure. Using ΔEDG, determine a Pythagorean identity.

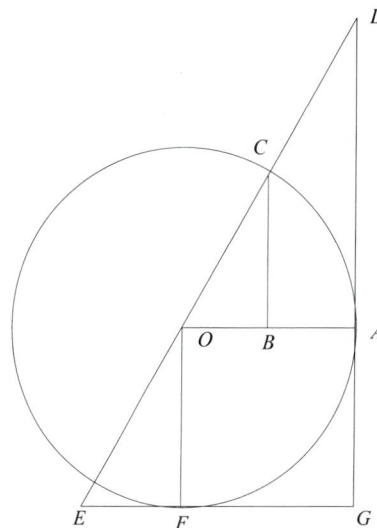

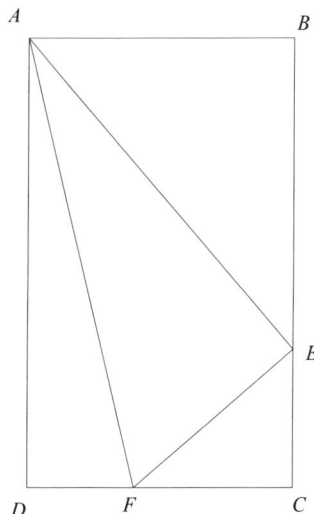

2. Make a copy of the diagram at the left on your answer sheet. Right triangle AEF (right angle at E) is inscribed in rectangle $ABCD$ as shown. If $\angle FAE = \alpha$ and $\angle EAB = \beta$ and the length of $AF = 1$, label the lengths of all segments in the diagram in terms of α, β, and $\alpha + \beta$. Comparing the lengths of the sides of rectangle $ABCD$, derive two familiar trigonometric identities.

3. Make a copy of the diagram at the right on your answer sheet. ΔOAD is a triangle with right angle OAD, $OA = 1$ and $\angle DOA = \alpha$. Cevian $\overline{OB}$ is drawn, forming $\angle BOA = \beta$. Point E is located on $\overline{OD}$ so that $\overline{EB} \perp \overline{OB}$ and point C is located on $\overline{AD}$ so that $\overline{EC} \perp \overline{AD}$. Label the lengths of all the segments of the diagram (except $\overline{OE}$, $\overline{ED}$, and $\overline{OD}$) in terms α, β, and $\alpha - \beta$. Using the fact that $AD - AB = BC + CD$, determine a familiar trigonometric identity.

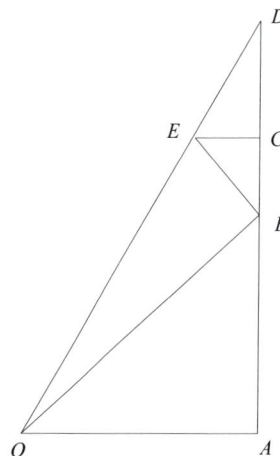

4. Make a copy of the diagram at the right on your answer sheet. Circle O is centered at O with diameters $\overline{AB}$ and $\overline{CD}$. Point E is placed on circle O so that $\overline{EB}$ intersects $\overline{CD}$ at point F and forms $\angle EBA = \theta$. If $OB = a$, $BF = b$, and $OF = c$, determine the lengths of $\overline{AO}$, $\overline{CO}$, $\overline{EF}$ and $\overline{FD}$ in terms of a, b, c, and θ. Use chords $\overline{AB}$, $\overline{BE}$ and $\overline{CD}$ to prove a familiar trigonometric identity.

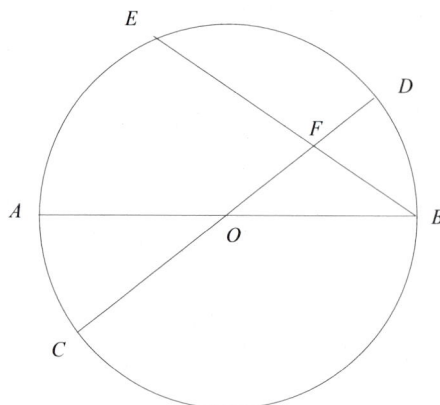

5. Make a copy of the diagram at the right on your answer sheet. Angle A is drawn and points B, C, and D are placed on the angle as shown so that $AB = BC = CD = 1$. Points E, F, and G are then placed so that $BE \perp AC$, $CF \perp AD$, and $DG \perp AG$. If $\angle A = \theta$, label all angles that are equal to θ, 2θ, and 3θ. Label the lengths of each remaining segment in the diagram in terms of θ, 2θ, and 3θ.

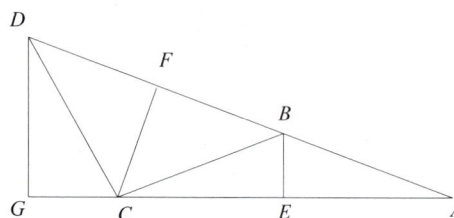

Use right triangle ACF to prove $\sin(2\theta) = 2\sin(\theta)\cos(\theta)$ and $\cos(2\theta) = 2\cos^2(\theta) - 1$. Use right triangle ADG to prove $\cos(3\theta) = 4\cos^3(\theta) - 3\cos(\theta)$ and $\sin(3\theta) = 3\sin(\theta) - 4\sin^3(\theta)$.

Part B Half Angle Identities

When you studied circle functions, you derived laws for the sine, cosine , and tangent of $\dfrac{\alpha}{2}$ in terms of α. In this

part of the contest, you will derive laws for the sine, cosine , and tangent of $\dfrac{\alpha}{2}$ in terms of sides a, b, and c. In

this section the variables s, r, and R will be used to signify the semi perimeter, the inradius, and the circumradius of a triangle, respectively.

6. Using the figure at the right, show that $\tan\left(\dfrac{\alpha}{2}\right) = \dfrac{r}{s-a}$.

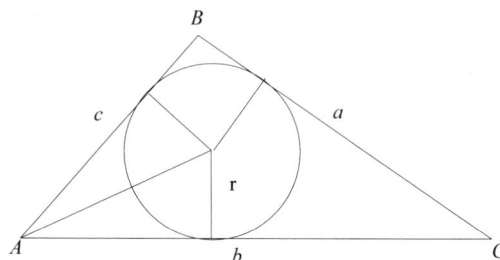

208

7. Starting with $\cos\left(\dfrac{\alpha}{2}\right) = \sqrt{\dfrac{1+\cos(\alpha)}{2}}$, show that $\cos\left(\dfrac{\alpha}{2}\right) = \sqrt{\dfrac{s(s-a)}{bc}}$.

8. Show that $\sin\left(\dfrac{\alpha}{2}\right) = \sqrt{\dfrac{(s-b)(s-c)}{bc}}$.

9. Use the results from questions 7 and 8 to prove Hero's formula for the area of a triangle,

$K = \sqrt{s(s-a)(s-b)(s-c)}$. (Hint: $\sin(2\theta) = 2\sin(\theta)\cos(\theta)$.)

10. Use the results from questions 6, 7, and 8 to prove $r = \sqrt{\dfrac{(s-a)(s-b)(s-c)}{s}}$.

11. Show that $2rR = \dfrac{abc}{a+b+c}$.

Part C

12. In right triangle ABC, angle C is $90°$. Using $n-1$ points, the hypotenuse is divided into n congruent segments. Then $n-1$ cevians are drawn from C to each of these points. It can be shown that the sum of the squares of the lengths of these cevians is equal to $R(n) \cdot c^2$, where $R(n)$ is a rational function. Find $R(n)$, expressing your answer as a ratio of two polynomials. Show your work and reduce your answer.

The Solutions

1. See diagram at right. $\left(\cot(\theta)+1\right)^2 + \left(\tan(\theta)+1\right)^2 = (\sec(\theta)+\csc(\theta))^2$

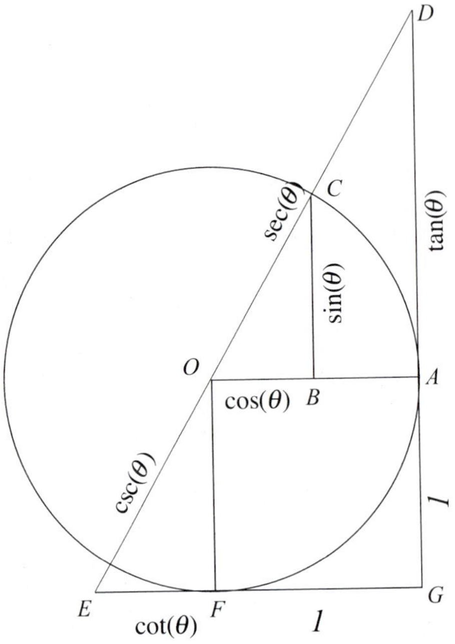

2.

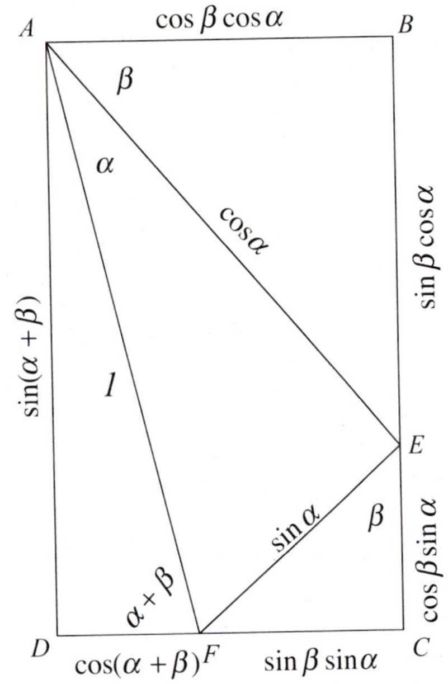

$AB = DC$

$\cos\beta\cos\alpha = \cos(\alpha+\beta) + \sin\beta\sin\alpha$

$\cos(\alpha+\beta) = \cos\alpha\cos\beta - \sin\alpha\sin\beta$

$AD = BC$

$\sin(\alpha+\beta) = \sin\beta\cos\alpha + \cos\beta\sin\alpha$

$\sin(\alpha+\beta) = \sin\alpha\cos\beta + \cos\alpha\sin\beta$

3.

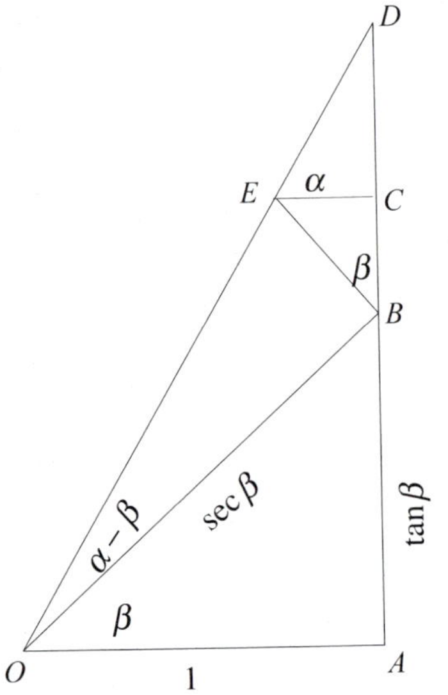

$EB = \tan(\alpha-\beta)\sec\beta$

$EC = \tan(\alpha-\beta)\tan\beta$

$CD = \tan\alpha\tan(\alpha-\beta)\tan\beta$

$BC = \tan(\alpha-\beta)$

$AD = \tan\alpha$

$AD - AB = BC + CD$

$\tan\alpha - \tan\beta = \tan(\alpha-\beta) + \tan\alpha\tan(\alpha-\beta)\tan\beta$

$\tan\alpha - \tan\beta = \tan(\alpha-\beta)(1 + \tan\alpha\tan\beta)$

$\dfrac{\tan\alpha - \tan\beta}{(1+\tan\alpha\tan\beta)} = \tan(\alpha-\beta).$

4. Add segment $\overline{AE}$ to the drawing. Because $\overline{AB}$ is a diameter $\angle AEB = 90°$. $\cos\theta = \dfrac{EB}{AB} = \dfrac{EB}{2a}$. Therefore,

$EB = 2a\cos\theta$ and $EF = 2a\cos\theta - b$. Since $\overline{CD}$ and $\overline{EB}$ are intersecting chords,

$$(a+c)(a-c) = b(2a\cos\theta - b)$$
$$a^2 - c^2 = 2ab\cos\theta - b^2$$
$$a^2 + b^2 - 2ab\cos\theta = c^2.$$

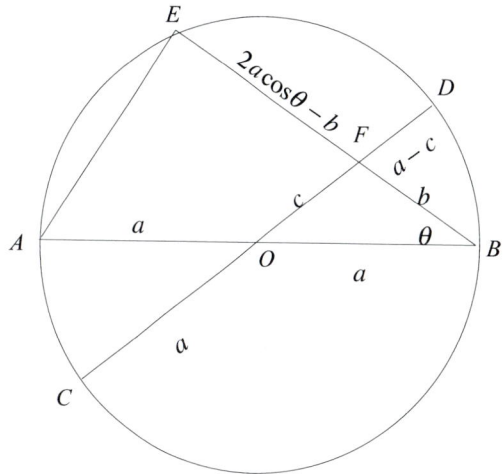

5. In triangle ACF, $\cos\theta = \dfrac{AF}{AC} = \dfrac{\cos 2\theta + 1}{2\cos\theta}$.

Therefore, $\cos 2\theta = 2\cos^2\theta - 1$.

In triangle ACF, $\sin\theta = \dfrac{CF}{AC} = \dfrac{\sin 2\theta}{2\cos\theta}$.

Therefore, $\sin 2\theta = 2\sin\theta\cos\theta$.

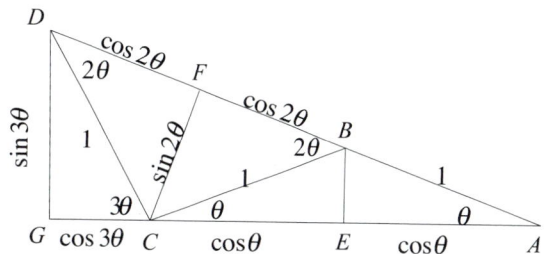

In triangle ADG, $\cos\theta = \dfrac{AG}{AD} = \dfrac{\cos 3\theta + 2\cos\theta}{2\cos 2\theta + 1}$.

Therefore, $\cos 3\theta = 2\cos 2\theta\cos\theta + \cos\theta - 2\cos\theta$

$\cos 3\theta = 2\cos\theta(2\cos^2\theta - 1) - \cos\theta$

$\cos 3\theta = 4\cos^3\theta - 3\cos\theta$

In triangle ADG, $\sin\theta = \dfrac{DG}{DA} = \dfrac{\sin 3\theta}{2\cos 2\theta + 1}$.

Therefore, $\sin 3\theta = 2\cos 2\theta\sin\theta + \sin\theta$

$\sin 3\theta = 2\sin\theta(2\cos^2\theta - 1) + \sin\theta$

$\sin 3\theta = 2\sin\theta(2(1 - \sin^2\theta) - 1) + \sin\theta$

$\sin 3\theta = 4\sin\theta - 4\sin^3\theta - 2\sin\theta + \sin\theta$

$\sin 3\theta = 3\sin\theta - 4\sin^3\theta.$

6. Label the tangent segments as shown.

$$c - (a - b + x) = x$$

$$b + c - a = 2x$$

$$\frac{b + c - a}{2} = x.$$

But $s - a = \dfrac{a + b + c}{2} - a$

$$s - a = \frac{a + b + c}{2} - \frac{2a}{2}$$

$$s - a = \frac{b + c - a}{2}.$$

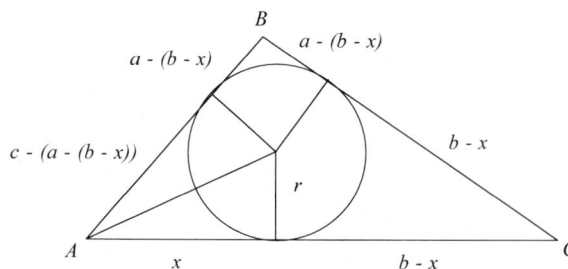

$$\tan\left(\frac{\alpha}{2}\right) = \frac{r}{x} = \frac{r}{\dfrac{b + c - a}{2}} = \frac{r}{s - a}.$$

7.

$$\cos\left(\frac{\alpha}{2}\right) = \sqrt{\frac{1 + \cos(\alpha)}{2}}$$

$$\cos^2\left(\frac{\alpha}{2}\right) = \frac{1 + \cos(\alpha)}{2}$$

$$\cos^2\left(\frac{\alpha}{2}\right) = \frac{1}{2} + \frac{b^2 + c^2 - a^2}{4bc}$$

$$\cos^2\left(\frac{\alpha}{2}\right) = \frac{2bc}{4bc} + \frac{b^2 + c^2 - a^2}{4bc}$$

$$\cos^2\left(\frac{\alpha}{2}\right) = \frac{(b + c)^2 - a^2}{4bc}$$

$$\cos^2\left(\frac{\alpha}{2}\right) = \frac{(b + c + a)(b + c - a)}{4bc}$$

$$\cos^2\left(\frac{\alpha}{2}\right) = \frac{s(s - a)}{bc}$$

$$\cos\left(\frac{\alpha}{2}\right) = \sqrt{\frac{s(s - a)}{bc}}.$$

8.

$$\sin\left(\frac{\alpha}{2}\right) = \sqrt{\frac{1 - \cos(\alpha)}{2}}$$

$$\sin^2\left(\frac{\alpha}{2}\right) = \frac{1 - \cos(\alpha)}{2}$$

$$\sin^2\left(\frac{\alpha}{2}\right) = \frac{1}{2} - \frac{b^2 + c^2 - a^2}{4bc}$$

$$\sin^2\left(\frac{\alpha}{2}\right) = \frac{2bc}{4bc} + \frac{a^2 - (b^2 + c^2)}{4bc}$$

$$\sin^2\left(\frac{\alpha}{2}\right) = \frac{a^2 - (b - c)^2}{4bc}$$

$$\sin^2\left(\frac{\alpha}{2}\right) = \frac{(a - b + c)(a + b - c)}{4bc}$$

$$\sin^2\left(\frac{\alpha}{2}\right) = \frac{(s - b)(s - c)}{bc}$$

$$\sin\left(\frac{\alpha}{2}\right) = \sqrt{\frac{(s - b)(s - c)}{bc}}.$$

9.

$$K = \frac{1}{2} bc \sin(\alpha)$$

$$K = \frac{1}{2} bc \sin\left(2\left(\frac{\alpha}{2}\right)\right)$$

$$K = \frac{1}{2} bc \cdot 2 \sin\left(\frac{\alpha}{2}\right) \cos\left(\frac{\alpha}{2}\right)$$

$$K = bc \sqrt{\frac{(s - b)(s - c)}{bc}} \sqrt{\frac{s(s - a)}{bc}}$$

$$K = \sqrt{s(s - a)(s - b)(s - c)}.$$

10. Using the results from questions 7 and 8, $\tan\left(\dfrac{\alpha}{2}\right) = \dfrac{\sin\left(\dfrac{\alpha}{2}\right)}{\cos\left(\dfrac{\alpha}{2}\right)} = \sqrt{\dfrac{(s-b)(s-c)}{s(s-a)}} = \dfrac{1}{s-a}\sqrt{\dfrac{(s-a)(s-b)(s-c)}{s}}$.

In question 6, you showed that $\tan\left(\dfrac{\alpha}{2}\right) = \dfrac{r}{s-a} = \left(\dfrac{1}{s-a}\right) \cdot r$. Therefore, $r = \sqrt{\dfrac{(s-a)(s-b)(s-c)}{s}}$.

11. If any of the sides of the triangle, say c, contain the center of the circumscribed circle, then $r = \dfrac{ab}{a+b+c}$

(proven in last year's Power Contest) and $c = 2R$. Combining, you get $2rR = \dfrac{abc}{a+b+c}$.

If none of the sides of the triangle go through the center of the circumscribed circle, then draw diameter $\overline{BD}$

and chord $\overline{CD}$. $\angle BCD$ must be a right angle and $\angle BDC = \alpha$ and the sine of $\angle BDC = \dfrac{a}{2R}$.

Therefore, $K = \dfrac{1}{2}bc\sin(\alpha) = \dfrac{1}{2}bc\dfrac{a}{2R} = \dfrac{abc}{4R}$. But $K = sr = r\left(\dfrac{a+b+c}{2}\right)$ and so $\dfrac{abc}{4R} = r\left(\dfrac{a+b+c}{2}\right)$ and

$2rR = \dfrac{abc}{a+b+c}$.

12. Solve by looking at simpler cases:

If $n = 2$, using the figure at the right, by the Law of Cosines,

$$d_1^2 = b^2 + \left(\dfrac{c}{2}\right)^2 - 2b\left(\dfrac{c}{2}\right)\cos\theta$$

$$d_1^2 = b^2 + \dfrac{c^2}{4} - bc\left(\dfrac{b}{c}\right)$$

$$d_1^2 = \dfrac{1}{4}c^2.$$

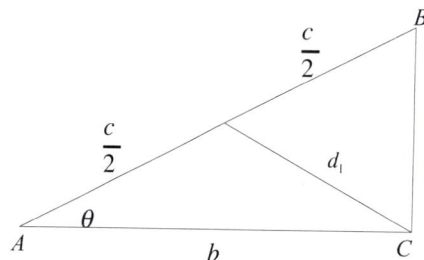

If $n = 3$, $d_1^2 + d_2^2 = b^2 + \left(\dfrac{c}{3}\right)^2 - 2b\left(\dfrac{c}{3}\right)\cos\theta + b^2 + \left(\dfrac{2c}{3}\right)^2 - 2b\left(\dfrac{2c}{3}\right)\cos\theta$

$$d_1^2 + d_2^2 = b^2 + \dfrac{c^2}{9} - 2b\left(\dfrac{c}{3}\right)\left(\dfrac{b}{c}\right) + b^2 + \dfrac{4c^2}{9} - 2b\left(\dfrac{2c}{3}\right)\left(\dfrac{b}{c}\right)$$

$$d_1^2 + d_2^2 = \dfrac{5}{9}c^2.$$

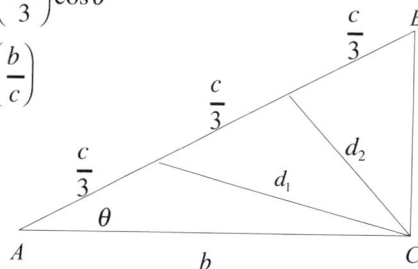

213

If $n = 4$, $d_1^2 + d_2^2 + d_3^2 = b^2 + \left(\dfrac{c}{4}\right)^2 - 2b\left(\dfrac{c}{4}\right)\cos\theta + b^2 + \left(\dfrac{2c}{4}\right)^2 - 2b\left(\dfrac{2c}{4}\right)\cos\theta + b^2 + \left(\dfrac{3c}{4}\right)^2 - 2b\left(\dfrac{3c}{4}\right)\cos\theta$

$d_1^2 + d_2^2 + d_3^2 = b^2 + \dfrac{c^2}{16} - 2b\left(\dfrac{c}{4}\right)\left(\dfrac{b}{c}\right) + b^2 + \dfrac{4c^2}{16} - 2b\left(\dfrac{2c}{4}\right)\left(\dfrac{b}{c}\right) + \dfrac{9c^2}{16} - 2b\left(\dfrac{3c}{4}\right)\left(\dfrac{b}{c}\right)$

$d_1^2 + d_2^2 + d_3^2 = \dfrac{14}{16}c^2$.

Continuing, when $n = 5$, $d_1^2 + d_2^2 + d_3^2 + d_4^2 = \dfrac{30}{25}c^2$ and when $n = 6$, $d_1^2 + d_2^2 + d_3^2 + d_4^2 + d_5^2 = \dfrac{55}{36}c^2$.

Therefore, $\displaystyle\sum_{i=1}^{n} d_i^2 = \left(\dfrac{\displaystyle\sum_{j=1}^{n-1}(j)^2}{n^2}\right)c^2 = \left(\dfrac{\dfrac{(n)(n-1)(2n-1)}{6}}{n^2}\right)c^2 = \left(\dfrac{2n^2 - 3n + 1}{6n}\right)c^2$.

Electing a Candidate

The Background

In a small Irish town on election day, instead of voting for a single candidate, each ballot requires the voter to *rank* the candidates in order of preference. For example, if there are four candidates and their names are listed on the ballot: Aidan, Brendan, Caitlin, and Deirdre and a voter marks the ballot with a 3, 4, 1, and 2 after each of their names respectively, then Caitlin has received one first-place vote, Deirdre a second-place vote, and Aidan and Brendan, a third and fourth-place vote respectively. A voter must rank each candidate and cannot give the same ranking to two candidates. The ordered *n*-tuple (a_1, a_2, a_3, a_4) represents the votes Aidan received, indicating a_1 first-place votes, a_2 second-place votes, and so on. It summarizes all the votes for Aidan and will be represented by the symbol $\overrightarrow{v_A}$, meaning the *voting vector* for candidate *A*.

An array of the voting vectors for all candidates will be called a *vote distribution matrix*. Note that in a vote distribution matrix, the sums of the numbers in each row and the sums of the numbers in each column will equal the total number of voters.

Before the election, a point value is assigned to each place. The ordered *n*-tuple (w_1, w_2, w_3, w_4) represents the point value assigned to each of the places. A first-place vote is worth w_1 points, a second-place vote is worth w_2 points, and so on. It is represented symbolically $\overrightarrow{w}$ and is called the *weight vector*. **In a weight vector it is required that $w_i \geq w_j$ whenever $i < j$.** Therefore, the same point value can be assigned to a second and a third-place vote but a third place vote cannot receive a higher point value than a second-place vote. **All weight values must be integers.**

Consider the following vote distribution matrix for a three candidate (*A, B, C*) election:

$$
\begin{array}{c}
 \\
A \\
B \\
C
\end{array}
\begin{array}{ccc}
1st & 2nd & 3rd \\
\left(\begin{array}{ccc}
4 & 1 & 4 \\
3 & 4 & 2 \\
2 & 4 & 3
\end{array}\right)
\end{array}
$$

If the weight vector $(2,1,0)$ was used, candidate *A* would receive nine points, candidate *B* would receive ten points, candidate *C* eight points, and therefore, candidate *B* would win. These values could be represented in a *points vector* $\overrightarrow{p} = (9,10,8)$. However, if the weight vector $(1,0,0)$ was used then the points vector would be $\overrightarrow{p} = (4,3,2)$ and candidate *A* would win. We say that a candidate wins an election if that candidate has more points than any other candidate. A winner is not declared if there is a tie for the most points.

The Problems

1. Consider the following vote distribution matrix:

$$
\begin{array}{cccc}
 & 1st & 2nd & 3rd & 4th \\
A & \begin{pmatrix} 5 & 8 & 3 & 4 \\
B & 5 & 9 & 0 & 6 \\
C & 6 & 1 & 6 & 7 \\
D & 4 & 2 & 11 & 3 \end{pmatrix}
\end{array}
$$

Show that is is possible for each of the candidates to win, given the proper weight vector.

2. Consider an election in which twenty-four voters rank three candidates. When the weight vector $\overline{w_A} = (1,0,0)$ is used candidate A wins. Using the weight vector $\overline{w_B} = (4,1,0)$, candidate B wins. Candidate C wins if $\overline{w_C} = (2,1,0)$ is used. Determine a vote distribution matrix satisfying these conditions.

3. Consider a two-candidate election. Prove that it is impossible to determine two weight vectors, $\overline{w_1}$ and $\overline{w_2}$, whereby candidate A wins if $\overline{w_1}$ is used and candidate B wins if $\overline{w_2}$ is used.

4. Determine all the possible ways to fill in the missing entries in this vote distribution matrix:

$$
\begin{array}{cccccc}
 & 1st & 2nd & 3rd & 4th & 5th \\
A & \begin{pmatrix} 8 & 7 & & 2 & 4 \\
B & 4 & & 5 & & \\
C & & 6 & 7 & 7 & 6 \\
D & 5 & & 2 & 8 & \\
E & & 7 & & 5 & 4 \end{pmatrix}
\end{array}
$$

5. Using the following vote distribution matrix, prove candidate C cannot win.

$$
\begin{array}{cccc}
 & 1st & 2nd & 3rd \\
A & \begin{pmatrix} 24 & 26 & 13 \\
B & 18 & 27 & 18 \\
C & 21 & 10 & 32 \end{pmatrix}
\end{array}
$$

6. For the following vote distribution matrix, determine (with proof) which candidates can win and which candidates cannot.

$$
\begin{array}{c}
 \quad 1st \;\; 2nd \;\; 3rd \;\; 4th \;\; 5th \;\; 6th \\
\begin{array}{c} A \\ B \\ C \\ D \\ E \\ F \end{array}
\left(
\begin{array}{cccccc}
7 & 10 & 10 & 8 & 10 & 5 \\
8 & 9 & 8 & 10 & 9 & 6 \\
9 & 6 & 3 & 10 & 7 & 15 \\
9 & 7 & 10 & 5 & 6 & 13 \\
8 & 9 & 8 & 10 & 11 & 4 \\
9 & 9 & 11 & 7 & 7 & 7
\end{array}
\right)
\end{array}
$$

7. If a candidate receives the fewest number of points (without tying another candidate) then that candidate is a *big time loser*. For the following vote distribution matrix, prove there is <u>exactly one</u> candidate who can neither be a winner nor a big time loser.

$$
\begin{array}{c}
 \quad 1st \;\; 2nd \;\; 3rd \;\; 4th \;\; 5th \\
\begin{array}{c} A \\ B \\ C \\ D \\ E \end{array}
\left(
\begin{array}{ccccc}
9 & 11 & 10 & 7 & 8 \\
8 & 11 & 8 & 6 & 12 \\
9 & 7 & 9 & 13 & 7 \\
10 & 6 & 7 & 13 & 9 \\
9 & 10 & 11 & 6 & 9
\end{array}
\right)
\end{array}
$$

8. Find all the possible weight vectors which would produce the following point totals for the following vote distribution matrix.

$$
\begin{array}{c}
 \quad 1st \;\; 2nd \;\; 3rd \;\; 4th \;\; 5th \\
\begin{array}{c} A \\ B \\ C \\ D \\ E \end{array}
\left(
\begin{array}{ccccc}
31 & 24 & 50 & 24 & 36 \\
31 & 33 & 32 & 33 & 36 \\
41 & 42 & 49 & 18 & 15 \\
25 & 24 & 2 & 60 & 54 \\
37 & 42 & 32 & 30 & 24
\end{array}
\right)
=
\begin{array}{c}
427 \\
409 \\
575 \\
241 \\
493
\end{array}
\end{array}
$$

Although not part of the contest, it can be shown that for any $n \geq 3$, a n-candidate vote distribution matrix can be formed along with n weight vectors whereby any of the n candidates can win!

The Solutions

1. Candidate C can win if $\vec{w} = (1,0,0,0)$. Candidate B wins if $\vec{w} = (1,1,0,0)$. Candidate D wins if $\vec{w} = (1,1,1,0)$. If $\vec{w} = (a,b,c,d)$, for candidate A to beat candidate B, c must be at least 1. Try $\vec{w} = (2,1,1,0)$, candidate A ties candidate D. Try $\vec{w} = (2,2,1,0)$ and candidate A wins. Obviously, other solutions are possible.

2. Let the vote distribution matrix, V, be equal to $\begin{array}{c} A \\ B \\ C \end{array}\begin{pmatrix} a & b & 24-a-b \\ c & d & 24-c-d \\ e & f & 24-e-f \end{pmatrix}$, where $e = 24 - a - c$ and

$f = 24 - b - d$. Out of the thousands of possible replacements for a, b, c, and d, only eight work! So trying to solve this problem by guessing and checking will not be very fruitful. Therefore, a little analysis would be helpful:

i) A wins if $\vec{w} = (1,0,0)$. Therefore, $a > c$ and $a > e$ and so $\boxed{a \geq 9}$.

ii) B wins if $\vec{w} = (4,1,0)$. Therefore, $4c + d > 4a + b$ and $4c + d > 4e + f$. Using the first inequality,

$$d - b > 4a - 4c$$
$$d - b > 4(a - c)$$
$$d - b > 4 \quad \text{(because } a > c)$$
Therefore, $d > b + 4$ or $\boxed{d \geq b + 5.}$

iii) C wins if $\vec{w} = (2,1,0)$. Therefore, $2e + f > 2a + b$ and $2e + f > 2c + d$. Rearranging this last inequality to $-2c - d + 2e + f > 0$ and adding it to the last inequality from part (ii) above (also rearranged to $4c + d - 4e - f > 0$), one gets $2c - 2e > 0$, implying that $\boxed{c > e}$ and $\boxed{a \geq e + 2.}$ Since $2e + f > 2c + d > 2e + d$, $\boxed{f > d.}$ Since $a \geq e + 2$, $4a \geq 4e + 8$ and therefore, $4e + f > 4a + b \geq 4e + 8 + b$, and so $f > 8 + b$ or $\boxed{f \geq b + 9.}$

Using the six highlighted inequalities, one can easily create one of the eight solutions to this problem:

$\begin{array}{c} A \\ B \\ C \end{array}\begin{pmatrix} 9 & 1 & 14 \\ 8 & 10 & 6 \\ 7 & 13 & 4 \end{pmatrix}$ $\begin{array}{c} A \\ B \\ C \end{array}\begin{pmatrix} 9 & 3 & 12 \\ 8 & 9 & 7 \\ 7 & 12 & 5 \end{pmatrix}$ $\begin{array}{c} A \\ B \\ C \end{array}\begin{pmatrix} 10 & 0 & 14 \\ 8 & 9 & 7 \\ 6 & 15 & 3 \end{pmatrix}$ $\begin{array}{c} A \\ B \\ C \end{array}\begin{pmatrix} 10 & 0 & 14 \\ 9 & 5 & 10 \\ 5 & 19 & 0 \end{pmatrix}$ $\begin{array}{c} A \\ B \\ C \end{array}\begin{pmatrix} 10 & 0 & 14 \\ 9 & 6 & 9 \\ 5 & 18 & 1 \end{pmatrix}$ $\begin{array}{c} A \\ B \\ C \end{array}\begin{pmatrix} 10 & 0 & 14 \\ 9 & 7 & 8 \\ 5 & 17 & 2 \end{pmatrix}$

$\begin{array}{c} A \\ B \\ C \end{array}\begin{pmatrix} 10 & 1 & 13 \\ 9 & 6 & 9 \\ 5 & 17 & 2 \end{pmatrix}$ $\begin{array}{c} A \\ B \\ C \end{array}\begin{pmatrix} 10 & 1 & 13 \\ 9 & 7 & 8 \\ 5 & 16 & 3 \end{pmatrix}$

3. Let n = the number of voters. If candidate A receives x first-place votes, the voting matrix would be:

$$A \begin{pmatrix} x & n-x \\ n-x & x \end{pmatrix}. \text{ Let } \vec{w}_A = (p,q) \text{ and } \vec{w}_B = (r,s), \text{ Candidate } A \text{ wins using } \vec{w}_A \text{ and candidate } B \text{ wins using}$$

$\vec{w}_B$. To eliminate ties, it must be true that $p > q$ and $r > s$ and so $p - q$ and $r - s$ are both positive.

When candidate A wins,
$$pa + q(n-a) > p(n-a) + qa$$
$$pa + qn - qa > pn - pa + qa$$
$$2pa - 2qa > pn - qn$$
$$2a(p-q) > n(p-q)$$
$$2a > n.$$

When candidate B wins,
$$r(n-a) + sa > ra + s(n-a)$$
$$rn - ra + sa > ra + sn - sa$$
$$rn - sn > 2ra - 2sa$$
$$n(r-s) > 2a(r-s)$$
$$n > 2a$$

But this is a contradiction! So a two-candidate cannot be created in which both candidates could win.

4. Assign the following variable names to the vote distribution matrix:

$$\begin{array}{c c c c c c} & 1st & 2nd & 3rd & 4th & 5th \\ A & 8 & 7 & A_3 & 2 & 4 \\ B & 4 & B_2 & 5 & B_4 & B_5 \\ C & C_1 & 6 & 7 & 7 & 6 \\ D & 5 & D_2 & 2 & 8 & D_5 \\ E & E_1 & 7 & E_3 & 5 & 4 \end{array}$$

Let r_X and c_Y denote the sum of the numbers in row X and column Y, respectively. Since the row and column sums for any vote distribution matrix must be equal, the following must be true:

$$0 = r_A + r_E - c_1 - c_3$$
$$= (21 + A_3) + (16 + E_1 + E_3) - (17 + C_1 + E_1) - (14 + A_3 + E_3)$$
$$= 6 - C_1$$
$$C_1 = 6$$

Therefore, the row and column sums must equal 32 and $A_3 = 11$, $E_3 = 7$, $E_1 = 9$, and $B_4 = 10$. This leaves four remaining cells: B_2, D_2, B_5, and D_5. Let $B_2 = x$, then $B_5 = 13 - x$, $D_2 = 12 - x$, and $D_5 = x + 5$. Since all the entries in a vote distribution matrix must be nonnegative integers, it must be true that $0 \le x \le 12$. Hence, there are thirteen possible vote distribution matrices.

5. Let $\vec{w} = (w_1, w_2, w_3)$ be the weight vector. By the property of decreasing weights, $w_1 \ge w_2 \ge w_3$ and so $w_1 - w_2 \ge 0$, $w_1 - w_3 \ge 0$, and $w_2 - w_3 \ge 0$. If $\sigma(X)$ denotes the number of points candidate X receives, then

$$\sigma(A) - \sigma(C) = 3w_1 + 16w_2 - 19w_3$$
$$= 3(w_1 - w_3) + 16(w_2 - w_3)$$
$$\ge 0.$$

Therefore, since the number of points A receives is always greater than the number of points C receives, candidate C can never win.

6. For a given weight vector $\vec{w} = (w_1, w_2, w_3, w_4, w_5, w_6)$, let $\sigma(X)$ denotes the number of points candidate X receives. Then $\sigma(E) - \sigma(B) = 2(w_5 - w_6) \geq 0$. Therefore, candidate B cannot ever win.

$\sigma(F) - \sigma(C) = 3w_2 + 8w_3 - 3w_4 - 8w_6 = 3(w_2 - w_4) + 8(w_3 - w_6) \geq 0$. Therefore, candidate C can never win.

$\sigma(F) - \sigma(D) = 2w_2 + w_3 + 2w_4 + w_5 - 6w_6 = 2(w_2 - w_6) + (w_3 - w_6) + 2(w_4 - w_6) + (w_5 - w_6) \geq 0$. Therefore, candidate D can never win. Now that it is known that candidates B, C, and D cannot win, it must be shown that candidates A, E, and F can win. It is easy to see that candidate F can win with $\vec{w} = (1,1,0,0,0,0)$ producing the points vector $\vec{p} = (17, 17, 15, 16, 17, 18)$. To allow E to win the weight vector needs to include nonzero values for w_4 and w_5. Trying $\vec{w} = (1,1,1,1,1,0)$ produces the points vector $\vec{p} = (45, 44, 35, 37, 46, 43)$ and a victory for candidate E. To allow candidate A to win, $w_5 > 2$. With a little experimentation, a desired weight vector can now be found. $\vec{w} = (5,5,5,3,3,0)$ produces the the desired result with the points vector $\vec{w} = (189, 182, 141, 163, 188, 187)$.

7. Using $\vec{w} = (1,0,0,0,0)$ produces $\vec{p} = (9,8,9,10,9)$ and so candidate D can be a winner and candidate B can be a big time loser. Using $\vec{w} = (1,1,0,0,0)$ produces $\vec{p} = (20, 19, 16, 17, 19)$ and so candidate A can be a winner and candidate C is a big time loser. Using $\vec{w} = (1,1,1,1,0)$ produces $\vec{p} = (37, 33, 38, 36, 36)$ and so candidate C can be a winner. To show that candidate E can never win, compare $\sigma(A)$ and $\sigma(E)$.

$$\sigma(A) - \sigma(E) = (9-9)w_1 + (11-10)w_2 + (10-11)w_3 + (7-6)w_4 + (8-9)w_5$$
$$= w_2 - w_3 + w_4 - w_5 = (w_2 - w_3) + (w_4 - w_5) \geq 0.$$

Therefore, candidate E can never beat candidate A. To show E cannot be a big time loser, compare $\sigma(E)$ and $\sigma(B)$ to show that candidate E always beats candidate B.

$$\sigma(E) - \sigma(B) = (9-8)w_1 + (10-11)w_2 + (11-8)w_3 + (6-6)w_4 + (9-12)w_5$$
$$= w_1 - w_2 + 3w_3 - 3w_5 = (w_1 - w_2) + 3(w_3 - w_5) \geq 0.$$

8. Using matrix multiplication on a calculator is helpful in finding the resulting point vector when given a vote distribution matrix and a weight vector. However, using the inverse matrix capabilities of a calculator to find the solution to this problem is not very helpful since the vote distribution matrix has no inverse. (Why?)

However, the vote distribution matrix can be augmented with the points vector to produce:

$$\begin{pmatrix} 31 & 24 & 50 & 24 & 36 & 427 \\ 31 & 33 & 32 & 33 & 36 & 409 \\ 41 & 42 & 49 & 18 & 15 & 575 \\ 25 & 24 & 2 & 60 & 54 & 241 \\ 37 & 42 & 32 & 30 & 24 & 493 \end{pmatrix}$$

By doing a series of *elementary row operations* on this matrix it can be transformed into *echelon form* or *reduced row echelon form*. The following steps produce the desired results and can be done on a calculator.

1. Multiply row 1 by 1/31. (On a TI84: *row(1/31,[A],1))
2. Add -31 times row 1 to row 2. (On a TI84: *row+(-31,[A],1,2))
3. Add -41 times row 1 to row 3.
4. Add -25 times row 1 to row 4.
5. Add -37 times row 1 to row 5.
6. Multiply row 2 by 1/9.
7. Add -318/31 times row 2 to row 3.
8. Add -144/31 times row 2 to row 4.
9. Add -414/31 times row 2 to row 5.
10. Multiply row 3 by 31/105.
11. Add 900/31 times row 3 to row 4.
12. Add 30/31 times row 3 to row 5.
13. Multiply row 4 by -7/1188.
14. Add 132/7 times row 4 to row 5.

$$\text{echelon form} = \begin{pmatrix} 1 & \dfrac{24}{31} & \dfrac{50}{31} & \dfrac{24}{31} & \dfrac{36}{31} & \dfrac{427}{31} \\ 0 & 1 & -2 & 1 & 0 & -2 \\ 0 & 0 & 1 & \dfrac{-248}{35} & \dfrac{-337}{35} & \dfrac{318}{35} \\ 0 & 0 & 0 & 1 & \dfrac{3}{2} & -1 \\ 0 & 0 & 0 & 0 & 0 & 0 \end{pmatrix}$$

Since this is just a computational algorithm, it can easily be done on a TI84 by using *ref*([A]), found under matrix math.

It is now in echelon form and parametric equations can be written...Or continue:

15. Add 248/35 times row 4 to row 3.
16. Add -1 times row 4 to row 2.
17. Add -24/31 times row 4 to row 1.
18. Add 2 times row 3 to row 2.
19. Add -50/31 times row 3 to row 1.
20. Add -24/31 times row 2 to row 1.

$$\text{reduced row echelon form} = \begin{pmatrix} 1 & 0 & 0 & 0 & -2 & 9 \\ 0 & 1 & 0 & 0 & \dfrac{1}{2} & 3 \\ 0 & 0 & 1 & 0 & 1 & 2 \\ 0 & 0 & 0 & 1 & \dfrac{3}{2} & -1 \\ 0 & 0 & 0 & 0 & 0 & 0 \end{pmatrix}$$

Simply, rref([A]) on the TI84.

The matrix is now in reduced row echelon form and produces the following set of equations:

$w_1 - 2w_5 = 9$, $w_2 + \dfrac{1}{2}w_5 = 3$, $w_3 + w_5 = 2$, $w_4 + \dfrac{3}{2}w_5 = -1$, and $0w_5 = 0$. Let $w_5 = t$ and the weight vector can

be written as $\vec{w} = (9 + 2t, 3 - .5t, 2 - t, -1 - 1.5t, t)$. Because $w_2 \geq w_3$, $t \geq$ -2 and because $w_4 \geq w_5$, $t \leq$ -.4, and

t must be an even integer lest some weights be fractions. Therefore, t = -2 is the only possibility and

$\vec{w} = (5, 4, 4, 2, -2)$ is the only possible weight vector.

Three's a Charm !

The Background

We ordinarily write numbers using the decimal system, that is, we use ten digits, namely 0, 1, 2, 3, 4, 5, 6, 7, 8, and 9, and when we write the numeral 145, we mean the number $1(10^2) + 4(10^1) + 5(10^0)$. Because the digits are multiplied by decreasing powers of 10, it is called the base ten or decimal numeration system. Computers do arithmetic using a base two or binary system, where the only digits are 0 and 1. The number 145 is written as 10010001_{TWO} because

$145 = 1(2^7) + 0(2^6) + 0(2^5) + 1(2^4) + 0(2^3) + 0(2^2) + 0(2^1) + 1(2^0) = 128 + 16 + 1$. Since base ten is the most commonly used numeration system, it is common to omit the subscript TEN when using this system. The most economical (see note at end of the problems) numeration system to use, however, is the base three or *ternary* system. In this system, there are three digits, namely 0, 1, and 2, and the number 145 is written as 12101_{THREE}

because $145 = 1(3^4) + 2(3^3) + 1(3^2) + 0(3^1) + 1(3^0) = 81 + 2(27) + 9 + 1$. So if binary is too small and decimal too big, Goldilocks would say ternary is just right!

The Problems

Part A Ternary Number System

1. Let k be a positive integer. What is the largest integer whose ternary notation contains k digits?

2. Here are the addition and multiplication tables for the binary system:

+	0	1
0	0	1
1	1	10

×	0	1
0	0	0
1	0	1

Write the addition and multiplication tables for the ternary system.

3. The decimal integers 0 through 15 can be placed in a 4×4 square array so that each of its <u>nine</u> 2×2 subsquares adds up to 30 as shown in figure 1 below. A method to accomplish this task is hinted at in figure 2, where each of the numbers from figure 1 is represented in its binary notation.

0	6	1	7
9	15	8	14
2	4	3	5
11	13	10	12

0000	0110	0001	0111
1001	1111	1000	1110
0010	0100	0011	0101
1011	1101	1010	1100

figure 1   figure 2

Place the decimal integers from 0 to 80 in a 9×9 square array so that the sum of the numbers in each of its <u>forty-nine</u> 3×3 subsquares is the same.

4. The First Martian has exactly one ear. Any Martian with $n < 729$ ears has exactly two children; one with $3n$ ears and the other with $3n + 1$ ears. Any Martian with $n \geq 729$ ears has no children. Every Martian is a direct descendent of the First Martian. No Martian has ever died.

a) Determine the number of ears of the children and grandchildren of the First Martian.

222

b) Is there a Martian with 11 ears? Justify your answer.

c) Is there a Martian with 16 ears? Justify your answer.

d) An integer will be called *eerie*, if it can be expressed in a unique way as the sum of the ears of two *different* Martians. Prove that 4 and 11 are eerie, while 3, 8, and 13 are not.

e) Determine how many of the first 728 positive integers are eerie.

5. A number that has the same value when read forwards or backwards, like 21012, is called a palindrome. If the first 10000 positive integers were written in ternary notation, what is the decimal representation of the hundredth palindrome in the list?

Part B The Balanced Ternary Number System

6. "Perhaps the prettiest number system of all," writes Donald Knuth in The Art of Computer Programming, "is the balanced ternary notation." As in ordinary ternary numbers, the digits of a *balanced ternary numeral* are used as coefficients of powers of 3, but instead of coming from the set {0, 1, 2}, the coefficients are -1, 0, and 1. They are "balanced" because they are symmetric about zero. For notational convenience the digits 1, 0, and N (where N = -1) will be used. In this notation, the numeral 10N0 represents the decimal number 24 because

$$24 = 1(3^3) + 0(3^2) + (-1)(3^1) + 0(3^0) = 27 - 3.$$

a) Write the integers from –13 to 13 (inclusive) in increasing order in balanced ternary notation.

b) Write the addition and multiplication tables for the balanced ternary system.

c) Tom has a balance pan scale and four weights: 1-gram, 3-grams, 9-grams, and 27-grams. How could he determine the weight of an object weighing 32 grams?

d) Let k be a positive integer. What are the smallest and largest integers whose balanced ternary representations contains k digits? How many integers contain k or fewer digits in their balanced ternary notation?

7. Ivo has a digital scale which can measure (in grams) any integral weight from 1 gram to 12100 grams. He has received seven sacks, each containing 1000 identical coins. The different sacks have coins which look identical but may have different weights. Some sacks may have real coins all weighing 10g each, some sacks may have counterfeit coins that all weigh 9g each, and some sacks may have counterfeit coins all weighing 11g. Explain how Ivo could determine which sacks contain the real coins using just one measurement on the digital scale.

8. In Trilandia the monetary system consists of five coins (1 centi, 3 centi, 9 centi, 27 centi, and 81 centi) and five bills (243 centi, 729 centi, 2187 centi, 6561 centi, and 19683 centi). Suppose Jenny went to a store and purchased a computer for 12614 centi (including taxes). If she and the cashier each had only one of each coin and bill, what coins and bills would she use for payment so that the cashier could give her exact change?

N.B. For a given integer, the *economy* of its numeral in a given base is determined by multiplying the numeral's *width* (how many digits it has) by its *depth* (how many different digits can occupy each place). The product which is smallest determines the most economical base representation. For example, the number $1537 = 1537_{TEN} = 11000000001_{TWO} = 2002221_{THREE}$. So for the number 1537, the economy of its base ten numeral is $9 + 3(10) = 39$, the economy of base two numeral is $1 + 10(2) = 21$, and the economy of base three numeral is $2 + 6(3) = 20$. In this, and almost all cases, the base three representation of a number is the most economical.

Many thanks to Ivaylo Kortezov, one of the coaches of the Sofia Math Circle from Bulgaria. The creation and much of the writing for this problem was done by him.

223

The Solutions

1. The largest k-digit ternary number is $222...2 = 2(3^0 + 3^1 + 3^2 + ... + 3^{k-1}) = 3^k - 1$.

2.

+	0	1	2
0	0	1	2
1	1	2	10
2	2	10	11

×	0	1	2
0	0	0	0
1	0	1	2
2	0	2	11

3. Use the ternary representations of the numbers from 0 to 80 and distribute these numerals in such a way that in each of the 3×3 subsquares each ternary digit is found three times in each of the four digital positions of the numeral. One way to achieve this is to fill a 9×9 square so that in the first row the first digit of every number is 0, the first digit in the second row is 1, the first digit in row three is 2, the first digit in row four is 0, row five is 1, and so on until the last row. In the first column, let the second digit of every number be 0. In the second column, let the second digit be 1; in the third column, let the second digit be 2; and continue this pattern of 0, 1, 2 for the second digit in each of the remaining columns. In the first three columns, let the third digits from top to bottom be 0, 1, 2, 0, 1, 2, 0, 1, 2. In the middle three columns, let the third digits be 1, 2, 0, 1, 2, 0, 1, 2, 0. In the last three columns, let the third digits be 2, 0, 1, 2, 0, 1, 2, 0, 1. Finally, in the first three rows, let the forth digits from left to right be 0, 1, 2, 0, 1, 2, 0, 1, 2; in the middle three rows, let the forth digits be 1, 2, 0, 1, 2, 0, 1, 2, 0; and in the last three rows, let the forth digits be 2, 0, 1, 2, 0, 1, 2, 0, 1. In the end the first table at the right is produced.

Each of the 3×3 subsquares contain each of the digits 0, 1, and 2 three times in each of the four digital positions.

0000	0101	0202	0010	0111	0212	0020	0121	0222
1010	1111	1212	1020	1121	1222	1000	1101	1202
2020	2121	2222	2000	2101	2202	2010	2111	2212
0001	0102	0200	0011	0112	0210	0021	0122	0220
1011	1112	1210	1021	1122	1220	1001	1102	1200
2021	2122	2220	2001	2102	2200	2011	2112	2210
0002	0100	0201	0012	0110	0211	0022	0120	0221
1012	1110	1211	1022	1120	1221	1002	1100	1201
1022	2120	2221	2002	2100	2201	2012	2110	2211

0	10	20	3	13	23	6	16	26
30	40	50	33	43	53	27	37	47
60	70	80	54	64	74	57	67	77
1	11	18	4	14	21	7	17	24
31	41	48	34	44	51	28	38	45
61	71	78	55	65	72	58	68	75
2	9	19	5	12	22	8	15	25
32	39	49	35	42	52	29	36	46
62	69	79	56	63	73	59	66	76

So the sum of the numbers in each 3×3 subsquare is $3(0 + 1 + 2)(27 + 9 + 3 + 1) = 3(3)(40) = 360$.

The second table is the decimal representation of the ternary table.

4a. Children: 3 and 4; Grandchildren: 9, 10, 12, and 13.

4b. No, the remainder of 11 modulo 3 must be 0 or 1 and it is not.

4c. No, its parents must have 5 ears and the remainder of 5 modulo 3 must be 0 or 1 and it is not.

4d. The unique representations of 4 and 11 are: $4 = 3 + 1$ and $11 = 10 + 1$.

Since there is no Martian with 2 ears, the integer 3 cannot be expressed as sum. Eight $= 1 + 7 = 2 + 6 = 3 + 5$ but there are no Martians with 7, 6, or 5 ears. Eight $= 4 + 4$ but these aren't different Martians. Thirteen equals $1 + 12 = 3 + 10 = 4 + 9$ and therefore does not have a unique representation.

4e. Looking at the first few generations, the number of Martian ears are represented by the following sequence: 1; 3, 4; 9, 10, 12, 13; 27, 28, 30, 31, 36, 37, 39, 40; ... Changing these integers to their ternary representation yields: 1; 10, 11; 100, 101, 110, 111; 1000, 1001, 1010, 1011, 1100, 1101, 1110, 1111; ... Notice each number consists only of 0's and 1's. (This makes sense since to multiply a ternary numeral by three just catenate a 0 on the end of it and to multiply a ternary number by three and add one just catenate a 1 on the end of it.) So if n is *eerie* it must be the sum of two of these types of numbers and if its ternary representation contains a 2 it must be the sum of two 1's and a 0 must be the sum of two 0's. A 1 in the ternary representation must be $0 + 1$ or $1 + 0$. For n not to be unique sum the ternary representation for n must contain more than one 1. There are several cases to consider:

If in the ternary representation of n there is exactly two 1's and the rest 0's then $n = 3^a + 3^b$ is a unique representation as the sum of the ears of two Martians (e.g. $1010_{THREE} = 1000_{THREE} + 0010_{THREE}$).

If in the ternary representation of n there is exactly one 1 and at least one 2, then n is a unique representation of the ears of Two Martians (e.g. $2102_{THREE} = 1101_{THREE} + 1001_{THREE}$).

If in the ternary representation of n there is exactly one 1 and no 2's, then n cannot be expressed as the unique sum of the ears of two Martians.

If in the ternary representation of n there are no 1's (i.e. only 0's and 2's), then n can be represented as the sum of the ears of two Martians (e.g. $20220_{THREE} = 10110_{THREE} + 10110_{THREE}$) but they are not different Martians and so n is not *eerie*.

If in the ternary representation of n there are at least two 1's and and at least one 2, then n can be expressed as the sum of the ears of two Martians but this sum is not unique (e.g. $1210_{THREE} = 1100_{THREE} + 0100_{THREE} = 1110_{THREE} + 0100_{THREE}$).

The numbers from 1 to 728 have six digits in their ternary representations (if some leading zeros are added).

The number of numbers with exactly two 1's are $\binom{6}{2} = 15$. The number of numbers with exactly one 1, at least one 2, and the rest 0's is $\binom{6}{1}(2^5 - 1) = 6(31) = 186$. Therefore, there are 201 *eerie* numbers among the first 728 integers.

5. There are 2 one-digit ternary palindromes, namely 1 and 2. There are 2 two-digit palindromes, namely 11 and 22. Because every three-digit palindrome is a two-digit ternary number with a 1 or a 2 added on the end, the number of three-digit palindromes is the same as the number of two-digit ternary numbers, namely $(2)(3) = 6$. Because every four-digit palindrome is a two-digit ternary number with the same digits added on the end in reverse order, the number of four-digit palindromes is the same as the number of two-digit ternary numbers, namely $(2)(3) = 6$. Likewise, five and six-digit palindromes start with a three-digit ternary number with the

necessary two or three digits added on the end. Since there are (2)(3)(3) = 18 three-digit ternary numbers, there 18 five-digit palindromes and 18 six-digit palindromes. Similarly, since a seven-digit palindrome starts with a four-digit ternary number, the number of seven-digit palindromes is (2)(3)(3)(3) = 54. Summing up, we now have 2 + 2 + 6 + 6 +18 + 18 + 54 = 106 ternary palindromes. Removing the last six ternary palindromes (2210122, 2211122, 2212122, 2220222, 2221222, and 222222) leaves the hundredth ternary palindrome, namely 2202022_{THREE}. This number's decimal representation is 2006!

6a. NNN, NN0, NN1, N0N, N00, N01, N1N, N10, N11, NN, NO, N1, N, 0, 1, 1N, 10, 11, 1NN, 1N0, 1N1, 10N, 100, 101, 11N, 110, 111.

6b.

+	0	1	N
0	0	1	N
1	1	1N	0
N	N	0	N1

×	0	1	N
0	0	0	0
1	0	1	N
N	0	N	1

6c. Place the object on one pan along with the 1g and 3 g weights and in the other pan place the 27g and 9g weights. They will balance!

6d. The smallest k-digit number : $NNN...N = -\left(3^0 + 3^1 + 3^2 + ... + 3^{k-1}\right) = \frac{1}{2}\left(1 - 3^k\right)$.

The largest k-digit number : $111...1 = -\left(3^0 + 3^1 + 3^2 + ... + 3^{k-1}\right) = \frac{1}{2}\left(1 - 3^k\right)$.

The total number of such numbers is $2\left(\frac{1}{2}\left(3^k - 1\right)\right) + 1 = 3^k$.

7. One way is to take 729 coins from the first sack, 243 from the second, 81 from the third, 27 from the fourth, 9 from the fifth, 3 from the sixth, and 1 from the seventh and place them all on the digital scale. The total number of weighed coins is 1093 and their total weight ($1093 \cdot 11 = 12023$) will be within the limits of the scale. Let their weight be $10930 + x$, where x is an integer whose absolute value does not exceed 1093. Then represent x in balanced ternary notation as a seven digit numeral, $x = a3^6 + b3^5 + c3^4 + ... + f3^1 + g3^0$. If the 3^6 coins from the first sack are real, then $a = 0$; if they are 1 g heavier, then $a = 1$; and if they are 1 g lighter, $a = -1$. In the same way the types of coins in each of the other sacks can be determined.

8. Convert the number 12614 to a balanced ternary representation The easiest way to do this is to first change it to a ternary representation by dividing by decreasing powers of three. Then, starting from the right, replace every digit 2 with an N and "carry" a 1 to the digit on the left. Using the addition table above, add each of the "carrys" to the digit, carrying a 1 if necessary.

For example, the number $12614 = 122022012_{THREE} = 1^1 N^1 N0^1 N^1 N01^1 N = 1N0N10N1NN_{BAL3}$.

Therefore, to pay for the computer, Jenny should give the cashier a 19683 centi bill, a 243 centi bill, and a 9 centi coin. She will receive in change a 6561 centi bill, a 729 centi bill, and 27, 3 and 1 centi coins. 19683 + 243 + 9 = 19935 and (12614) + 6561 + 729 + 27 + 3 + 1 = 19935.

The Stretch Method

<u>The Background</u>

Given the equation of a circle C, $(x - h)^2 + (y - k)^2 = r^2$, and (p, q), the coordinates of point P on circle C. When asked to find the equation of the line tangent to C through P, most students will attack the problem in the following way:

    1. Find O the center of the circle, and use it to find a, the slope of $\overline{OP}$.

    2. Since the line tangent to a circle at point P is perpendicular to the radius $\overline{OP}$, the slope m of the tangent line must be $-\frac{1}{a}$.

    3. Use the point-slope formula, $y - q = m(x - p)$, to write the equation of the tangent line.

Let's call the above method "method 1". There is a another, much quicker, method which I will call the "stretch method":

    1. Rewrite the equation, "stretching" or expanding the squares $(x - h)(x - h) + (y - k)(y - k) = r^2$.

    2. Replace <u>one</u> of the x's with p and <u>one</u> of the y's with q: $(p - h)(x - h) + (q - k)(y - k) = r^2$. The resulting equation is the equation of a line, the line tangent to the circle C at point P!

<u>The Problems</u>

<u>Part A</u>

1. Let C be the circle defined by the equation $(x - 6)^2 + (y + 4)^2 = 100$ and P be the point $(-2, -10)$.

    a) Find the equation of the line tangent to C at P using method 1.
    b) Find the equation of the line tangent to C at P using the "stretch method".
    c) Show the linear equations are equivalent.

2. Let C be the circle defined by the equation $(x - h)^2 + (y - k)^2 = r^2$ and P be the point (p, q) on circle C. Prove algebraically the two methods will always produce equivalent results. (Hint: The algebra is simpler if you first translate C and P so the circle is centered at the origin.

3. Let E be the ellipse defined by the equation $9x^2 + 8y^2 - 36x + 64y + 83 = 0$ and P be the point $(1, -7)$.

    a) Find the equation of the line tangent to E at P. This can be done by finding the value of m that produces only one solution when solving the system of equations: $\left\{ \begin{array}{c} 9x^2 + 8y^2 - 36x + 64y + 83 = 0 \\ y + 7 = m(x - 1) \end{array} \right\}$ when

    $(x, y) = (1, -7)$ or by some other technique of your choice. Again, a translation to the origin may greatly simplify your algebra.

    b) Find the equation of the line tangent to E at P using the "stretch method".
    c) Are the linear equations equivalent?

4. Let E be the ellipse defined by the equation $\dfrac{x^2}{a^2} + \dfrac{y^2}{b^2} = 1$ and P be the point (p,q) on ellipse E. Prove the

   equation of the line tangent to E at P is $\dfrac{px}{a^2} + \dfrac{qy}{b^2} = 1$.

Amazingly, the "stretch method" can also be used to find the equation of the line tangent to a hyperbola at a given point but cannot be used to find the equation of a line tangent to a parabola at a given point. Now let's look at other aspects of the "stretch method".

Part B – What happens if the "stretch method" is used on the equation of circle C but this time point P is exterior to C? A line is still produced, but how is this line related to P and C?

5. Let C again be the circle defined by the equation $(x-6)^2 + (y+4)^2 = 100$ and let $(4,-18)$ be P, a point that is exterior to circle C. Find the equation of the line produced by the stretch method. Find where this line intersects C Call the two points of intersection Q and R How are these points related to point P and circle C? If you need more "nice" external points in order to arrive at a conjecture, the following may be useful values to use for point P: $(-4,-24)$, $(8,-18)$, $(-4,-14)$, or $(16,-24)$.

6. Let C be the circle defined by the equation $x^2 + y^2 = r^2$ and P be the point (m,n) exterior to circle C. Prove your conjecture from question 5.

Part C – What happens if the "stretch method" is used on the equation of circle C but point P is interior to C?

7a. Let C again be the circle defined by the equation $(x-6)^2 + (y+4)^2 = 100$ and let $(2,-7)$ be P, a point that is interior to circle C Find the equation of the line produced by the stretch method.

You have probably heard of translations, reflections, rotations, and dilations, but here is another very useful geometric transformation:

> Consider a circle P'. with center O and radius r. If point P is not O, the **inverse** of P with respect to P'. is the point P' lying on ray $\overrightarrow{OP}$ such that $(OP)(OP') = r^2$ P'. is called the **circle of inversion** and O is called the **center of inversion**.

It is follows from this definition that:

   If P' is the inverse of P, then P is the inverse of P'.

   If P is in the interior of C, then P' is in the exterior of C.

   If P is in the exterior of C, then P' is in the interior of C.

   If P is on C, then P' is also on C. This is an **invariant** point, i.e., this point is its own inverse.

7b. What are the coordinates of P', the inverse of point P, in question 7a? Is point P' on the line whose equation you found in 7a?

7c. Use your previous answers to make a general conjecture about the "stretch method":

"If circle C is defined by $x^2 + y^2 = r^2$ and (m,n) is any point P other than the origin, O, then $mx + ny = r^2$ is the equation of the line that_____

_____."

Part D

8a. Given a circle of radius r, centered at point O, and point P such that $OP > r$, the following procedures can be used to construct P', the inverse of P :

Draw segment $\overline{OP}$.

Construct an arc centered at P with radius OP, intersecting the circle. Label this intersection Q.

Construct an arc centered at Q with radius OQ, intersecting $\overline{OP}$. Label this point of intersection P'.

Using this construction, prove that P' is the inverse of P.

8b Given a circle of radius r, centered at point O, and point P such that $OP < r$, and using the diagram from question 8a with P and P' interchanged, write a set of procedures that can be used to construct P', the inverse of P.

9. Given a circle C_1 centered at O, with radius OP, and circle C_2 whose diameter is $\overline{OP}$, prove for any point Q on C_2 other than O, the inverse of Q is on the line tangent to C_1 at point P It is therefore true that this tangent line is the inverse of C_2 with respect to C_1.

10. Let C_1 be defined by $x^2 + y^2 = 36$ and C_2 be defined by $(x-2)^2 + y^2 = 1$. Using C_1 as the circle of inversion, what is the equation of the inverse of C_2 ? (Hint: It's another circle!)

The Solutions

1a. The center of the circle, O, is $(6,-4)$ and the slope of radius $\overline{OP}$ is $\dfrac{3}{4}$. Therefore the equation of the

tangent line is $y + 10 = -\dfrac{4}{3}(x - 2)$ or $4x + 3y = -38$.

1b/c. $-8(x - 6) - 6(y + 4) = 100$

$-8x + 48 - 6y - 24 = 100$

$-8x - 6y = 76$

$4x + 3y = -38$

2. Translating by the vector (h,k), the equation of C becomes $x^2 + y^2 = r^2$ and point P becomes

$(m + h, n + k)$. Using the stretch method, the equation of the tangent line is $(m + h)x + (n + k)y = r^2$.

Using method 1, the slope of the radius to point P is $\dfrac{n + k}{m + h}$ and so the equation of the tangent line is

$$y - (n + k) = -\frac{m + h}{n + k}\left(x - (m + h)\right)$$

$$(y - n - k)(n + k) = (-m - h)(x - m - h)$$

$$ny - n^2 - nk + ky = m^2 + 2mn + h^2 + 2nk + k^2$$

$$mx + hx + ny + ky = m^2 + 2mn + h^2 + n^2 + 2nk + k^2$$

$$= (m + h)^2 + (n + k)^2$$

$$= r^2 \text{ because point } P \text{ is on circle } C.$$

3a. You may use calculus to arrive at the solution, but here is a non-calculus solution:

$$9x^2 + 8y^2 - 36x + 64y + 83 = 0$$

$$9x^2 - 36x + 8y^2 + 64y = -83$$

$$9\left(x^2 - 4x\right) + 8\left(y^2 + 8y\right) = -83$$

$$9\left(x^2 - 4x + 4\right) + 8\left(y^2 + 8y + 16\right) = -83 + 36 + 128$$

$$9(x - 2)^2 + 8(y + 4)^2 = 81, \text{ the equation of the ellipse } E \text{ with point } P \text{ being } (1,-7).$$

Transform these using the translation vector $(-2,4)$, and the ellipse becomes $9x^2 + 8y^2 = 81$ and point P

becomes $(-1,-3)$. $9x^2 + 8y^2 = 81$ with $x = -1$ and $y = -3$ becomes $9 + 7 = 81$. Subtracting these two

equations yields:

$$9x^2 - 9 + 8y^2 - 72 = 0$$

$$9(x^2 - 1) + 8(y^2 - 9) = 0$$

$$9(x - 1)(x + 1) + 8(y - 3)(y + 3) = 0$$

Let the equation of the line tangent to E at P be $y + 3 = m(x + 1)$ Substituting this into the above equation:

$$9(x - 1)(x + 1) + 8(y - 3)\left(m(x + 1)\right) = 0$$

$$(x + 1)(9x - 9 + 8my - 24m) = 0.$$

But because there is only one tangent to ellipse E at point P, this equation can have only one solution when

$x = -1$ and $y = -3$. Therefore, $9(-1) - 9 + 8m(-3) - 24 = 0$ and $m = -\dfrac{3}{8}$. So translating back again, the

equation of the tangent line must be $y + 7 = -\dfrac{3}{8}(x - 1)$ or $3x + 8y = -53$.

3b. Stretching $9(x - 2)^2 + 8(y + 4)^2 = 81$ and substituting $x = -1$ and $y = -7$ results in

    $-9(x - 2) - 24(y + 4) = 81$ or $3x + 8y = -53$.

3c. Done.

4. $\dfrac{x^2}{a^2} + \dfrac{y^2}{b^2} = 1$ implies $b^2x^2 + a^2y^2 = a^2b^2$. If (m, n) is on the ellipse then $b^2m^2 + a^2n^2 = a^2b^2$. Subtracting the

two equations yields $b^2\left(x^2 - m^2\right) + a^2\left(y^2 - n^2\right) = 0$. Let $y - n = c(x - m)$ be the tangent to E at point P

Then the following system can only have one solution:

$$\begin{cases} b^2(x^2 - m^2) + a^2(y^2 - n^2) = 0 \\ y = c(x - m) + n \end{cases}$$

$$b^2(x^2 - m^2) + a^2\left((c(x - m) + n)^2 - n^2\right) = 0$$
$$b^2(x^2 - m^2) + a^2(c^2(x - m)^2 + 2cn(x - m) + n^2 - n^2) = 0$$
$$b^2(x^2 - m^2) + a^2c^2(x - m)^2 + 2a^2cn(x - m) = 0$$
$$(x - m)\left(b^2(x + m) + a^2c^2(x - m) + 2a^2cn\right) = 0$$

But since $x = m$ is a zero of the left factor, it must also cause the right factor to be zero. Therefore,

$b^2(2m) + 2a^2cn = 0$ and the slope $c = -\dfrac{b^2m}{a^2n}$. So

$$y - n = -\dfrac{b^2m}{a^2n}(x - m)$$
$$a^2ny - a^2n^2 = -b^2mx + b^2m^2$$
$$b^2mx + a^2ny = b^2m^2 + a^2n^2$$
$$= a^2b^2$$
$$\dfrac{mx}{a^2} + \dfrac{ny}{b^2} = 1$$

5. The "stretch" line $x + 7y = -72$ intersects the circle C at points Q $(-2,-10)$ and R $(12,-12)$, where $\overrightarrow{PQ}$

     $(4x + 3y = -38)$ and $\overrightarrow{PR}$ $(3x - 4y = 84)$ are tangents to circle C.

6. Let (a,b) be the coordinates of point Q. If Q is on the circle C, then $a^2 + b^2 = r^2$. If Q is on the "stretch"

     line, then $ma + nb = r^2$. If $\overrightarrow{PQ}$ is also a tangent line, then $\overline{OQ}$ must be perpendicular to $\overrightarrow{PQ}$. This would

     be true if and only if the slope of $\overrightarrow{PQ}$ is the opposite reciprocal of $\overline{OQ}$. Slope of $\overrightarrow{PQ}$ is $\dfrac{b-n}{a-m}$ and the

     slope of $\overline{OQ}$ is $\dfrac{b}{a}$.

     $\dfrac{b-n}{a-m} = -\dfrac{a}{b}$ implies that $b^2 - bn = -a^2 + am$ and $a^2 + b^2 = am + bn$. The equations above show that both

     the left side and the right side of this equation equal r^2.

7a. $-4(x - 6) - 3(y + 4) = 100$

       $-4x + 24 - 3y - 12 = 100$

            $4x + 3y = -88$

7b. $(OP)(OP') = 100$ and $OP = 5$. Therefore, $OP' = 20$. The dilation factor $k = \dfrac{OP'}{OP} = 4$. So

     $P' = (6 - 4(4), -4 - 3(4)) = (-10,-16)$.

     $4x + 3y = -88$ the line is perpendicular to $\overrightarrow{OP}$ through P'.

7c. "... is perpendicular to $\overrightarrow{OP}$ through P', the inverse of P."

8a. $\triangle POQ$ is isosceles and so $m\angle OPQ = 180 - 2(m\angle POQ)$.

     $\triangle QOP'$ is isosceles and so $m\angle OQP' = 180 - 2(m\angle POQ)$.

     $\therefore \angle POQ \cong \angle OQP'$ and $\dfrac{PO}{PQ} = \dfrac{QO}{QP'} = 1$.

     $\therefore \triangle POQ \sim \triangle QOP'$ by SAS.

     $\dfrac{OP}{OQ} = \dfrac{OQ}{OP'}$ and $(OP)(OP') = (OQ)(OQ) = r^2$.

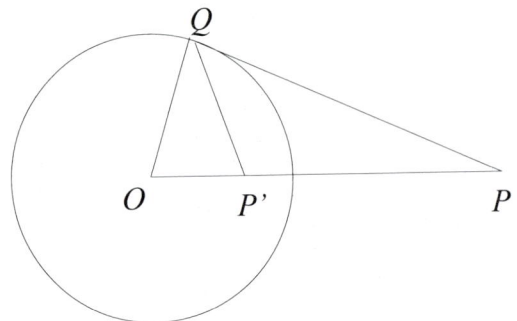

8b. Draw ray $\overrightarrow{OP}$.

Construct the perpendicular bisector of $\overline{OP}$, and where it

intersects the circle label point Q. Draw $\overline{OQ}$.

Construct the perpendicular bisector of $\overline{OQ}$, and where it

intersects $\overrightarrow{OP}$ label point P'. $\triangle OQP \sim \triangle OPQ'$.

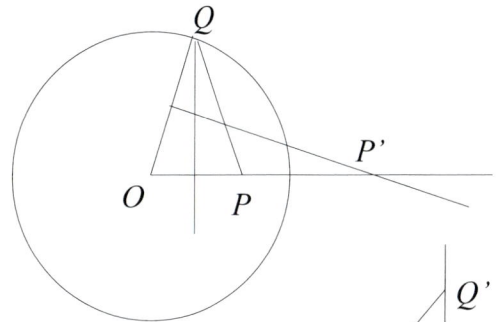

9. Draw circles C_1 and C_2 with points O and P as stated in the problem. Let

line ℓ be tangent to both circles at P. Let Q be any point on C_2 other

than O or P. Draw ray $\overrightarrow{OQ}$ until it intersects ℓ at some point.

Conjecture: This point is Q'. Proof: $\angle OQP$ is right and, therefore,

$\triangle OQP \sim \triangle OPQ'$ and $\dfrac{OQ}{OP} = \dfrac{OP}{OQ'}$ and $(OQ)(OQ') = (OP)(OP)$.

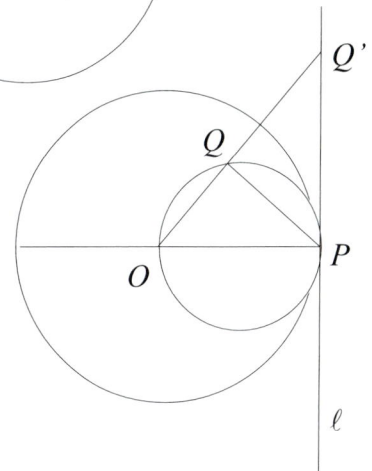

10. The segment $\overline{OQ}$ includes $\overline{PQ}$, a diameter of

C_2. As R traces C_2, ray $\overrightarrow{OR}$ intercepts

C_2 at points R and S. Points R' and S'

are their respective inverses.

$(OR)(OR') = (OS)(OS') = r^2$

$OS' = \dfrac{r^2}{OS}$

$OS' = \dfrac{r^2}{(OS)(OR)}(OR)$

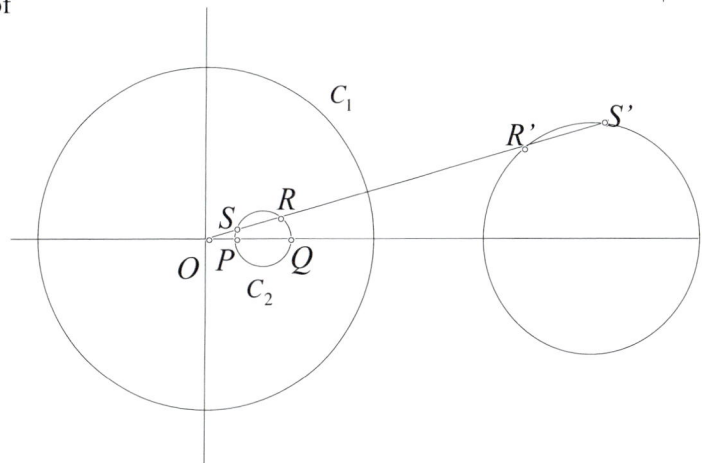

But $(OS)(OR) = (OP)(OQ)$. Why?

Therefore, $OS' = \dfrac{r^2}{(OP)(OQ)}(OR)$, and this shows that S' is the dilation of R with O as the center of dilation

and $\dfrac{r^2}{(OP)(OQ)}$ the dilation factor. In the problem given, $r = 6$, $OP = 1$, and $OQ = 3$, and so the dilation

factor is 12. Therefore, $P' = (12,0)$, $Q' = (36,0)$, and so the inverse of C_2 is a circle of radius 12, centered at

$(24,0)$, and defined by the equation $(x - 24)^2 + y^2 = 144$.

Random Walks In Trees

<u>The Background</u>

Although the title may conjure up thoughts of rambling through a forest or arboretum, this problem will look at the probabilities associated with a set of vertex-edge graphs called (rooted) trees. The vertex-edge graph in Figure 1 is an example of a tree. In any tree, two vertices are connected with at most one edge and the graph is connected, i.e., between any two vertices there is always a path. A rooted tree has one vertex which is designated as the <u>root</u> of the tree. In the tree in Figure 1, vertex R is the root and vertices A, B, and C are called the <u>leaves</u> of the tree. Each <u>leaf</u> is connected via an edge to only one other vertex. <u>A walk in a tree</u> is a path

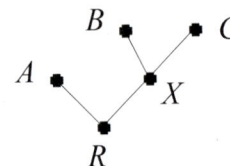

Figure 1

that always starts at the root and ends at one of the leaves. *RA*, *RXB*, and *RXC* are typical walks but, by thinking about the edges as being bi-directional, there are infinitely many others: *RXRA*, *RXRXB*, etc. Once a walk arrives at a leaf the walk is complete; so *RXRARXC* will not be considered a walk in a tree in this problem.

Simple walks that don't retrace edges such as *RA*, *RXB*, and *RXC* can be thought of as <u>branches</u> of the tree. The <u>length</u> of a branch is the number of edges it contains. Therefore, branch *RA*, or just branch A, has a length of 1 while branch B and branch C are each of length 2.

A walk in a tree is called <u>a random walk in a tree</u> if the probability of taking any edge out of a vertex is equally likely. Therefore, in Figure 1, starting at R, the probability of going to A or X is $\frac{1}{2}$ and when at X, the probability of going to R, B, or C is $\frac{1}{3}$. $P(A)$, $P(B)$, and $P(C)$ are defined as the probabilities that a random walk (starting at R) will end at leaf A, B, or C, respectively. It is obvious from the shape of the graph that $P(B) = P(C)$. $P(A)$ must be greater than $\frac{1}{2}$ since the walk *RA* will occur half the time of all possible random walks but there are more walks that end at A, namely *RXRA*, *RXRXRA*, etc. In this problem set you will be calculating the exact probabilities of ending a walk at each of the leaves of a tree. Knowledge of conditional probability, infinite geometric series, recursion, and symmetries may be helpful in this competition.

<u>The Problems</u>

1. Calculate *P(A)* and *P(B)* for each of these trees:

a)

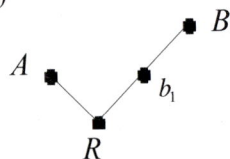

b)

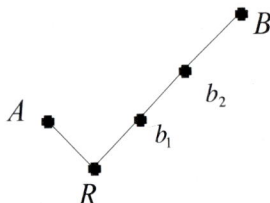

c)

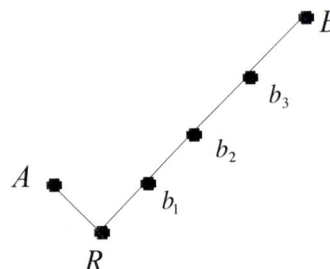

2. Branch A has length 1 and branch B has length n. Make a conjecture as to the formulas for $P(A)$ and $P(B)$ for this tree. Prove your conjecture is always true.

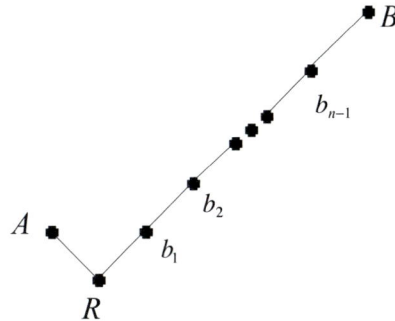

3. Calculate $P(A)$ and $P(B)$ for each of these trees:

Hint: In 3a, to arrive at A you must go through a_1 and from problem 1c you already know $P(a_1)$.

a)

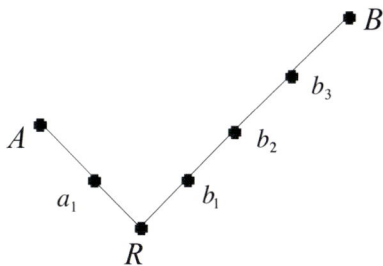

b)

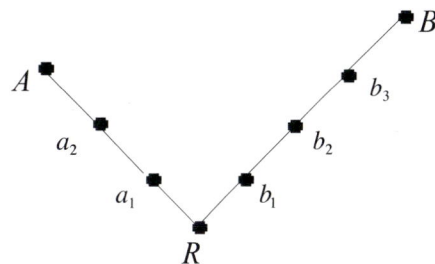

4. Branch A has length a and branch B has length b. Make a conjecture as to the formulas for $P(A)$ and $P(B)$ for this tree. Prove your conjecture is always true.

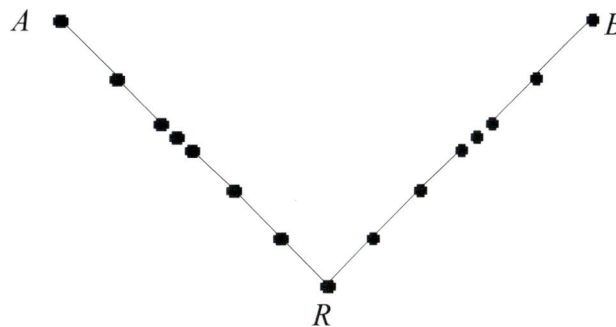

5. Calculate $P(A)$, $P(B)$, and $P(C)$ for each of these trees:

a)

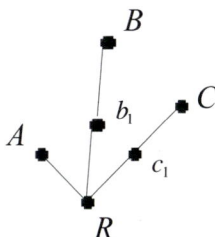

b)

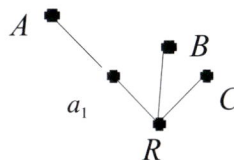

c)

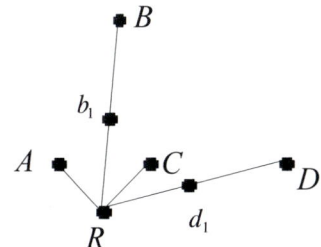

6. In the tree in Figure 6a, each of the n branches, A_k, has length a_k where k goes from 1 to n.

   a) Make a conjecture as to the formulas for $P(A_k)$ for this tree. b) Find $P(A)$, $P(B)$, and $P(C)$ for the tree in Figure 6b, showing the use of your conjecture. c) Prove your conjecture is always true.

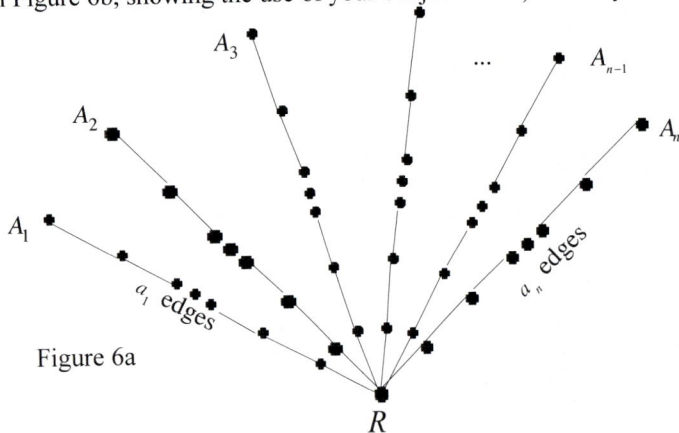

Figure 6a

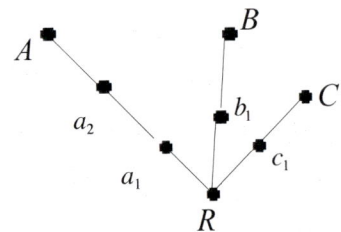

Figure 6b

7. For the tree in Figure 7a, $\left(P(A), P(B), P(C), P(D)\right) = \left(\dfrac{3}{7}, \dfrac{3}{14}, \dfrac{1}{7}, \dfrac{3}{14}\right)$. Use this fact to determine

   $\left(P(A), P(B), P(C), P(D)\right)$ for Figure 7b. (Hint: The two trees are identical except they have different roots. The root in Figure 7b is the vertex b_1 in Figure 7a.)

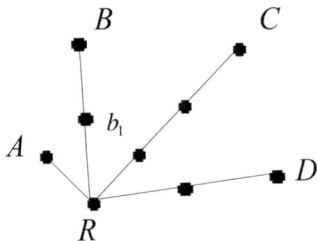

Figure 7a

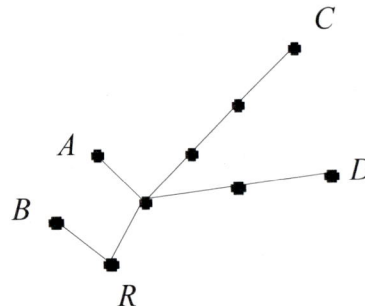

Figure 7b

8. A tree has the same shape as the tree in Figure 6a. If $a_1 + a_2 + a_3 + ... + a_k = 2007$, what is the smallest possible value for $P(A_1)$?

9. Calculate $P(A)$, $P(B)$, $P(C)$ and $P(D)$ for this tree:

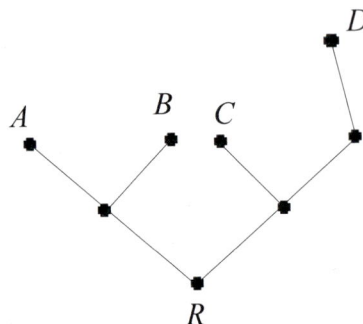

The Solutions

1. a) Paths to A: $RA + Rb_1 RA + Rb_1 Rb_1 RA + Rb_1 Rb_1 Rb_1 RA + \ldots$ So $P(A) = \dfrac{1}{2} + \dfrac{1}{2} \cdot \dfrac{1}{2} \cdot \dfrac{1}{2} + \dfrac{1}{2} \cdot \dfrac{1}{2} \cdot \dfrac{1}{2} \cdot \dfrac{1}{2} \cdot \dfrac{1}{2} + \ldots =$

$\dfrac{1}{2} + \dfrac{1}{8} + \dfrac{1}{32} + \ldots = \dfrac{\dfrac{1}{2}}{1 - \dfrac{1}{4}} = \dfrac{2}{3}$. $\quad P(B) = Rb_1 B + Rb_1 Rb_1 B + Rb_1 Rb_1 Rb_1 B + \ldots$

$\dfrac{1}{2} \cdot \dfrac{1}{2} + \dfrac{1}{2} \cdot \dfrac{1}{2} \cdot \dfrac{1}{2} \cdot \dfrac{1}{2} + \dfrac{1}{2} \cdot \dfrac{1}{2} \cdot \dfrac{1}{2} \cdot \dfrac{1}{2} \cdot \dfrac{1}{2} \cdot \dfrac{1}{2} + \ldots = \dfrac{1}{4} + \dfrac{1}{16} + \dfrac{1}{64} + \ldots = \dfrac{\dfrac{1}{4}}{1 - \dfrac{1}{4}} = \dfrac{1}{3}.$

b) *Paths to* A: $RA + Rb_1 RA + Rb_1 xb_1 RA + Rb_1 xb_1 xb_1 RA + \ldots$ *where* $x \in \{R, b_2\}$.

$P(A) = \dfrac{1}{2} + \dfrac{1}{8} + 2^1 \cdot \dfrac{1}{32} + 2^2 \cdot \dfrac{1}{128} + 2^3 \cdot \dfrac{1}{512} + \ldots = \dfrac{1}{2} + \dfrac{1}{8} + \dfrac{1}{16} + \dfrac{1}{32} + \ldots = \dfrac{1}{2} + \text{a geometric series}$

$= \dfrac{1}{2} + \dfrac{\dfrac{1}{8}}{1 - \dfrac{1}{2}} = \dfrac{1}{2} + \dfrac{1}{4} = \dfrac{3}{4}. \quad P(B) = 1 - P(A) = \dfrac{1}{4}.$

c) We could try the same approach as in parts a and b, but this produces:

Paths to A: $RA + Rb_1 RA + Rb_1 xb_1 RA + (Rb_1 xb_1 xb_1 RA + Rb_1 b_2 b_3 b_2 b_1 RA) + \ldots$ where $x \in \{R, b_2\}$

$P(A) = \dfrac{1}{2} + \left(\dfrac{1}{2}\right)^3 + 2 \cdot \left(\dfrac{1}{2}\right)^5 + 5 \cdot \left(\dfrac{1}{2}\right)^7 + 13 \cdot \left(\dfrac{1}{2}\right)^9 + \ldots$, a geometric-looking series with some nasty coefficients.

(N.B. 1, 1, 2, 5, 13, … is produced by the recursive formula $a_n = 3 \cdot a_{n-1} - a_{n-2}$.)

So let's try another approach:

$P(A) = P(\text{ending at } A, \text{ not going through } b_3) + P(\text{ending at } A, \text{ going through } b_3)$

$\qquad = P(\text{ending at } A, \text{ not going through } b_3) + P(\text{arriving at } b_3) \cdot P(\text{ending at } A \text{ when starting at } b_3).$

But $P(\text{ending at } A, \text{ not going through } b_3)$ is just $P(A)$ from 1b and $P(\text{arriving at } b_3)$ is $P(B)$ from 1b.

Because of the symmetry in this tree, $P(\text{ending at } A \text{ when starting at } b_3)$ is the same as $P(B)$ in this problem

and equals $1 - P(A)$. And so, $P(A) = \dfrac{3}{4} + \dfrac{1}{4} \cdot (1 - P(A))$. Solving, $P(A) = \dfrac{4}{5}$ and $P(B) = \dfrac{1}{5}$.

2. Conjecture: $P(A) = \dfrac{n}{n+1}$ and $P(B) = \dfrac{1}{n+1}$.

Proof by induction: We already know it is true when $n = 1, 2, 3,$ and 4. Assume we know it's true in a tree

with two branches: a of length 1 and b of length k. In this tree $P(A) = \dfrac{k}{k+1}$ and $P(B) = \dfrac{1}{k+1}$. Now consider another tree with two branches: a of length 1 and b of length $k+1$. Let b_k be the last node before

leaf B. $P(A) = P(ending\ at\ A,\ not\ going\ through\ b_k) + P(ending\ at\ A,\ going\ through\ b_k) =$

$P(ending\ at\ A,\ not\ going\ through\ b_3) + P(arriving\ at\ b_k) \cdot P(ending\ at\ A\ when\ starting\ at\ b_k)$. But

$P(ending\ at\ A,\ not\ going\ through\ b_k) = \dfrac{k}{k+1}$ from the induction hypothesis and $P(arriving\ at\ b_k) = \dfrac{1}{k+1}$.

Because of the symmetry in this tree, $P(ending\ at\ A\ when\ starting\ at\ b_k)$ is the same as $P(B)$ in this problem

which equals $1 - P(A)$. So $P(A) = \dfrac{k}{k+1} + \dfrac{1}{k+1} \cdot (1 - P(A))$. Therefore, $(k+1)P(A) = k + (1 - P(A))$ and

$(k+1)P(A) + P(A) = k+1$ and $P(A) = \dfrac{k+1}{k+2}$. $P(B) = 1 - P(A) = 1 - \dfrac{k+1}{k+2} = \dfrac{1}{k+2}$.

3. a) To get to A you must go through a_1. From 1c, $P(a_1) = \dfrac{4}{5}$. To determine the probability of getting to A

starting from a_1 you could just rearrange the tree with a_1 as the root and, using the conjecture from problem 2,

$P(A,\ starting\ from\ a_1) = \dfrac{5}{6}$. Therefore, $P(A) = P(ending\ at\ a_1) \cdot P(A,\ starting\ from\ a_1) = \dfrac{4}{5} \cdot \dfrac{5}{6} = \dfrac{4}{6}$.

$P(B) = 1 - P(A) = 1 - \dfrac{4}{6} = \dfrac{2}{6}$.

b) Using the answer from part a and the same argument as in part a,

$P(A) = P(ending\ at\ a_2) \cdot P(A,\ starting\ from\ a_2) = \dfrac{4}{6} \cdot \dfrac{6}{7} = \dfrac{4}{7}$ and $P(B) = \dfrac{3}{7}$.

4. Conjecture: $P(A) = \dfrac{b}{a+b}$ and $P(B) = \dfrac{a}{a+b}$. Proof by Induction:

The case for $a = 1$ was proven in problem 2. Assume that in a tree with two branches of length a and b,

$P(A) = \dfrac{b}{a+b}$ and $P(B) = \dfrac{a}{a+b}$, we must show that in a tree with two branches of lengths $a + 1$ and b,

$P(A) = \dfrac{b}{a+b+1}$ and $P(B) = \dfrac{a+1}{a+b+1}$. Let A_k be the last node before you get to leaf A.

$P(A) = P(A_k) \cdot P(A \mid A_k)$. By the induction hypothesis, $P(A_k) = \dfrac{b}{a+b}$. $P(A \mid A_k)$, the probability of getting

to A when starting from A_k, equals $\dfrac{a+b}{a+b+1}$ by the theorem in problem 2. Therefore,

$P(A) = \left(\dfrac{b}{a+b}\right)\left(\dfrac{a+b}{a+b+1}\right) = \dfrac{b}{a+b+1}$. $P(B) = 1 - P(A) = 1 - \dfrac{b}{a+b+1} = \dfrac{a+b+1-b}{a+b+1} = \dfrac{a+1}{a+b+1}$.

5. a) *Paths to A* : $RA + RxRA + RxRxRA + RxRxRxRA + \ldots$ where $x \in \{b_1,\ c_1\}$

$$P(A) = \frac{1}{3} + 2\left(\frac{1}{3}\cdot\frac{1}{2}\cdot\frac{1}{3}\right) + 2^2\left(\frac{1}{3}\cdot\frac{1}{2}\cdot\frac{1}{3}\cdot\frac{1}{2}\cdot\frac{1}{3}\right) + 2^3\left(\frac{1}{3}\cdot\frac{1}{2}\cdot\frac{1}{3}\cdot\frac{1}{2}\cdot\frac{1}{3}\cdot\frac{1}{2}\cdot\frac{1}{3}\right) + \ldots = \frac{1}{3} + \frac{2}{18} + \frac{4}{108} + \frac{8}{648} + \ldots =$$

$$\frac{\frac{1}{3}}{1 - \frac{2}{6}} = \frac{2}{4} = \frac{1}{2}. \quad P(B) = P(C) = \frac{1}{4}.$$

b) *Paths to A* : $Ra_1 A + Ra_1 Ra_1 A + Ra_1 Ra_1 Ra_1 A + Ra_1 Ra_1 Ra_1 Ra_1 A + \ldots$

$$P(A) = \frac{1}{3}\cdot\frac{1}{2} + \frac{1}{3}\cdot\frac{1}{2}\cdot\frac{1}{3}\cdot\frac{1}{2} + \frac{1}{3}\cdot\frac{1}{2}\cdot\frac{1}{3}\cdot\frac{1}{2}\cdot\frac{1}{3}\cdot\frac{1}{2} + \ldots = \frac{1}{6} + \frac{1}{36} + \frac{1}{216} + \ldots = \frac{\frac{1}{6}}{1 - \frac{1}{6}} = \frac{1}{5}. \quad P(B) = P(C) = \frac{2}{5}.$$

c) *Paths to A* : $RA + RxRA + RxRxRA + RxRxRxRA + \ldots$ where $x \in \{b_1, d_1\}$

$$P(A) = \frac{1}{4} + 2\left(\frac{1}{4}\cdot\frac{1}{2}\cdot\frac{1}{4}\right) + 2^2\left(\frac{1}{4}\cdot\frac{1}{2}\cdot\frac{1}{4}\cdot\frac{1}{2}\cdot\frac{1}{4}\right) + 2^3\left(\frac{1}{4}\cdot\frac{1}{2}\cdot\frac{1}{4}\cdot\frac{1}{2}\cdot\frac{1}{4}\cdot\frac{1}{2}\cdot\frac{1}{4}\right) + \ldots = \frac{1}{4} + \frac{1}{16} + \frac{1}{64} + \ldots = \frac{\frac{1}{4}}{1 - \frac{1}{4}} = \frac{1}{3}.$$

$$P(A) = P(C) = \frac{1}{3} \text{ and } P(B) = P(D) = \frac{1}{6}.$$

6. a) <u>Method 1:</u> From problem 4, $P\left(\text{walk ends at } A_1 \mid \text{walk ends at } A_1 \text{ or } A_2\right) = \frac{a_2}{a_1 + a_2}$ and

$$P\left(\text{walk ends at } A_2 \mid \text{walk ends at } A_1 \text{ or } A_2\right) = \frac{a_1}{a_1 + a_2}.$$

Therefore, $\dfrac{P\left(\text{walk ends at } A_1\right)}{P\left(\text{walk ends at } A_1 \text{ or } A_2\right)} = \dfrac{a_2}{a_1 + a_2}$ and $\dfrac{P\left(\text{walk ends at } A_2\right)}{P\left(\text{walk ends at } A_1 \text{ or } A_2\right)} = \dfrac{a_1}{a_1 + a_2}$ (*See (6c)) .

$$\frac{P\left(A_1\right)}{P\left(A_1 \text{ or } A_2\right)} = \frac{a_2}{a_1 + a_2} \quad \text{and} \quad \frac{P\left(A_2\right)}{P\left(A_1 \text{ or } A_2\right)} = \frac{a_1}{a_1 + a_2}$$

$$\frac{a_1 + a_2}{P\left(A_1 \text{ or } A_2\right)} = \frac{a_2}{P\left(A_1\right)} \quad \text{and} \quad \frac{a_1 + a_2}{P\left(A_1 \text{ or } A_2\right)} = \frac{a_1}{P\left(A_2\right)}.$$

Thus, $\dfrac{a_2}{P\left(A_1\right)} = \dfrac{a_1}{P\left(A_2\right)}$ and $P\left(A_2\right) = \dfrac{a_1}{a_2}P\left(A_1\right)$. Sweet! We have a relationship among all the $P\left(A_k\right)$'s .

We know $P\left(A_1\right) + P\left(A_2\right) + P\left(A_3\right) + \ldots + P\left(A_n\right) = 1$ and so $P\left(A_1\right)\left(1 + \dfrac{a_1}{a_2} + \dfrac{a_1}{a_3} + \ldots + \dfrac{a_1}{a_n}\right) = 1$.

$a_1 \cdot P(A_1) \cdot \sum\limits_{k=1}^{n} \dfrac{1}{a_k} = 1$ and $P(A_1) = \dfrac{1}{a_1} \cdot \left(\sum\limits_{k=1}^{n} \dfrac{1}{a_k} \right)^{-1}$. Set $\Sigma = \sum\limits_{k=1}^{n} \dfrac{1}{a_k}$ and doing the same calculations for each of

the probabilities, we get $\left(P(A_1),\ P(A_2),\ P(A_3),\ ...,\ P(A_n) \right) = \left(\dfrac{1}{a_1 \Sigma},\ \dfrac{1}{a_2 \Sigma},\ \dfrac{1}{a_3 \Sigma},\ ....,\ \dfrac{1}{a_n \Sigma} \right)$.

<u>Method 2:</u> For each branch, k, the numerator of $P(A_k)$ is the product of the lengths of all the other branches.

The denominator of $P(A_k)$ is the sum of all the numerators!

b) Method 1: $\Sigma = \dfrac{1}{3} + \dfrac{1}{2} + \dfrac{1}{2} = \dfrac{4}{3}$. $\left(P(A),\ P(B),\ P(C) \right) = \left(\dfrac{1}{3 \left(\dfrac{4}{3} \right)},\ \dfrac{1}{2 \left(\dfrac{4}{3} \right)},\ \dfrac{1}{2 \left(\dfrac{4}{3} \right)} \right) = \left(\dfrac{1}{4}, \dfrac{3}{8}, \dfrac{3}{8} \right)$.

Method 2: $\left(P(A),\ P(B),\ P(C) \right) = \left(\dfrac{2 \cdot 2}{4+6+6}, \dfrac{2 \cdot 3}{4+6+6}, \dfrac{2 \cdot 3}{4+6+6} \right) = \left(\dfrac{4}{16}, \dfrac{6}{16}, \dfrac{6}{16} \right)$.

c) See (6a), Method 1. (N.B. (*) By definition, $P(A \mid B) = \dfrac{P(A \text{ and } B)}{P(B)}$. Replacing B with $A \text{ or } B$, produces

$P\left(A \mid \left(A \text{ or } B \right) \right) = \dfrac{P\left(A \text{ and } (A \text{ or } B) \right)}{P(A \text{ or } B)}$. But $A \text{ and } (A \text{ or } B) = A$. Therefore, $P\left(A \mid \left(A \text{ or } B \right) \right) = \dfrac{P(A)}{P(A \text{ or } B)}$.

7. Let X be the vertex common to branches A, C, and D. The paths to A are $RX...A$ and so

$P(A) = \dfrac{1}{2} \cdot P(\text{path starts at } X \text{ and ends at } A) = \dfrac{1}{2} \left(\dfrac{3}{7} \right) = \dfrac{3}{14}$. The paths to B are RB and $AX....B$ and so

$P(B) = \dfrac{1}{2} + \dfrac{1}{2} \cdot P(\text{path starts at } X \text{ and ends at } B) = \dfrac{1}{2} + \dfrac{1}{2} \left(\dfrac{3}{14} \right) = \dfrac{17}{28}$. The paths to C are $RX...C$, giving

$P(C) = \dfrac{1}{2} \cdot P(\text{path starts at } X \text{ and ends at } C) = \dfrac{1}{2} \left(\dfrac{1}{7} \right) = \dfrac{1}{14}$. The paths to D are $RX...D$, resulting in

$P(D) = \dfrac{1}{2} \cdot P(\text{path starts at } X \text{ and ends at } D) = \dfrac{1}{2} \left(\dfrac{3}{14} \right) = \dfrac{3}{28}$.

8. From problem 6, $P(A_1) = \dfrac{1}{a_1 \Sigma} = \left(1 + \dfrac{a_1}{a_2} + \dfrac{a_1}{a_3} + \dfrac{a_1}{a_4} + \ldots + \dfrac{a_1}{a_k}\right)^{-1}$. To minimize $P(A_1)$, the series inside the

parentheses must be maximized. This will happen when we let $a_2 = a_3 = a_4 = \ldots = a_k = 1$.

Therefore, $P(A_1) = \left(1 + (n-1)a_1\right)^{-1}$. But $a_1 + (n-1) = 2007$, implying $(n-1) = 2007 - a_1$. So we must

maximize $1 + (2007 - a_1)a_1$. This is a parabola with vertex at $\dfrac{2007}{2}$. Therefore, the maximal integer values

occur at 1003 and 1004 and so $P(A_1) = \dfrac{1}{1 + 1003 \cdot 1004} = \dfrac{1}{1007013}$.

9. Because of the symmetry of the tree, $P(A) = P(B)$ (Why?) Consider the *two* steps following the first visit to

Z. We can walk directly to D with a probability of $\dfrac{1}{2}$. Or we could head back to Y also with a probability of

$\dfrac{1}{2}$. Once at Y our next step heads to C, R, or Z, each

with a probability of $\dfrac{1}{3}$. If we go to C, the probability of ending up

at D is zero. If we go to R, the probability of ending up at D is $P(D)$.
If we go to Z, the probability of ending up at D is $P(D|Z)$. Therefore,

$$P(D \mid Z) = \frac{1}{2} + \frac{1}{2}\left(\frac{1}{3}(0) + \frac{1}{3}P(D) + \frac{1}{3}P(D \mid Z)\right)$$

$$P(D \mid Z) = \frac{1}{2} + \frac{1}{6}P(D) + \frac{1}{6}P(D \mid Z)$$

$$6P(D \mid Z) = 3 + P(D) + P(D \mid Z)$$

$$5P(D \mid Z) = 3 + P(D)$$

$$P(D \mid Z) = \frac{3}{5} + \frac{1}{5}P(D)$$

Since $P(D) = P(Z) \cdot P(D \mid Z)$, we get $P(D) = \dfrac{1}{4}\left(\dfrac{3}{5} + \dfrac{1}{5} \cdot P(D)\right) = \dfrac{3}{20} + \dfrac{1}{20}P(D)$, giving $P(D) = \dfrac{3}{19}$. Since paths

ending at C and D must go through Y, $CYZD$ can be considered a tree rooted at Y and from the theorem in

problem 2, because the length of D is twice the length of C, $P(C)$ must be twice $P(D)$ or $\dfrac{6}{19}$. Finally, since

$P(A) = P(B)$, $\left(P(A), P(B), P(C), P(D)\right) = \left(\dfrac{5}{19}, \dfrac{5}{19}, \dfrac{6}{19}, \dfrac{3}{19}\right)$.

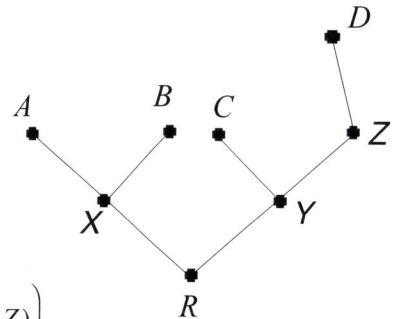

Mathematical Billiards

The Background

Harold Jacobs begins his book, Mathematics - A Human Endeavor, with a lesson on the path of a billiards ball. In his lesson the ball is always hit from the lower left-hand corner at a 45° angle to the sides and it continues to travel in straight segments, rebounding or caroming off the sides of the table until it comes to rest in a corner. When the ball hits the side or cushion of the table, it rebounds at the same angle at which it struck the cushion (or for you physics majors, the angle of incidence always equals the angle of reflection.) The gist of the problem is to predict at which corner the ball will end up.

This problem is an extension of Jacobs' idea. Like Jacobs' tables, our mathematical billiard tables in part A will be rectangular with integral side lengths and have frictionless felt so the ball can travel without losing momentum until it ends up in one of the corner pockets. The ball will always start in the lower left corner, but rather than always travelling at a 45° angle, on our table we will aim the ball at one of the diamonds along the sides marking the unit lengths. A side of length s will have $s-1$ equally-spaced diamonds. The dimensions of our table will be H by V (both integers) , with V always greater than or equal to H . The lower left corner of the table could be thought of as the origin, with $(H,0)$ the lower right pocket, $(0,V)$ the upper left pocket, and (H,V) the upper right pocket. The diamond which is aimed at will then be represented by the ordered pair (m,n) in which either $m = H$ or $n = V$. Given H, V, m, and n you will be investigating the mathematics behind predicting the final pocket, the number of caroms (or bounces) and the length of the path.

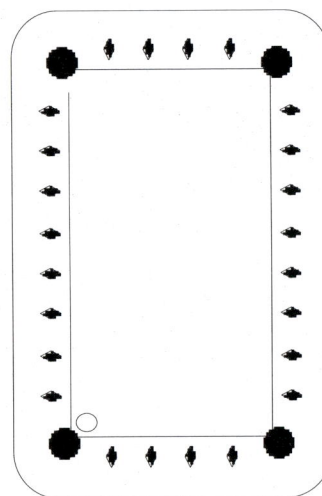

A 5 x 9 Mathematical Billiards Table

On a 5 by 9 table, when a ball is aimed at the (5, 6) diamond, it caroms three times, travels $3\sqrt{61}$ units, and ends up in the Lower-Right (LR) corner.

On a 5 by 9 table, when a ball is aimed at the (5, 3) diamond, it caroms two times, travels $3\sqrt{34}$ units, and ends up in the Upper-Right (UR) corner.

The length of the path will always be of the form $x\sqrt{m^2 + n^2}$.

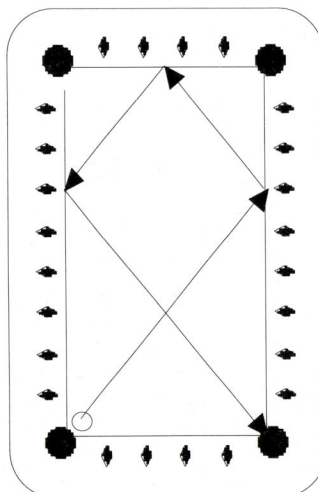

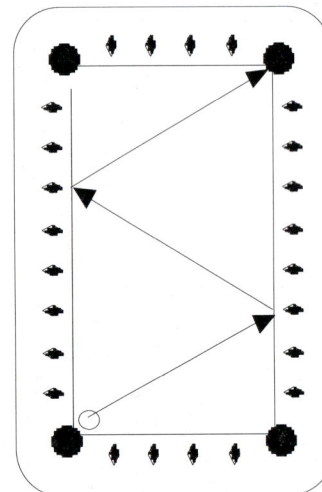

In part B you will be considering equilateral triangular billiards tables. The ball will still be hit from the lower left corner (A) and aimed at a diamond (D) on the opposite cushion ($\overline{BC}$). If the table has a side length of s, the $s-1$ diamonds along each side divide the side into s segments of length 1.

Let $\dfrac{m}{n} = \dfrac{BD}{DC}$ where m and n are relatively prime integers. You will use m, n, and s to predict the pocket the ball will end up in, the number of caroms it will make, and the length of the path.

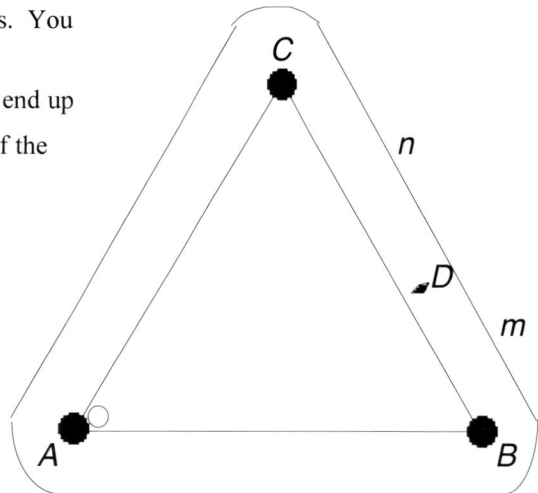

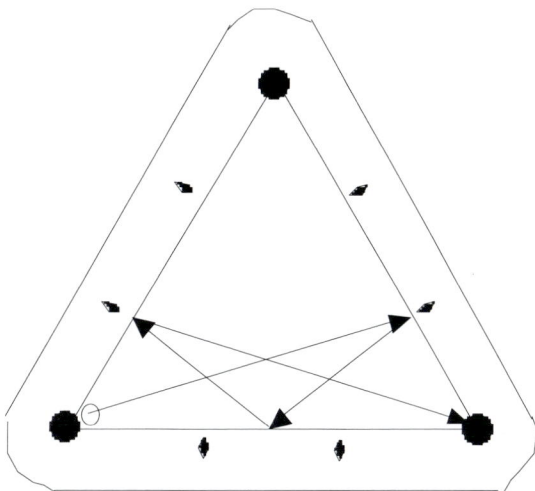

The path of a ball aimed at the (1:2) diamond on a triangular table of length 3

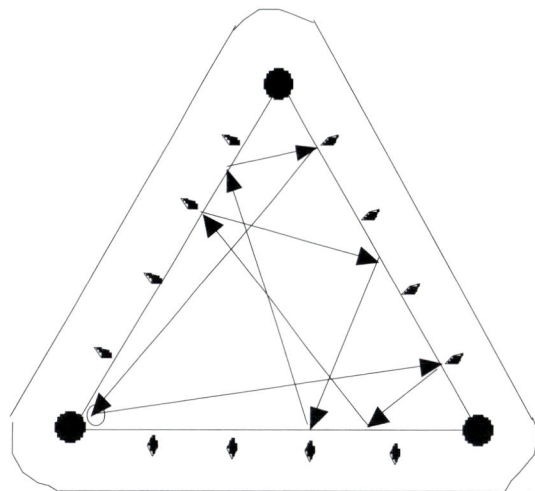

The path of a ball aimed at the (1:4) diamond on a triangular table of length 5

As you can see from the diagrams above, these drawings are diffcult to make so rather than having you draw many diagrams, the results for several tables are tabulated on the next page.

Table Length(s)	m:n	Final Pocket	Number of Caroms	Length of Path
2	1:1	A	1	$2\sqrt{3}$
3	1:2	B	3	$3\sqrt{7}$
	2:1	C	3	$3\sqrt{7}$
4	1:3	C	5	$4\sqrt{13}$
	1:1	A	1	$4\sqrt{3}$
	3:1	B	5	$4\sqrt{13}$
5	1:4	A	7	$5\sqrt{21}$
	2:3	B	7	$5\sqrt{19}$
	3:2	C	7	$4\sqrt{19}$
	4:1	A	7	$5\sqrt{21}$
6	1:5	B	9	$6\sqrt{31}$
	1:2	B	3	$6\sqrt{7}$
	1:1	A	1	$6\sqrt{3}$
	2:1	C	3	$6\sqrt{7}$
	5:1	C	9	$6\sqrt{31}$
7	1:6	C	11	$7\sqrt{43}$
	2:5	A	11	$7\sqrt{39}$
	3:4	B	11	$7\sqrt{37}$
	4:3	C	11	$7\sqrt{37}$
	5:2	A	11	$7\sqrt{39}$
	6:1	B	11	$7\sqrt{43}$
8	1:7	A	13	$8\sqrt{57}$
	1:3	C	5	$8\sqrt{13}$

The Problems

Set A

1. On the special answer sheet #1, carefully draw the paths the ball will take on a 3 by 5 mathematical billiards table, if it is aimed at each of the six diamonds along the top and right side cushions. Below each graph, indicate the pocket the ball ends up in, the number of caroms, and the length of the path in the form:

$$x\sqrt{m^2 + n^2}.$$

2. On the special answer sheet #2, carefully draw the paths the ball will take on a 5 by 6 mathematical billiards table, if it is aimed each of the nine diamonds along the top and right side cushions. Below each graph, indicate the pocket the ball ends up in, the number of caroms, and the length of the path in the form:

$$x\sqrt{m^2 + n^2}.$$

3. Let N and D be two relatively prime integers such that $\dfrac{N}{D} = \dfrac{m \cdot n}{H \cdot V}$. Use N and D to create a formula to predict the pocket (LL, LR, UL, or UR) a ball will end up at when you hit a ball from the lower left corner of a H by V table when aiming at the (m,n) diamond.

4. Use N and D to create a formula to predict the number of caroms a ball will make when you hit a ball from the lower left corner of a H by V table when aiming at the (m,n) diamond.

5. Use N, D, m, and n to create a formula to predict the length of the path a ball will make when you hit a ball from the lower left corner of a H by V table when aiming at the (m,n) diamond.

6. On the new 2008 model table with dimensions H by V, the salesman claimed that a ball hit from the lower left corner and aimed at the diamond (H, H) on the right cushion would carom 2008 times before falling in a pocket! But he forgot what dimensions the new models came in. If H and V are integers with $V > H$, how many different-sized (non-similar) tables can the new 2008 model come in?

Set B

7. Use m and n to create a formula to predict the pocket $(A, B, \text{or } C)$ the ball will end up in. (Hint: Think mod 3).

8. Use m and n to create a formula to predict the number of caroms the ball will take in its path to the pocket.

9. Use m, n, and s to create a formula to predict the length of the path of the ball.

10. While shopping for a new table, I noticed the 2007 model was now on sale for half off. The same crazy salesman claimed that a ball hit from the lower left corner (A) and aimed at some of the diamonds along cushion $\overline{BC}$ would carom 2007 times but he couldn't remember which diamonds to aim at! For how many of the diamonds along cushion $\overline{BC}$ would this be true?

ARML Power Contest
February 2008
Special Answer Sheet #1

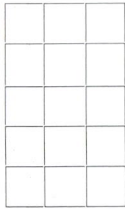  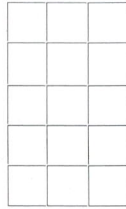 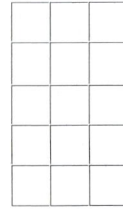 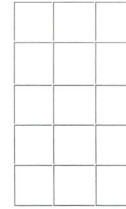

P = _____   P = _____   P = _____   P = _____   P = _____

C = _____   C = _____   C = _____   C = _____   C = _____

L = _____   L = _____   L = _____   L = _____   L = _____

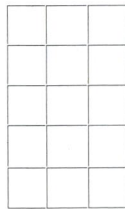 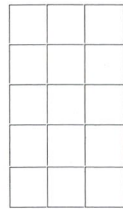 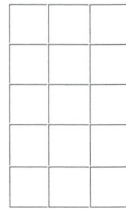 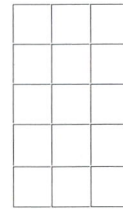 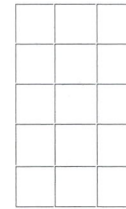

P = _____   P = _____   P = _____   P = _____   P = _____

C = _____   C = _____   C = _____   C = _____   C = _____

L = _____   L = _____   L = _____   L = _____   L = _____

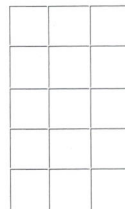 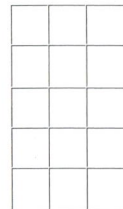 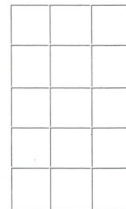 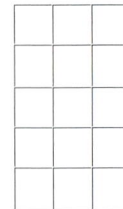 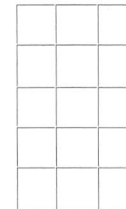

P = _____   P = _____   P = _____   P = _____   P = _____

C = _____   C = _____   C = _____   C = _____   C = _____

L = _____   L = _____   L = _____   L = _____   L = _____

ARML Power Contest
February 2008
Special Answer Sheet #2

P = _____

C = _____

L = _____

P = _____

C = _____

L = _____

P = _____

C = _____

L = _____

P = _____

C = _____

L = _____

P = _____

C = _____

L = _____

P = _____

C = _____

L = _____

P = _____

C = _____

L = _____

P = _____

C = _____

L = _____

P = _____

C = _____

L = _____

P = _____

C = _____

L = _____

P = _____

C = _____

L = _____

P = _____

C = _____

L = _____

The Solutions

1.

P = UR	P = UL	P = LR	P = UR	P = LR	P = UR
C = 2	C = 3	C = 7	C = 6	C = 5	C = 4
L = $3\sqrt{26}$	L= $3\sqrt{29}$	L = $5\sqrt{25}$	L = $5\sqrt{18}$	L= $5\sqrt{13}$	L= $5\sqrt{10}$
		= 25	= $15\sqrt{2}$		

P = UR	P = UL
C = 2	C = 5
L = $3\sqrt{29}$	L = $6\sqrt{26}$

2.

P = UR	P = UL	P = UR	P = UL	P = UL	P = LR	P = UL
C = 4	C = 5	C = 6	C = 7	C = 9	C = 3	C = 1
L = $5\sqrt{37}$	L = $5\sqrt{40}$	L = $5\sqrt{45}$	L = $5\sqrt{52}$	L = $6\sqrt{50}$	L = $3\sqrt{41}$	L = $2\sqrt{34}$
	= $10\sqrt{10}$	= $15\sqrt{5}$	= $10\sqrt{13}$	=$30\sqrt{2}$		

3. If the ball caroms off the TOP RAIL first:

   If N is even and D is odd, the ball will end up in the Upper Left pocket.

   If N is odd and D is odd, the ball will end up in the Upper Right pocket.

   If N is odd and D is even, the ball will end up in the Lower Right pocket. There are no examples of this, so try a 2 by 2 table and aim at the (1,2) diamond.

If the ball caroms off the SIDE RAIL first:

   If N is even and D is odd, the ball will end up in the Lower Right pocket.

   If N is odd and D is odd, the ball will end up in the Upper Right pocket.

   If N is odd and D is even, the ball will end up in the Upper Left pocket.

   It is impossible for the ball to end up in the Lower Left pocket.

4. $C = N + D - 2$

5. $L = D\sqrt{m^2 + n^2}$

6. By the formula in question #5, $N + D - 2 = 2008$ or $N + D = 2010$ where N and D have no common factors. Any common factor of N and D must also be a factor of 2010. The factors of 2010 are 1, 2010, 2, 1005, 3, 670, 5, 402, 6, 335, 10, 201, 15, 134, 30, and 67. Of the 2010 possibilities for N, 1005 are multiples of 2, 670 are multiples of 3, 402 are multiples of 5, 30 are multiples of 67, 335 are multiples of 2 and 3, 201 are multiples of 2 and 5, 134 are multiples of 3 and 5, 15 are multiples of 2 and 67, 10 are multiples of 3 and 67, 6 are multiples of 5 and 67, 67 are multiples of 2, 3, and 5, 5 are multiples of 2, 3 and 67, 3 are multiples of 3, 5, and 67, and 1 is a multple of all four prime factors of 2010. Therefore, by the principle of inclusion/exclusion, the number of possibilities for N are

$2010 - (1005 + 670 + 402 + 30) + (335 + 201 + 134 + 15 + 10 + 6) - (67 + 5 + 3 + 2) + 1 = 528$. So the total number of non-congruent tables is $528/2 = 256$.

7. Let $X = (2m + n) \bmod 3$.

If $X = \begin{cases} 0, \text{ the ball ends up in pocket } A. \\ 1, \text{ the ball ends up in pocket } B. \\ 2, \text{ the ball ends up in pocket } C. \end{cases}$

(This diagram (for $s = 4$) should give you an idea of where this formula came from.)

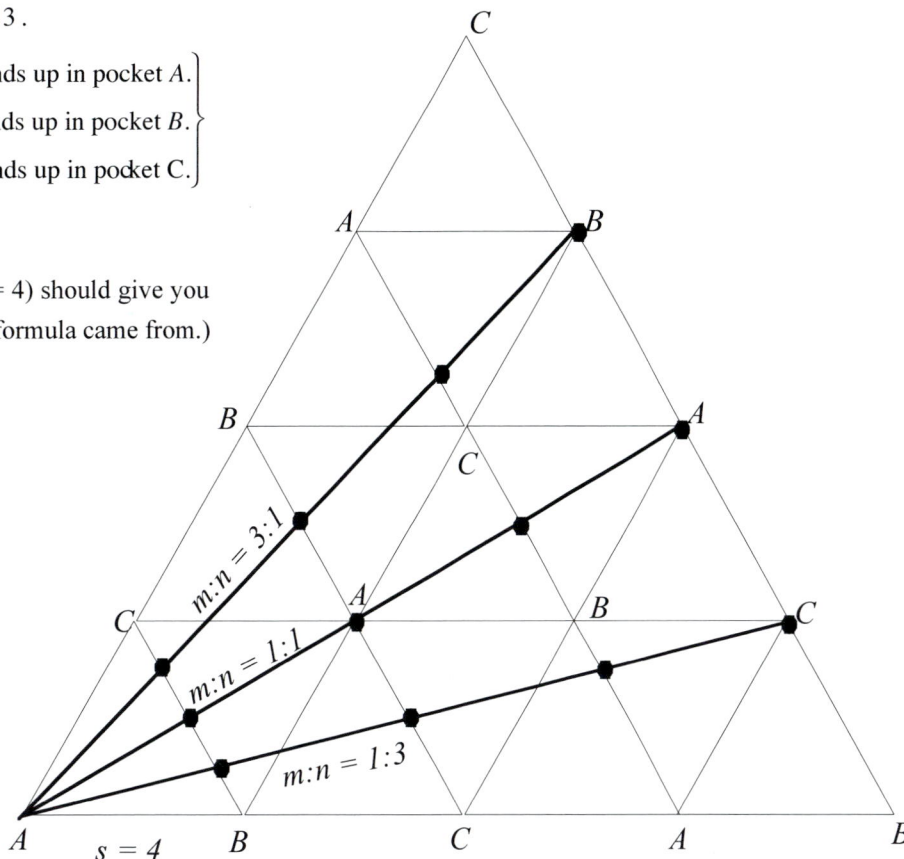

8. $C = 2(m + n) - 3$

9. $L = s\sqrt{m^2 + n^2 + mn}$

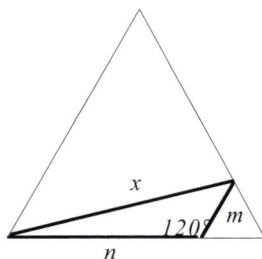

$x^2 = m^2 + n^2 - 2mn \cos(120°) = m^2 + n^2 + mn$

(The s in the formula comes from the equally-spaced dots in the diagram above.)

10. By the formula in question #8, $2(m + n) - 3 = 2007$ or $m + n = 1005$ where m and n have no common factors. Any common factor of m and n must also be a factor of 1005. The factors of 1005 are 1, 1, 1005, 3, 335, 5, 201, 15, and 67. Of the 1005 possibilities for m, 335 are multiples of 3, 201 are multiples of 5, 15 are multiples of 67, 67 are multiples of 3 and 5, 5 are multiples of 3 and 67, 3 are multiples of 5 and 67, and 1 is a multple of all three prime factors of 1005. Therefore, by the principle of inclusion/exclusion, the number of possibilities for m are $1005 - (335 + 201 + 15) + (67 + 5 + 3) - 1 = 528$. Also this problem and #6 can be

solved using Euler's phi function, $\varphi(1005) = 1005\left(1 - \frac{1}{3}\right)\left(1 - \frac{1}{5}\right)\left(1 - \frac{1}{67}\right) = 528$.

The Game of Yahtzee

The Background

The Yacht Game, a poker dice game, was invented by a Canadian couple in 1954 while sailing aboard their yacht. Wanting to distribute copies to their friends, they sold exclusive production rights to Edwin S. Lowe in exchange for the first 1,000 copies. Lowe changed the name to Yahtzee and began actively marketing his product as "The Fun Game That Makes Thinking Fun." From 1956 to 1973 over 40,000,000 Yahtzee games were sold. In 1973 Lowe, after making a handsome profit, sold his company to Milton Bradley, now Hasbro.

In 2003 Phil Woodward of Pfizer Global Research and Development "solved" the game by computing the 1,279,054,096,320 possible outcomes and working out the optimal playing strategies. His results have been confirmed by Tom Verhoeff and Erick Scheffers of Einhoven University of Technology in the Netherlands. They have created an online applet "Optimal Solitaire Yahtzee Player" which analyzes your playing of a game of Yahtzee.

The object of the game is to roll five dice and obtain one of thirteen "poker hand" categories listed on the score card. On each turn you can roll the dice up to three times. On the first roll you roll all five dice but on subsequent rolls, you can keep some of the dice and reroll the others. You must then decide in which category you want to score the final outcome. During a game each category may be used only once. Therefore, a game consists of thirteen turns, one for each category. The points scored for obtaining each category is either a fixed amount or the total of your five dice. On some turns you may have to enter a zero for a category.

Although the official rules for the game have had some slight modifications over the years, I have enclosed a set of the original 1956 rules.

How to Play

Yahtzee®

the FUN game that makes
THINKING ...*fun!*

Your YAHTZEE game consists of the following equipment.

1 Dice Cup
1 Set of 5 Dice
1 YAHTZEE Score Pad
2 Pencils
20 YAHTZEE Bonus Chips

YAHTZEE RULES

YAHTZEE may be played by any number of people. Each player keeps his own score on a score card marked with his name. The object of the game is to obtain the highest score. The player with the highest grand total score wins the difference between his score and that of his opponents.

The players each throw five dice once; the one with the highest total starts the play. The players then continue clockwise.

Let's start the play. Each player on his turn shakes and rolls out of cup the 5 YAHTZEE dice. Each player is entitled to 3 rolls of the dice on each turn. And it's the skillful use of this option that can turn an unlucky roll into a high-scoring turn.

Note that on the YAHTZEE score card there are 13 scoring boxes — aces, twos, threes, etc., through Large Straight, YAHTZEE and Chance. The player must decide in which of these 13 boxes he wishes to score, for each possibility has a different point value. Depending on his particular goal, and remembering that the player with the highest total score is the winner, the player may stop and take his score on the first roll; or he may pick up any number of dice and roll again. On this second roll he may stop and take his score or he may elect to roll a third time. Again he may pick up any number of dice and roll; on this last roll he must take his score.

On completion of each turn the player marks the score in the appropriate box on his score card. If there is no appropriate box open to mark his score, the player must enter a zero in any open box of his choice. Only one blank box may be filled at the end of each turn. The boxes in the column may be filled in any order, according to the player's best judgment.

The game is completed after each player has had 13 turns and has filled every box in the column with a score or an optional zero. The scores are then totalled and the player with the highest grand total wins.

HOW TO SCORE

It's simple. See score pad. The score pad is divided into 2 sections, the Upper and Lower. In the **Upper section** there are boxes to score aces, twos, threes, fours, fives and sixes.

The player counts and adds only the dice with the same number and enters the total in the appropriate box. Thus, if the three box is chosen, the combination 2, 5, 3, 3, 3 would score 9, for the 3 three's. The maximum score in the 3's box is, of course, 15; in the 5's box 25.

The minimum score to earn a bonus of 35 points is a score of 63 points or more. Sixty-three must be reached by scoring a minimum of 3 of a kind of each of the numbers on the dice from 1 to 6. (See score card).

The **Lower section** is played exactly as shown on the score card.

3 of a kind may be chosen only when a roll includes any 3 of a kind. The total on all 5 dice is scored, e.g.,

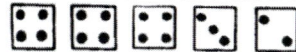

would be scored as 17.

4 of a kind scores the total of all 5 dice provided they include any 4 of a kind, e.g.,

would be scored as 22.

Full House may be chosen only when the roll includes any 3 of a kind and any pair. Score 25.

Small Straight is any sequence of four numbers. Score 30.

Large Straight is any sequence of five numbers. Score 40.

YAHTZEE IS ANY 5 OF A KIND. Score 50.

Chance is the opportunity the player has to score on any turn which doesn't fill any other requirement. Mark score by totalling number of points on all dice.

If the player should throw a YAHTZEE (five of a kind) for the first time, and the YAHTZEE box has previously been filled with a zero and the appropriate numbered box of the upper section has been used, he may use this turn as a Joker and mark his score in any of the boxes open in the lower section. For example, if he has

he may score 20 points in any of the following boxes: 3 of a kind, 4 of a kind or Chance box; or score 25 points in the Full House, 30 points in Small Straight, or 40 points in Large Straight boxes. If all these boxes in the lower section are filled he must enter a zero in a box of his choice in the upper section. He does not receive a YAHTZEE Bonus Chip.

A player receives one YAHTZEE Bonus Chip only when he tosses a second YAHTZEE during a game (13 turns). He must also use this second YAHTZEE as a Joker, and score as explained in the previous paragraph.

The YAHTZEE Bonus Chips are each worth 100 points. At the end of each game, players score the number of points each has in YAHTZEE Bonus Chips and then return the chips to the kitty. When two tables are playing YAHTZEE, divide the Bonus Chips by color.

© 1956, 1961 E. S. LOWE COMPANY, INC.

The Problems

Part A: One Roll of the Dice

1. On one roll of the five dice, what is the probability of rolling

   a) a Yahtzee?

   b) Four of a Kind? (N.B. Although 33333 could be scored as "Four of a Kind", do NOT count this as "Four of a Kind.")

   c) Three of a Kind? (N.B Do NOT count 33344, 33335, and 33333 as "Three of a Kind".)

   d) a Pair? (N.B. Do NOT count 22333 but DO count 22334.)

   e) a Full House?

   f) a Large Straight?

   g) a Small Straight? (N.B Although 12345 could be scored as a "Small Straight", do NOT count this as a "Small Straight.")

2. On one roll of the five dice, how many distinct outcomes are there? Justify your answer.
   (N.B. A roll of 1, 1, 1, 1, 2 is the same outcome as a roll of 1, 2, 1, 1, 1.)

3. According to the "Optimal Solitaire Yahtzee Player," the expected value for the "Chance" category when playing a game of Yahtzee is 22.01. On one roll of the five dice, what is the probability of rolling a total of 22?

4. After two rolls, the dice show three 3's and two 1's. Should you take a Full House and score 25 points or should you reroll the two 1's and try to score a Yahtzee, Four of a Kind, Three of a Kind or Chance? Justify you answer by determining the expected score of each possibility.

Part B: The Two Final Rolls of the Dice

5. If you roll and keep two 6's, what is the probability of getting a Yahtzee of five 6's in your remaining two rolls of that turn?

6. If you roll and keep two 6's, what is the probability of getting a Full House in your remaining two rolls of that turn?

7. If you roll and keep a 2, a 3, and a 4, what is the probability of getting a Small Straight or a Large Straight in the remaining two rolls of the turn? (N.B. On the second roll, if you roll a 1 and a 5 or a 5 and a 6, you will keep them and end your turn; if you roll a 1 or a 5, you will keep it and reroll the other die; any other values will be rerolled.)

Part C: One Complete Turn (Three Rolls of the Dice)

8. Jean says the probability of getting "any" Yahtzee in a turn (3 rolls of the dice) is six times the probability of getting a Yahtzee of 1's in any turn. Do you agree? Justify your answer.

9. What is the highest possible score you could obtain in a game of Yahtzee? (Remember to count your points for Bonus Yahtzees.) What's the lowest possible score? Justify your answers.

10. A scoring curiosity? A Full House, which scores 25 points, occurs twice as often as Four of a Kind, which scores from 6 to 29 points. How many points would you expect to score in the category "Four of a Kind"?

11. What is the probability of rolling a Yahtzee of 6's in a given turn?

12. On the last turn of a game, the only category remaining is Sixes in the upper half of the score card. You need to get eighteen points to get the bonus. What is the expected value for Sixes in this turn?

The Solutions

1. Each solution has the following format: Pick the values, arrange the values, roll the dice.

a) AAAAA. $\binom{6}{1}\left(\dfrac{5!}{5!}\right)\left(\dfrac{1}{6}\right)^5 = \dfrac{6}{7776} = \dfrac{1}{1296}$.

b) AAAAX $\binom{6}{1}\binom{5}{1}\left(\dfrac{5!}{4!}\right)\left(\dfrac{1}{6}\right)^5 = \dfrac{25}{1296}$.

c) AAAXY $\binom{6}{1}\binom{5}{2}\left(\dfrac{5!}{3!}\right)\left(\dfrac{1}{6}\right)^5 = \dfrac{200}{1296} = \dfrac{25}{162}$.

d) AAXXY or AAXYZ $\binom{6}{2}\binom{4}{1}\left(\dfrac{5!}{2!2!}\right)\left(\dfrac{1}{6}\right)^5 + \binom{6}{1}\binom{5}{3}\left(\dfrac{5!}{2!}\right)\left(\dfrac{1}{6}\right)^5 = \dfrac{300}{1296} + \dfrac{600}{1296} = \dfrac{900}{1296} = \dfrac{25}{36}$.

e) AAAXX $\binom{6}{1}\binom{5}{1}\left(\dfrac{5!}{3!2!}\right)\left(\dfrac{1}{6}\right)^5 = \dfrac{50}{1296} = \dfrac{25}{648}$.

f) 12345 or 23456 $2\cdot\left[\binom{5}{5}(5!)\left(\dfrac{1}{6}\right)^5\right] = \dfrac{40}{1296} = \dfrac{5}{162}$.

g) The possibilities are: 1234X (where X ≠ 5) or 2345X (where X ≠ 1 and X ≠ 6) or 3456X (where X ≠ 2). This is equivalent to: 12346 or 13456 or 1234X (where X = 1, 2, 3, or 4) or 2345X (where X = 2, 3, 4, 5) or 3456X (where X = 3, 4, 5, or 6)

$$2\left[\binom{5}{5}(5!)\left(\dfrac{1}{6}\right)^5\right] + 3\left[\binom{4}{4}\binom{4}{1}\left(\dfrac{5!}{2!}\right)\left(\dfrac{1}{6}\right)^5\right] = \dfrac{5}{162} + \dfrac{5}{154} = \dfrac{10}{81}.$$

2. On one roll of the dice the following distinct outcomes can occur:

5 of a Kind $\binom{6}{1} = 6$

4 of a Kind $\binom{6}{1}\binom{5}{1} = 30$

Full House $\binom{6}{1}\binom{5}{1} = 30$

3 of a Kind $\binom{6}{1}\binom{5}{2} = 60$ Total = 252

Two Pair $\binom{6}{2}\binom{4}{1} = 60$

One Pair $\binom{6}{1}\binom{5}{3} = 60$

All different $\binom{6}{5} = 6$

3. The following is a list of all the ways of scoring 22 points on a roll of the dice:

66631	66433	64444
66622	65551	55552
66541	65542	55543
66532	65533	55444
66442	65443	

Of these fourteen rolls, two have the form XXXXY; two have the form XXXYY; three have the form XXXYZ; three have the form XXYYZ; and four have the form XXYZW.
Therefore, the probability of rolling a score of 22 would be:

$$\left[2\left(\tfrac{5!}{4!}\right)+2\left(\tfrac{5!}{3!2!}\right)+3\left(\tfrac{5!}{3!}\right)+3\left(\tfrac{5!}{2!2!}\right)+4\left(\tfrac{5!}{2!}\right)\right]\cdot\left(\tfrac{1}{6}\right)^5 = \frac{35}{648} = 0.0540123457.$$

4. Taking the Full House, the expected value would be 25 points. Rerolling the ones, the possible outcomes are 33333, 333XX, 3333X, 333XY, where $X \neq 3$, $Y \neq 3$, and $X \neq Y$. 33333 is a Yahtzee and it's expected value is

$\dfrac{1}{36}(50) = 1.3\overline{8}$. 333XX is one of five possible Full Houses and their combined expected values are

$\dfrac{1}{36}(5)(25) = 3.47\overline{2}$. 3333X (and 333X3) can be used for Four of a Kind or Chance and both earn points equal to

the sum of the five dice. Their combined expected values are $2 \cdot \dfrac{1}{36}(13+14+16+17+18) = 4.\overline{3}$. Likewise

333XY (and 333YX) can be used for Three of a Kind or Chance and both earn points equal to the sum of the five

dice. Their combined expected values are $2 \cdot \dfrac{1}{36}(12+14+15+16+15+16+17+18+19+20) = 9$. The

expected value when the ones are rerolled is the sum of all these expected values or $\dfrac{655}{36} = 18.19\overline{4}$. So keep the Full

House!

5. The result of the second roll could be 666, 66X, 6XX, or XXX, where X represents a non-six. For the last three, a third roll would be needed, resulting in 6, 66, 666, respectively. Therefore, the probability of rolling a Yahtzee of sixes after rolling two sixes on the first roll, would be

$$\left[\left(\tfrac{1}{6}\right)^3\right]+\left[\left(\tfrac{3!}{2!}\right)\left(\tfrac{1}{6}\right)^2\left(\tfrac{5}{6}\right)\right]\left(\tfrac{1}{6}\right)+\left[\left(\tfrac{3!}{2!}\right)\left(\tfrac{1}{6}\right)^1\left(\tfrac{5}{6}\right)^2\right]\left(\tfrac{1}{6}\right)^2+\left[\left(\tfrac{5}{6}\right)^3\right]\left(\tfrac{1}{6}\right)^3 =$$

$$\left(\tfrac{1}{6}\right)^3\left(1+3\left(\tfrac{5}{6}\right)+3\left(\tfrac{5}{6}\right)^2+\left(\tfrac{5}{6}\right)^3\right)=\left(\tfrac{1}{6}\right)^3\left(1+\tfrac{5}{6}\right)^3=\frac{1331}{46656}.$$

6. The result of the second roll could be 6XX, 6XY, XYZ, XXY, or XXX, where X, Y, and Z represent distinct non-sixes. The first and the last result in a Full House. The three others would require a third roll which would have to be WW for 6XY, 6WW or WWW for XYZ, 6 or X for XXY.

$$P(6XX)=\left[\binom{5}{1}\frac{3!}{2!}\left(\tfrac{1}{6}\right)^3\right]=\frac{15}{216}=\frac{5}{72}.$$

$$P(6XY \text{ then } WW)=\left[\binom{5}{2}(3!)\left(\tfrac{1}{6}\right)^3\right]\left[\binom{5}{1}\left(\tfrac{1}{6}\right)^2\right]=\frac{50}{1296}=\frac{25}{648}.$$

$$P(XYZ \text{ then } 6WW) = \left[\binom{5}{3}(3!)\left(\frac{1}{6}\right)^3\right]\left[\binom{5}{1}\frac{3!}{2!}\left(\frac{1}{6}\right)^3\right] = \frac{25}{1296}.$$

$$P(XYZ \text{ then } WWW) = \left[\binom{5}{3}(3!)\left(\frac{1}{6}\right)^3\right]\left[\binom{5}{1}\left(\frac{1}{6}\right)^3\right] = \frac{25}{3888}.$$

$$P(XXY \text{ then } 6) = \left[\binom{5}{2}\left(\frac{3!}{2!}\right)\left(\frac{1}{6}\right)^3\right]\left[\left(\frac{1}{6}\right)\right] = \frac{5}{216}.$$

$$P(XXY \text{ then } X) = \left[\binom{5}{2}\left(\frac{3!}{2!}\right)\left(\frac{1}{6}\right)^3\right]\left[\left(\frac{1}{6}\right)\right] = \frac{5}{216}.$$

$$P(XXX) = \left[\binom{5}{1}\left(\frac{1}{6}\right)^3\right] = \frac{5}{216}.$$

Therefore, after rolling two sixes on the first roll, the probability of rolling a Full House, either 666WW or 66WWW, would be $\frac{395}{1944}$. (Although not intended by the author, some teams may accept 66666 as a Full House. In this case the probability increases to $\frac{449}{1944}$.)

7.

On the second roll, four of the possible thirty-six outcomes (boxed) will result in a large straight while nine of the outcomes (small ovals) will result in a 1234 small straight and seven of the outcomes (large ovals) will result in a 2345 small straight. Probabilities for each of these outcomes would be $\frac{1}{9}$, $\frac{1}{4}$, and $\frac{7}{36}$, respectively, and the probability of no straight is $\frac{4}{9}$. So after the third roll, the probability of a large straight is

$$\frac{1}{9} + \frac{1}{4}\cdot\frac{1}{6} + \frac{7}{36}\cdot\frac{2}{6} + \frac{4}{9}\cdot\frac{1}{9} = \frac{173}{648}$$ and the probability of a small straight is $\frac{1}{4}\cdot\frac{5}{6} + \frac{7}{36}\cdot\frac{4}{6} + \frac{4}{9}\cdot\frac{4}{9} = \frac{347}{648}$. So the probability of getting a large or a small straight after rolling a 2, 3, and 4 on the first roll is

$$\frac{173}{648} + \frac{347}{648} = \frac{520}{648} = \frac{65}{81}.$$

8. When determining the probability of rolling a Yahtzee of 1's, everytime a 1 is rolled, it is set aside and the non-1's are rerolled. But this does not account for the possibility of changing the value of the Yahtzee during the roll. For example, if on the first roll, the outcome is 11234 and the 1's are held and the other three are rerolled, the result could be 11555. If any Yahtzee was now the goal, the 5's would be held and the 1's would be rerolled in hopes of getting 55555. This possibility would not be included if the original goal had been a Yahtzee of 5's.

9. To get the highest possible score one would need to roll thirteen Yahtzees and use Yahtzees of 6's as Chance, 3 of a Kind, and 4 of a Kind, and any kind of Yahtzee as Jokers in the Full House, Small Straight and Large Straight. Twelve hundred bonus points would be awarded. So the score card would read
$5 + 10 + 15 + 20 + 25 + 30 = 105 + 35 = 140$ in the Upper Section and $30 + 30 + 25 + 30 + 40 + 50 + 30 = 235$ in the Lower Section. Including the bonus points for the multiple Yahtzees, the highest total score would be $140 + 235 + 1200 = 1575$.
To get the lowest possible score, one would have to try (?) very hard but could score zero in the Upper Section and zero in the first six categories in the Lower Section and roll five 1's for Chance. The lowest possible score would be 5.

10. Four of a Kind with 1's could score from 5 to 10 points, Four of a Kind with 2's could score from 9 to 14 points, Four of a Kind with 3's could score from 13 to 18 points, Four of a Kind with 4's could score from 17 to 22 points, Four of a Kind with 5's could score from 21 to 26 points, Four of a Kind with 6's could score from 25 to 30 points. The sum of these thirty-six possible scores is 630. So, on the average, if a player scores a Four of a Kind, a score of $\dfrac{360}{36} = 17.5$ points will be earned. The expected score for a Full House is $25 \cdot \dfrac{24}{648} = \dfrac{25}{27} = .925926$, while the expected value for Four of a Kind is $(17.5)\dfrac{25}{1296} = \dfrac{875}{2592} = 0.337577$.

11. If one has 1 six and rerolls the 4 non-sixes, the probability of ending up with 3 sixes, i.e. 2 more sixes, is $\dbinom{4}{2}\left(\dfrac{1}{6}\right)^2\left(\dfrac{5}{6}\right)^2$. If one has 2 sixes and rerolls the 3 non-sixes, the probability of ending up with 5 sixes (i.e. 3 more sixes) is $\dbinom{3}{3}\left(\dfrac{1}{6}\right)^3\left(\dfrac{5}{6}\right)^0$. In general, if one has i sixes and rerolls the $5-i$ non-sixes, the probability of ending up with j sixes, where $0 \le i \le j \le 5$, is $\dbinom{5-i}{j-i}\left(\dfrac{1}{6}\right)^{j-i}\left(\dfrac{5}{6}\right)^{5-j}$. Using this fact, a transition matrix can be formed in which the value in cell (i, j) is the probability of getting $j-i$ sixes when you roll $5-i$ dice, i.e. it's the probability of increasing the number of sixes from i to j:

from \ to	0	1	2	3	4	5
0	$\binom{5}{0}\left(\frac{1}{6}\right)^0\left(\frac{5}{6}\right)^5$	$\binom{5}{1}\left(\frac{1}{6}\right)^1\left(\frac{5}{6}\right)^4$	$\binom{5}{2}\left(\frac{1}{6}\right)^2\left(\frac{5}{6}\right)^3$	$\binom{5}{3}\left(\frac{1}{6}\right)^3\left(\frac{5}{6}\right)^2$	$\binom{5}{4}\left(\frac{1}{6}\right)^4\left(\frac{5}{6}\right)^1$	$\binom{5}{5}\left(\frac{1}{6}\right)^5\left(\frac{5}{6}\right)^0$
1	0	$\binom{4}{0}\left(\frac{1}{6}\right)^0\left(\frac{5}{6}\right)^4$	$\binom{4}{1}\left(\frac{1}{6}\right)^1\left(\frac{5}{6}\right)^3$	$\binom{4}{2}\left(\frac{1}{6}\right)^2\left(\frac{5}{6}\right)^2$	$\binom{4}{3}\left(\frac{1}{6}\right)^3\left(\frac{5}{6}\right)^1$	$\binom{4}{4}\left(\frac{1}{6}\right)^4\left(\frac{5}{6}\right)^0$
$[T]=$ 2	0	0	$\binom{3}{0}\left(\frac{1}{6}\right)^0\left(\frac{5}{6}\right)^3$	$\binom{3}{1}\left(\frac{1}{6}\right)^1\left(\frac{5}{6}\right)^2$	$\binom{3}{2}\left(\frac{1}{6}\right)^2\left(\frac{5}{6}\right)^1$	$\binom{3}{3}\left(\frac{1}{6}\right)^3\left(\frac{5}{6}\right)^0$
3	0	0	0	$\binom{2}{0}\left(\frac{1}{6}\right)^0\left(\frac{5}{6}\right)^2$	$\binom{2}{1}\left(\frac{1}{6}\right)^1\left(\frac{5}{6}\right)^1$	$\binom{2}{2}\left(\frac{1}{6}\right)^2\left(\frac{5}{6}\right)^0$
4	0	0	0	0	$\binom{1}{0}\left(\frac{1}{6}\right)^0\left(\frac{5}{6}\right)^1$	$\binom{1}{1}\left(\frac{1}{6}\right)^1\left(\frac{5}{6}\right)^0$
5	0	0	0	0	0	$\binom{0}{0}\left(\frac{1}{6}\right)^0\left(\frac{5}{6}\right)^0$

Let $[A] = [1\ 0\ 0\ 0\ 0\ 0\ ]$, representing the probabilities that one has 0, 1, 2, 3, 4, or 5 sixes at the start of the round. $[A]\cdot[T]$ would represent the probability that one has 0, 1, 2, 3, 4, or 5 sixes after one roll of the dice, and

$[A]\cdot[T]^2$ would represent the probability that one has 0, 1, 2, 3, 4, or 5 sixes after two rolls of the dice, and

$[A]\cdot[T]^3$ would represent the probability that one has 0, 1, 2, 3, 4, or 5 sixes after three rolls of the dice. From this last matrix multiplication, it can be seen that .0001286 is the probability of rolling a Yahtzee of sixes in a given turn.

12.

Let $C = \begin{bmatrix} 0 & 0 & 0 & 0 & 0 & 0 \\ 0 & 1 & 0 & 0 & 0 & 0 \\ 0 & 0 & 2 & 0 & 0 & 0 \\ 0 & 0 & 0 & 3 & 0 & 0 \\ 0 & 0 & 0 & 0 & 4 & 0 \\ 0 & 0 & 0 & 0 & 0 & 5 \end{bmatrix}$ and let $D = \begin{bmatrix} 1 \\ 1 \\ 1 \\ 1 \\ 1 \\ 1 \end{bmatrix}$.

Multiplying $[A][T]^3$ by $[C]$ will multiply the numbers in column 1 by 0, column 2 by 1, column 3 by 2, column 4 by 3, column 4 by 5 and column 6 by 5 to get the expected values of each of the six possible number of sixes after three rolls of the dice. Multiplying $[A][T]^3[C]$ by $[D]$ will total the individual probabilities. Then multiply by 6 because each probability is worth six points. $[A]\cdot[T]^3\cdot[C]\cdot[D]\cdot6 = 12.63888$. So on the average, even though 18 points are needed in Sixes in the Upper Section to get the bonus, on a given turn you can expect to get only 12.6 points!

Sponsor: D.E. Shaw Group

The D.E. Shaw Group is a global investment and technology development firm. It employs a substantial number of top-notch computer scientists and mathematicians, many of whom joined the firm directly from leading university math and science programs. A number of them are former ARML competitors. Given the nature and challenges of its work, D.E. Shaw has a particular interest in promoting excellence in mathematics. It is especially proud of its years-long association with ARML and of its current sponsorship of this national competition.

Supporters:

American Mathematical Society	ams.org
Art of Problem Solving	artofproblemsolving.com
Awesome Math	awesomemath.org
Canada/USA Mathcamp	mathcamp.org
Casualty Actuarial Society	casact.org
Cogito.org	cogito.org
Design Science	dessci.com
Geometry Expressions	geometryexpressions.com
John Wiley & Sons, Inc.	wiley.com/wiley.cda
Hampshire College Summer Program (HCSSiM)	hcssim.org
Key Curriculum Press	keypress.com
The Learning Tree	learningteam.org
MATHCOUNTS	mathcounts.org
Math League	mathleague.com
Math Zoom	mathzoom.com
MathPro Press	mathpropress.com
Mathematics Association of America	maa.org
Mu Alpha Theta	mualphatheta.org
Pi Mu Epsilon	pme_math.org
PROMYS (Boston University)	promys.org
Ross Program (Ohio State University)	math.ohio-state.edu/ross/
Society of Actuaries	soa.org
Texas Instruments	ti.com
USAMTS	usamts.org
William K. Bradford Publishing	wkbradford.com
Wolfram Research	wolfram.com

Unfortunately, we don't have pictures of all the authors from 2004 to 2008. Missing are Ed Early, Bridget Tenner, Eric Wepsic, and Gabriel Carroll.

From left to right: Zuming Feng, Andy Niedermaier, PJ Karafiol, Don Barry, Leo Schneider.

From left to right: Andy Niedermaier, Chris Jeuell, Paul Dreyer, Don Barry, Zac Franco, PJ Karafiol, and Leo Schneider.